W9-BDK-371

# ELECTRIC CIRCUITS AND MACHINES

# ELECTRIC CIRCUITS

*Third Edition*

McGRAW-HILL BOOK COMPANY, INC.

*An Introduction to Practical Electricity*

# AND MACHINES

## EUGENE C. LISTER

*Chief Electrical Engineer,*
*Stanley Engineering Company*
*Member, American Institute of*
*Electrical Engineers*

**NEW YORK    TORONTO    LONDON    1960**

ELECTRIC CIRCUITS AND MACHINES

Copyright © 1960 by the McGraw-Hill Book Company, Inc.
Copyright, 1945, 1952, by the McGraw-Hill Book Company, Inc.
Printed in the United States of America.
All rights reserved. This book, or parts thereof,
may not be reproduced in any form
without permission of the publishers.

*Library of Congress Catalog Card Number:* 51-13590

38020

THE MAPLE PRESS COMPANY, YORK, PA.

# PREFACE

It has been the objective of the author in the preparation of this book and previous editions to present, in concise form, a practical text covering the fundamentals of electric circuits and machines which would be suitable for use in technical high schools, technical institutes, community colleges, home study, adult education and job training courses, training programs in the Armed Forces, and survey courses for nonelectrical engineering students.

To achieve a concise yet broad text, the author has omitted detailed mathematical analyses of the theories involved. Rather, he has emphasized the presentation of fundamental principles without rigorous mathematical proofs; and in so far as possible he has stressed the descriptions of the physical actions taking place. Enough of the essentials are presented to enable the student to gain a general understanding of each subject, and yet the student or instructor is allowed the opportunity to enlarge upon those subjects which are of particular interest. To this end, a list of references and a visual bibliography appear following the Appendix. The book has proved to be suitable for students with varied educational backgrounds and for use in courses with varied objectives.

Mathematics is limited to simple algebra and to the use of a few trigonometric relationships. The trigonometry used is explained in a section of the Appendix, and a table of trigonometric functions is also included. For those students or instructors desiring to use the complex quantity notation for vector representation, the Appendix includes a brief discussion of this notation.

The material covered in the text includes the fundamentals of both d-c and a-c circuits together with the principles of magnetism and electromagnetic induction, to serve as a foundation for the presentation of the principles of the operation of electric machinery. Application of these fundamentals is made in the discussion of electric machinery in chapters covering d-c generators, d-c motors, transformers, a-c generators, induction motors, synchronous motors, and single-phase motors. Special features of the text are the inclusion of chapters or sections covering primary and secondary cells, feeder voltage regulators, circuit switching and protective equipment, self-synchronous apparatus, electrical measurements, and electron tubes and devices.

Many numerical examples are worked out in detail in the text, and a list of problems is included in those chapters in which the solution of problems will illustrate the application of the principles involved. Review questions at the end of each chapter may be used for class discussion or as a study aid by the student for evaluating his grasp of the subject matter.

Acknowledgment is made of the valuable assistance given in the preparation of the original manuscript by J. A. DeWild and S. K. Fosholt. The numerous helpful comments and criticisms offered by the many users of previous editions of this book are also gratefully acknowledged. These suggestions and criticisms have been most helpful in the preparation of this revised edition.

*Eugene C. Lister*

# CONTENTS

# ELECTRIC CIRCUITS AND MACHINES

# CHAPTER 1

## FUNDAMENTAL UNITS

While the exact nature of electricity is unknown, a great deal is known about what it can do. By the mere closing of a switch, buildings are lighted, wheels are turned, ice is made, food is cooked, distant voices are heard, and countless other tasks—ordinary and extraordinary—are performed. Although a great number of uses for electricity have been discovered and applied, the field is by no means exhausted. Electric machines and devices that have been in use for many years are being improved and are now finding wider fields of application. Extensive research is constantly bringing forth and developing new devices. Much is still to be learned about electricity.

Electricity is a convenient form of energy. It is well known that when fuels such as coal, oil, and gas are burned, energy is released. A waterfall, whether it is man-made or natural, also possesses energy. Yet, to be of value, this energy must be made available at points where it can be used conveniently. Electricity furnishes the most practicable and convenient means yet devised for doing this. The energy of burning fuel or of falling water is changed to a more convenient form—electricity—by *electric machines*. It is transmitted to distant points over *electric circuits*. It is controlled by other electric machines. At points where it is to be used, it is converted into useful work by still other electric machines and devices.

Since electricity is a form of energy, the study of electricity is the study of energy, its conversions from one form to another, and its transmission from one point to another. Electric machines are energy-conversion devices, and electric circuits are energy-transmission devices.

Although no one knows precisely what electricity is, it has been possible to develop theories about electricity through experiment and by observation of its behavior. As a result, it is now believed that all matter is essentially electrical in nature.

1

**1-1. The Structure of Matter**    *Matter* has been defined as anything that occupies space and has weight.    Familiar examples of matter are water, air, copper, tin, smoke, iron, and salt.    Matter is made up of extremely small particles called *molecules*.    A molecule is the smallest particle into which a given substance may be divided without changing its identity.    For instance, water is composed of two parts hydrogen and one part oxygen.    If a drop of water were divided and subdivided into smaller and smaller particles, the smallest particle into which it could be divided and still contain two parts hydrogen and one part oxygen would be called a molecule of water.    If this particle were subdivided further, the resulting parts would be hydrogen and oxygen, both of which are gases and obviously do not have the physical properties of water.

Small as they are, molecules may be divided chemically into *atoms*. There are as many kinds of molecules as there are kinds of matter, but there are only about one hundred different kinds of atoms corresponding to the number of known chemical elements.    While it is not now believed to be entirely correct, the atomic model proposed by the Danish scientist Niels Bohr is still useful in describing the structure of the atom.

The atom as described by Bohr, is a solar system in miniature.    The core of the atom, corresponding to the sun in the solar system, is called the *nucleus*.    The nucleus is formed of subatomic particles called *protons* and *neutrons*.    Surrounding the nucleus and in a state of continual motion similar to the orbiting of the planets about the sun are other subatomic particles called *electrons*.    Atoms of different elements contain different numbers of electrons, although the electrons of all the approximately 100 different kinds of atoms are alike.

It has been found that protons and electrons exert forces on one another over and above the forces of gravitational attraction between them.    This force is attributed to a property of the protons and electrons known as *electric charge*.    Protons exert forces of repulsion on other protons and likewise electrons exert forces of repulsion on other electrons.    However, protons and electrons attract one another. There are, therefore, two kinds of electric charge arbitrarily designated as *positive* and *negative*.

It has been found that all electrons have precisely the same negative charge and that all protons have precisely the same positive charge.    Neutrons have no charge, or are electrically neutral.    In the normal atom there are equal numbers of electrons and protons and therefore the atom is uncharged since the positive charges just balance the negative charges.    Furthermore, a particular body made up of uncharged or neutral atoms is uncharged or neutral. However, nearly all atoms have some electrons which are loosely bound to their nuclei. These electrons are called *free electrons* and may be dislodged by one means or another and transferred from one atom to another.

If a body is caused to lose some of its electrons or negative charges, the body is said to be positively charged. Similarly, if a body is caused to gain electrons, it is said to be negatively charged. For example, a dry glass rod may be charged positively if it is rubbed vigorously with a silk cloth. Some of the electrons on the glass rod are transferred to the silk cloth, leaving the rod positively charged and causing the cloth to assume a negative charge.

The forces of attraction and repulsion of electrically charged bodies form the basis for a fundamental rule of electricity; that is, *similarly charged bodies repel one another and oppositely charged bodies attract one another*. The force of attraction or repulsion depends on the distance between the charged bodies: the greater the separation, the weaker the force. If the distance between two charged bodies is doubled, the force is decreased to one-fourth as much. Stated in mathematical terms, the force is inversely proportional to the square of the distance between the charged bodies.

The atoms of some materials such as copper, zinc, silver, and aluminum have many free electrons. Such materials are called *conductors*. The atoms of nonmetallic materials such as glass, slate, mica, and porcelain have electrons that are held rather rigidly to their nuclei; that is, they have few free electrons. These materials are called nonconductors or *insulators*.

**1-2. Electric Current**  In a conductor material, some of the free electrons are freely moving at random or "migrating" from atom to atom. When, in addition to this random motion, there is a drift or general movement of electrons along the conductor, this is called an *electric current*.

When a strip of zinc and a strip of copper are immersed in a solution of sulfuric acid to form a simple *electric cell*, the resulting chemical action causes the zinc strip to gain electrons from the solution, thereby causing it to become negatively charged. At the same time the copper strip has a tendency to lose some of its electrons, causing it to become positively charged. When the two plates are connected by a copper wire, which is a good conductor, the electrons on the zinc strip flow through the wire to the copper strip. This movement of the electrons from the zinc strip through the copper wire to the copper strip and back through the solution constitutes an electric current, and the entire path through which it flows is called a *circuit*.   Thus, *an electric current is merely the movement of electrons or negative charges through a conductor.*

Early experimenters recognized the fact that an electric current was a movement of charges along a conductor.   Since the direction of the flow of current was not known, unfortunately it was arbitrarily chosen to be from a positively charged body to a negatively charged body (positive to negative), and this convention has been so firmly established that it is still in use.   Thus, the conventional direction or positive direction of current flow is taken to be from positive to negative even though it is now known that the direction of electron flow, which actually constitutes an electric current, is from negative to positive.

**1-3. Unit of Current: the Ampere**   The smallest quantity of electricity is the electron.   This particle of electricity is so small that the flow of one electron could not be detected by even the most sensitive current-detecting instrument.   A *coulomb* is a much larger unit of quantity of electricity or electric charge and is used for practical measurements.   One coulomb is equal to approximately $628 \times 10^{16}$ electrons. Since a coulomb is a quantity of electricity, then a *rate of flow* of electricity may be specified in *coulombs per second*.   In practice, the term coulombs per second is seldom used; a shorter term, *ampere*, is used instead.

For example, an ordinary 100-watt lamp used on a house-lighting circuit takes a current of about 0.83 ampere.   This means that electricity is passing through the lamp at the rate of 0.83 coulomb every second, or more simply, the current is 0.83 ampere.

An international agreement, legalized in the United States by an act of Congress in 1894, has defined the ampere as a steady current which, when passed through a solution of nitrate of silver in water under standard conditions, deposits silver at a specified rate (0.001118 gram per sec).

The relation of the terms coulomb per second and ampere is similar to the measurement of rate of motion or speed of a ship.   The speed of a ship may be indicated in nautical miles per hour or more simply in knots.   Coulombs per second and amperes mean the same thing, just as do nautical miles per hour and knots.

The flow of an electric current through a conductor is sometimes compared with the flow of water through a pipe.   The quantity of electricity, measured in coulombs, is compared with the quantity of water, measured in gallons.   The rate of flow of electricity measured in amperes is compared with the rate of flow of water measured in gallons per minute. This comparison is often helpful in learning the units of measurement of electricity.

**1-4. Resistance: the Ohm** It was pointed out in Art. 1-1 that materials which have many free electrons are called conductors, while materials having few free electrons are called insulators. Conductors are said to offer a low *resistance* to the flow of an electric current, and insulators offer a high resistance to current flow. Electrical resistance, then, is defined as the opposition offered by a material to the flow of an electric current.

The practical unit of measurement of resistance is the *ohm*. The ohm has been defined legally as the resistance of a column of mercury of certain dimensions under specified conditions. As practical examples of resistance, an ordinary 100-watt electric lamp used on a 120-volt circuit has a resistance of about 144 ohms when hot. A 1,000-ft length of No. 10 American Wire Gauge copper wire (0.1 in. in diameter) has a resistance of about 1 ohm. A 240-volt 2,500-watt electric heater has a resistance of about 23 ohms.

Resistance depends not only on the material used for the conductor, but also on the size and temperature of the conductor. In a conductor of large cross-sectional area, the number of electrons free to move is larger than in a wire of small cross-sectional area. Thus, the larger the conductor, the lower its resistance.

Resistance also depends on the length of a conductor. A conductor 20 ft long has twice as much resistance as a conductor of the same material and size only 10 ft long.

It has also been found that temperature affects the resistance of most materials. The resistance of most materials increases with an increase in temperature. For example, a tungsten lamp filament has a much lower resistance when it is cold than it has when it is red hot.

Summarizing, the resistance of a conductor depends on

1. The material
2. The cross-sectional area
3. The length
4. The temperature

**1-5. Potential Difference and Electromotive Force: the Volt** Just as there must be a difference in water pressure to cause water to flow between two points, so must there be a difference in electric pressure to cause an electric current to flow between two points in an electric circuit.    This difference in electric pressure is called *potential difference*, and it is measured in *volts*.    The volt is the amount of potential difference that will cause one ampere to flow through a resistance of one ohm.

Potential differences in common use vary from a few millionths of a volt to several million volts.    The potential difference between the terminals of a common dry cell is about $1\frac{1}{2}$ volts; between terminals of an automobile storage battery, about 12 volts.    Common potential differences applied to the terminals of electric motors are 115, 208, 220, 440, 550, and 2,300 volts.    Potential differences between conductors on long power-transmission lines are as high as 345,000 volts.    Experimental lines have been operated with even higher potential differences.

If two bodies have different amounts of charge, a potential difference exists between the two bodies.    Potential difference is then merely a difference in electric charge.    When two points having a potential difference between them are joined by a conductor, a current flows along the conductor attempting to equalize the difference in charge on the two points.    When the two charges are equalized, the flow of current stops.    Therefore, if a current is to be maintained between two points, the potential difference between the points must be maintained.

A device that has the ability to maintain a potential difference or a difference in charge between two points, even though a current is flowing between those points, is said to develop an *electromotive force* (emf).

There are several ways in which an emf may be developed.    The simple electric cell described in Art. 1-2 develops an emf by *chemical* means.    The electric generator in which conductors are moved through magnetic fields develops an emf by *mechanical* means.    When a junction of two dissimilar metals is heated, a small emf is developed.    This is the principle of the *thermocouple*.    When certain substances are placed in contact with metals and the junction is illuminated, a small emf is developed.    The *photoelectric cell* operates on this principle. If, when any of the above-mentioned devices is in operation, the terminals of the device are connected by a conductor, a continuous current flows through the completed circuit because the potential difference at the terminals is maintained.

Since the result of the action of an emf in a circuit is a potential difference measured in volts, emf is also expressed in volts.

Thus, a potential difference causes current to flow, and an emf maintains the potential difference.    Since both are measured in volts, a common term, *voltage*, is used to indicate a measure of either.    Although the terms potential difference, emf, and voltage do not mean exactly the same thing, they are often used interchangeably.

**1-6. Measurement of Current, Voltage, and Resistance** A simple electric circuit consisting of a generator supplying a lamp is represented in Fig. 1-1.* The assumed or conventional direction of current flow is out of the positive terminal of the generator, through the lamp, and back to the negative terminal of the generator as shown by the arrows.

Electric current is measured by an *ammeter*. An ammeter measures the number of coulombs per second or *amperes* flowing in a circuit. To measure the current flowing through the lamp of Fig. 1-1, an ammeter is connected into the circuit as shown in Fig. 1-2. Note that the ammeter is *inserted into* or made a part of the circuit.

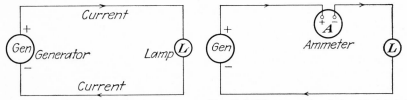

Fig. 1-1. A simple electric circuit consisting of a generator, a lamp, and the connecting conductors.

Fig. 1-2. The ammeter is inserted into the circuit of Fig. 1-1 to measure the electric current.

For the purpose at hand, electricity may be considered as a fluid that cannot be compressed. If electricity is thought of in this way, it should be easy to see that in the circuit of Fig. 1-2 the same current must flow through both the ammeter and the lamp. Because an ammeter is always connected directly into the circuit, it must have a very low resistance so as not to hinder the flow of current. The ammeter is connected so that the current enters it through the positive (+) terminal and leaves it through the negative (−) terminal.

Potential difference or voltage is measured with a *voltmeter*. A voltmeter must be connected *between* or *across* the two points whose difference in potential is to be measured.

Figure 1-3 shows the method of connecting a voltmeter to measure the voltage across the lamp. Note that the current flowing through the lamp *does not* flow through the voltmeter; the voltmeter is merely *tapped* on the circuit.

Compare the methods of connecting ammeters and voltmeters in Figs. 1-2 and 1-3. The *ammeter* is *inserted into* the circuit, while the

* For a table of symbols used in circuit diagrams refer to Appendix 1.

*voltmeter* is *connected across* the circuit. An ammeter should never be connected across a circuit, since it has such a low resistance that it would be ruined by the large rush of current through it. A voltmeter is not damaged by its connection across the circuit because it has a very high resistance.

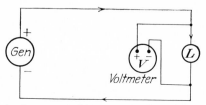

FIG. 1-3. The voltmeter is connected to measure the voltage applied to the lamp.

Resistance may be measured by means of a Wheatstone bridge, an ohmmeter, or by the voltmeter-ammeter method, all of which are discussed in Chap. 17.

### 1-7. Summary of Important Ideas Concerning Electricity   *Electric current* is the movement of *electric charges* along a conductor.

An *electric circuit* is a path over which an *electric current* may flow.

The *ampere* is the unit of measurement of *current* and is a *rate of flow* of *one coulomb* of electricity *per second*.

*Resistance* is the *opposition* to the flow of an electric current.

The *ohm* is the unit of measurement of *resistance*.

*Resistance* depends on the *material, cross-sectional area, length,* and *temperature* of the conductor.

*Potential difference* is that which causes current to flow, and its unit of measurement is the *volt*.

*Electromotive force,* or *emf,* is required to maintain a potential difference between two points when a current flows between the two points.

An emf may be produced *chemically, mechanically,* or by means of *light* or *heat*.

*Voltage* is a common term used to indicate a measure of either *potential difference* or *emf*.

*Current* may be measured by means of a low-resistance *ammeter* that is *inserted into* the circuit.

*Voltage* may be measured by means of a high-resistance *voltmeter* that is tapped *across* the circuit.

*Resistance* may be measured by means of a *Wheatstone bridge,* an *ohmmeter,* or by the *voltmeter-ammeter method*.

## Table 1. Electrical Units

| Quantity | Unit | Symbol | Measuring device |
|---|---|---|---|
| Current | Ampere | $I$ | Ammeter |
| Potential difference<br>Electromotive force<br>Voltage | Volt | $E$ | Voltmeter |
| Resistance | Ohm | $R$ | Wheatstone bridge<br>Ohmmeter<br>Voltmeter-ammeter |

## REVIEW QUESTIONS

**1.** Why is electricity a convenient form of energy?

**2.** What is matter? Give examples.

**3.** What is a molecule? What is an atom?

**4.** The nucleus of an atom is associated with what kind of charge?

**5.** What are the negative charges in an atom called?

**6.** What is the relation between the positive and negative charges in an uncharged or neutral atom?

**7.** Give the rules for attraction and repulsion of electric charges.

**8.** What is a conductor? Give examples.

**9.** What is an insulator? Give examples.

**10.** Describe the nature of an electric current.

**11.** What is an electric circuit?

**12.** Is the assumed or conventional flow of current in the same direction as the electron flow in a circuit?

**13.** What is the unit of electric charge used in practical measurements? How is this unit related to the ampere?

**14.** What is electrical resistance? What is its unit of measurement?

**15.** Upon what things does the resistance of a conductor depend?

**16.** What is potential difference? What is its unit of measurement?

**17.** How is a potential difference maintained between two points, even though a current is flowing between the points?

**18.** What is the common term used to indicate a measure of either potential difference or emf?

**19.** How are ammeters and voltmeters connected in an electric circuit?

**20.** What precaution is necessary in connecting voltmeters and ammeters?

**21.** As a summary, write the units of measurement of electric charge, current, voltage, and resistance.

# CHAPTER 2

## DIRECT-CURRENT CIRCUITS

There are two basic ways of connecting two or more pieces of electric apparatus: they may be connected in *series* or in *parallel*.

When electric devices are connected end-to-end or in tandem to form a single continuous circuit, they are said to be connected in *series*. The three resistances $R_1$, $R_2$, and $R_3$ in Fig. 2-1 are connected in series. Note that in Fig. 2-1 there is only one path over which current may flow.

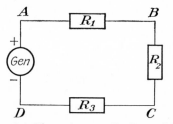

FIG. 2-1. The resistances $R_1$, $R_2$, and $R_3$ are connected in series.

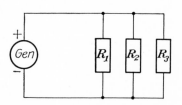

FIG. 2-2. The resistances $R_1$, $R_2$, and $R_3$ are connected in parallel.

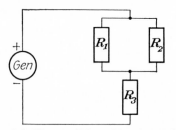

FIG. 2-3. The parallel combination of $R_1$ and $R_2$ is connected in series with $R_3$.

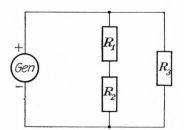

FIG. 2-4. The series combination of $R_1$ and $R_2$ is connected in parallel with $R_3$.

When the apparatus is connected so that there is a divided path over which current may flow—two or more alternate routes between two points in a circuit—the arrangement is called a *parallel* circuit. This combination, shown in Fig. 2-2, is also known as the multiple or shunt connection.

Other connections are combinations or variations of the two basic circuits. For example, in Fig. 2-3, the parallel combination of $R_1$ and $R_2$ is in series with $R_3$. In Fig. 2-4, the series combination of $R_1$ and $R_2$ is in parallel with $R_3$. As still more apparatus is connected into a circuit, the combinations become more complex.

**2-1. Series Circuits: Current Relations** The same amount of current must flow in every part of a series circuit. This should be evident from a diagram of a series circuit. For example, in Fig. 2-1 the current that flows out of the positive terminal of the generator must flow successively through resistances $R_1$, $R_2$, and $R_3$ before returning to the negative terminal of the generator since there is only one path over which the current may flow. This is true regardless of the values of the several resistances in series. This may be easily verified experimentally by inserting an ammeter at several different points in a series circuit, such as at the points $A$, $B$, $C$, or $D$ in Fig. 2-1. It will be found that the amount of current flowing at any of these points is the same.

*The current is the same in all parts of a series circuit.*

This rule may be expressed mathematically by the expression

$$I = I_1 = I_2 = I_3 = \cdots \tag{1}$$

where $I$ is the current supplied by the generator and $I_1$, $I_2$, and $I_3$ are the currents in the several parts of the circuit.

This does not imply that the current of a series circuit cannot be changed by altering the circuit. A change in either the applied voltage or the resistance of the circuit will change the value of the current flowing. However, for any given value of circuit resistance and applied voltage, the same current must flow in every part of the circuit.

**2-2. Series Circuits: Voltage Relations** Water pressure is required to cause water to flow through a pipe. More pressure is required to force water to flow at a given rate through a small pipe than through a large pipe since more resistance is offered to the flow in the small pipe.

Likewise, in an electric circuit an electric pressure or voltage is necessary to cause a current to flow. The greater the resistance of a circuit, the greater the voltage must be to cause a given current to flow through that circuit.

In Fig. 2-5, voltmeters $V_1$, $V_2$, and $V_3$ are connected across $R_1$, $R_2$, and $R_3$, respectively. These voltmeters indicate the voltage required to cause the current of 2 amperes (amp), as indicated by the ammeter $A$, to flow through each of the three resistors. Voltmeter $V$ indicates the voltage at the generator terminals, or the total voltage applied to the three resistors, which in Fig. 2-5 is 72 volts.

Voltmeter $V_1$ indicates a voltage of 12 volts across $R_1$. This means that 12 of the total of 72 volts is used in causing the current to flow through $R_1$. Stated another way, there is a drop in voltage of 12 volts across $R_1$. Voltmeter $V_2$ indicates 36 volts, or three times the voltage required across $R_1$. This is to be expected since $R_2$ has three times the resistance of $R_1$ and the same current of 2 amp is being caused to flow through both resistors. The voltage across $R_3$ is only 24 volts since $R_3$ is only twice as large as $R_1$. In general, it may be stated that the voltage required to cause a current to flow in a d-c circuit is directly proportional to the resistance of the circuit; that is, the higher the resistance, the higher the voltage must be.

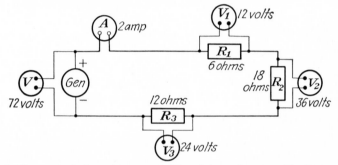

FIG. 2-5. The sum of the voltages as indicated by voltmeters $V_1$, $V_2$, and $V_3$ is equal to the voltage indicated by voltmeter $V$.

Note that in Fig. 2-5 the sum of the voltage drops across the three resistors is equal to the voltage applied to the circuit

$$12 + 36 + 24 = 72$$

The entire applied voltage is used in causing the current to flow through the three resistors.

*In a series circuit, the sum of the voltages across the several parts is equal to the total voltage applied to the circuit.*

Stated mathematically,

$$E = E_1 + E_2 + E_3 + \cdots \qquad (2)$$

where $E$ is voltage applied to the circuit and $E_1$, $E_2$, and $E_3$ are the voltages across the several parts.

**2-3. Parallel Circuits: Voltage Relations** Figure 2-6 shows three lamps $L_1$, $L_2$, and $L_3$ connected as three independent circuits to a

110-volt generator. Obviously, a voltage of 110 volts is applied to each of the three lamps since each lamp is connected directly to the same generator. Now if instead of making three separate circuit connections as in Fig. 2-6, the connecting wires are replaced by one outgoing and one returning wire, the same condition exists. That is, there is still a voltage of 110 volts applied to each of the three lamps. The connecting wires of Fig. 2-7 may be considered to be merely extensions of the generator terminals so that the same voltage is supplied to each lamp. The connection shown in Fig. 2-7 is called a

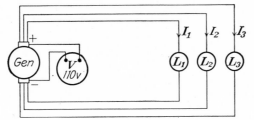

Fig. 2-6. The three lamps are connected as three separate circuits to the same generator.

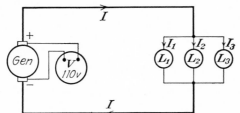

Fig. 2-7. The three lamp circuits of Fig. 2-6 are combined to form a parallel circuit.

*parallel connection,* and the rule for voltages in a parallel circuit may be stated as follows:

*The voltage across each branch of a parallel combination is the same as the voltage applied to the entire combination.*

Stated mathematically,

$$E = E_1 = E_2 = E_3 = \cdots \qquad (3)$$

where $E$ is the voltage across the combination and $E_1$, $E_2$, and $E_3$ are the voltages across the several branches.

**2-4. Parallel Circuits: Current Relations** Since in Fig. 2-6 the generator supplies current to each of the three independent circuits, the total current supplied must be the sum of the currents in the three circuits. Then since Fig. 2-6 is equivalent to the parallel circuit shown in Fig. 2-7, the rule for currents in a parallel circuit may be stated as follows:

*The total current supplied to a parallel circuit is the sum of the branch currents.*

Mathematically,

$$I = I_1 + I_2 + I_3 + \cdots \tag{4}$$

where $I$ is the total current and $I_1$, $I_2$, and $I_3$ are the currents in the several branches.

## 2-5. Ohm's Law

Ohm's law states that the amount of steady current flowing in a circuit is equal to the applied emf divided by the resistance of the circuit. This law, experimentally determined by Georg Simon Ohm in 1826, is of the utmost importance as it forms the basis for nearly all d-c circuit calculations. The law may be written briefly

$$\text{Current} = \frac{\text{emf}}{\text{resistance}}$$

or

$$\text{Amperes} = \frac{\text{volts}}{\text{ohms}}$$

Written mathematically it is

$$I = \frac{E}{R} \tag{5}$$

where $I$ = current, amp
$E$ = emf, volts
$R$ = resistance, ohms

**Example 1**  How much current will flow through a 12-ohm electric heater when a voltage of 120 volts is applied?

$$I = \frac{E}{R}$$

$$I = \frac{120}{12} = 10 \text{ amp}$$

Equation (5) may be transposed and written

$$E = IR \tag{6}$$

That is, the voltage across a circuit is equal to the product of the current in amperes and the resistance in ohms.

**Example 2**  What voltage is required to cause a current of 2 amp to flow through a resistance of 55 ohms?

$$E = IR$$
$$E = 2 \times 55 = 110 \text{ volts}$$

Since $E = IR$, the difference in voltage between two points is often referred to as the "$IR$ drop" between the two points.

The third form of Ohm's law, by again transposing Eq. (5), is

$$R = \frac{E}{I} \tag{7}$$

That is, the resistance of a circuit is equal to the voltage across the circuit divided by the current through the circuit.

**Example 3** What is the resistance of a lamp that draws 1.5 amp from a 120-volt line?

$$R = \frac{E}{I}$$

$$R = \frac{120}{1.5} = 80 \text{ ohms}$$

The three forms of Ohm's law are summarized in Table 2. It is important that the student become familiar with all three forms of Ohm's law, since he will be using them as long as he works with electricity.

### Table 2. Ohm's Law

| | | |
|---|---|---|
| $I = \frac{E}{R}$ | Current $= \frac{\text{voltage}}{\text{resistance}}$ | Amperes $= \frac{\text{volts}}{\text{ohms}}$ |
| $E = IR$ | Voltage $=$ current $\times$ resistance | Volts $=$ amperes $\times$ ohms |
| $R = \frac{E}{I}$ | Resistance $= \frac{\text{voltage}}{\text{current}}$ | Ohms $= \frac{\text{volts}}{\text{amperes}}$ |

**2-6. Applying Ohm's Law** Frequently mistakes in electrical calculations are made because Ohm's law is not used properly. The law may be applied to an *entire circuit* or to *any part of a circuit*. When used for the entire circuit, values of current, voltage, and resistance must be used for the entire circuit. When used for a certain part of a circuit, values of current, voltage, and resistance must be used from only that certain part of the circuit.

**Example 4** In the circuit represented in Fig. 2-8, find the current flowing in and the voltage across each of the two series resistances.

$$I \text{ (entire circuit)} = \frac{E \text{ (entire circuit)}}{R \text{ (entire circuit)}}$$

$$I = \frac{240}{(40 + 20)} = \frac{240}{60} = 4 \text{ amp}$$

$$E \text{ (across } R_1) = I \text{ (through } R_1) \times R_1$$
$$E_1 = 4 \times 40 = 160 \text{ volts}$$
$$E \text{ (across } R_2) = I \text{ (through } R_2) \times R_2$$
$$E_2 = 4 \times 20 = 80 \text{ volts}$$

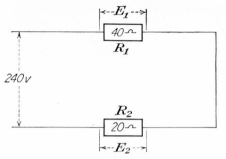

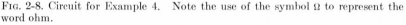

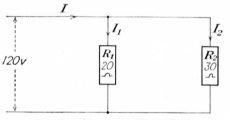

FIG. 2-8. Circuit for Example 4.   Note the use of the symbol Ω to represent the word ohm.

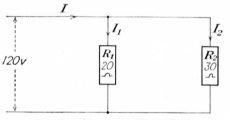

FIG. 2-9. Circuit for Example 5.

**Example 5**   Find the current in each branch and the line current in the parallel circuit shown in Fig. 2-9.   What is the combined resistance of the two branches?

$$I \text{ (branch 1)} = \frac{E \text{ (branch 1)}}{R \text{ (branch 1)}}$$

$$I_1 = \frac{120}{20} = 6 \text{ amp}$$

$$I \text{ (branch 2)} = \frac{E \text{ (branch 2)}}{R \text{ (branch 2)}}$$

$$I_2 = \frac{120}{30} = 4 \text{ amp}$$

$$\text{Line current } I = I_1 + I_2$$
$$I = 6 + 4 = 10 \text{ amp}$$

$$R \text{ (entire circuit)} = \frac{E \text{ (entire circuit)}}{I \text{ (entire circuit)}}$$

$$R = \frac{120}{10} = 12 \text{ ohms}$$

Notice that the combined resistance of $R_1$ and $R_2$ in parallel in Example 5 is less than the value of either $R_1$ or $R_2$.   Resistances in parallel are discussed in Art. 2-8.

**2-7. Resistance in a Series Circuit** It was shown in Art. 2-1 that the same current flows through every part of a series circuit. Resistance is the opposition offered by a circuit to the flow of current. All parts of a series circuit have resistance, and each part of the circuit offers a part of the total resistance to the flow of current. Thus, the following rule may be stated for combining resistances in series:

*The total or combined resistance of a series circuit is the sum of the resistances of the several parts.*

Stated mathematically,

$$R = R_1 + R_2 + R_3 + \cdots \qquad (8)$$

where $R$ is the total resistance and $R_1$, $R_2$ and $R_3$, are the resistances of the several parts of a series circuit.

**2-8. Resistance of a Parallel Circuit** When one 120-ohm lamp is connected to a 120-volt generator, 1 amp of current flows. When another lamp of the same size is added in parallel, 1 amp flows through the second lamp and the generator must supply a total of 2 amp. Applying Ohm's law to the entire circuit with two lamps in parallel,

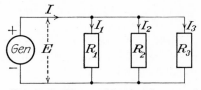

$$R = \frac{E}{I} = \frac{120}{2} = 60 \text{ ohms}$$

where $R$ is the resistance of the entire circuit. Thus the combined resistance of resistances in parallel is *less* than the resistance of either

Fig. 2-10. The combined resistance of a parallel circuit is less than the resistance of any one branch.

branch. This is true since as more paths are added through which current may flow the easier it is for current to flow, or in other words, the lower is the combined resistance of the circuit.

The equation for combining resistances in parallel may be developed by means of Ohm's law and the current and voltage rules for parallel circuits. Applying Ohm's law to the entire circuit of Fig. 2-10, $I = E/R$ where $R$ is the resistance of the entire parallel combination. Applying Ohm's law to the individual branches

$$I_1 = \frac{E}{R_1} \qquad I_2 = \frac{E}{R_2} \qquad \text{and} \qquad I_3 = \frac{E}{R_3}$$

From the current rule for parallel circuits given by Eq. (4)

$$I = I_1 + I_2 + I_3 \qquad (4)$$

Substituting the Ohm's law values of the currents in Eq. (4) results in

$$\frac{E}{R} = \frac{E}{R_1} + \frac{E}{R_2} + \frac{E}{R_3}$$

and, canceling out $E$ from each term,

$$\frac{1}{R} = \frac{1}{R_1} + \frac{1}{R_2} + \frac{1}{R_3} \tag{9}$$

Equation (9) is the rule for combining resistances in parallel. It may be extended for any number of parallel branches.

**Example 6**   What is the combined resistance of a circuit that has resistances of 20, 10, 40, and 80 ohms all connected in parallel?

$$\frac{1}{R} = \frac{1}{R_1} + \frac{1}{R_2} + \frac{1}{R_3} + \frac{1}{R_4}$$

$$\frac{1}{R} = \frac{1}{20} + \frac{1}{10} + \frac{1}{40} + \frac{1}{80}$$

$$\frac{1}{R} = \frac{4 + 8 + 2 + 1}{80} = \frac{15}{80}$$

$$15R = 80 \qquad \text{or} \qquad R = \frac{80}{15} = 5.33 \text{ ohms}$$

Note in Example 6 that the combined resistance is less than the resistance of any one of the branch resistances. This is true in any parallel circuit.

The resistance of two resistances in parallel may be found by simplifying Eq. (9) to

$$R = \frac{R_1 R_2}{R_1 + R_2} \tag{10}$$

That is, the combined resistance of any two resistances in parallel is equal to their product divided by their sum. This is true only for *two* resistances.

**Example 7**   What is the combined resistance of a circuit composed of a 20-ohm resistor and a 30-ohm resistor connected in parallel?

$$R = \frac{R_1 R_2}{R_1 + R_2} = \frac{20 \times 30}{20 + 30} = \frac{600}{50} = 12 \text{ ohms}$$

The application of Eq. (9) or (10) to a circuit composed of two equal resistances in parallel shows that the combined resistance is one-half that of either resistance. Likewise, the combined resistance of three equal resistances in parallel is one-third that of any one branch; the combined resistance of four equal resistances in parallel is one-fourth that of any one branch and so on.   In general, the combined resistance of any number of equal resistances in parallel is equal to the resistance of one branch divided by the number of branches.

**2-9. Series-Parallel Circuits**   Thus far, only simple series and simple parallel circuits have been considered.   Practical electric circuits very often consist of combinations of series and parallel resistances.

Table 3. Summary of the Laws of Series and Parallel Circuits

|  | Series circuits | Parallel circuits |
|---|---|---|
| Diagram | | |
| Current | The current is the same in all parts of the circuit $I = I_1 = I_2 = I_3 \cdots$ | The total current supplied to the circuit equals the sum of the currents through the several branches $I = I_1 + I_2 + I_3 \cdots$ |
| Voltage | The total voltage equals the sum of the voltages across the different parts of the circuit $E = E_1 + E_2 + E_3 \cdots$ | The voltage across a parallel combination is the same as the voltage across each branch $E = E_1 = E_2 = E_3 \cdots$ |
| Resistance | The total resistance equals the sum of the resistances of the separate parts $R = R_1 + R_2 + R_3 \cdots$ | The reciprocal of the equivalent or combined resistance equals the sum of the reciprocals of the resistances of the individual branches $\frac{1}{R} = \frac{1}{R_1} + \frac{1}{R_2} + \frac{1}{R_3} \cdots$ |

Such circuits may be solved by the proper application of Ohm's law and the rules for series and parallel circuits to the various parts of the complex circuit.   There is no definite procedure to be followed in solving complex circuits, the solution depending on the known facts concerning the circuit and the quantities which one desires to find. One simple rule may usually be followed, however—reduce the parallel branches to an equivalent series branch and then solve the circuit as a simple series circuit.

The following examples will illustrate the solution of typical series-parallel circuits.

**Example 8**   A resistor of 30 ohms is connected in parallel with a resistor of 60 ohms.   In series with the parallel combination is a 20-ohm resistor as shown in Fig. 2-11*a*.   What is the resistance of the entire circuit?

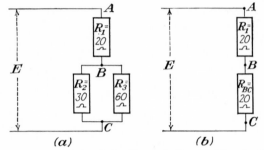

Fɪɢ. 2-11. (*a*) Series-parallel circuit for Example 8.   (*b*) The circuit shown in (*a*) may be reduced to this equivalent circuit.

The resistance between points $B$ and $C$ is

$$R_{BC} = \frac{R_2 R_3}{R_2 + R_3} = \frac{30 \times 60}{30 + 60} = \frac{1,800}{90} = 20 \text{ ohms}$$

Since $R_2$ and $R_3$ in parallel are equivalent to one 20-ohm resistance, the circuit may be reduced to the equivalent circuit shown in Fig. 2-11*b*.   The total circuit resistance is then

$$R = R_1 + R_{BC} = 20 + 20 = 40 \text{ ohms}$$

**Example 9**   Two resistors of 40 and 60 ohms in parallel are connected in series with two 0.5-ohm resistors as shown in Fig. 2-12*a*.   Find the voltage across the series resistors and across the parallel resistors when 125 volts is applied to the entire circuit.

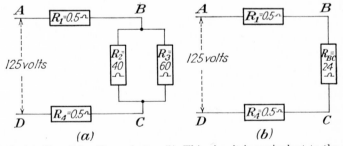

Fɪɢ. 2-12. (*a*) Circuit for Example 9.   (*b*) This circuit is equivalent to the circuit shown in (*a*).

The resistance between $B$ and $C$ is

$$R_{BC} = \frac{R_2 R_3}{R_2 + R_3} = \frac{40 \times 60}{40 + 60} = \frac{2,400}{100} = 24 \text{ ohms}$$

The circuit may now be represented as shown in Fig. 2-12b from which the total circuit resistance is

$$R = R_1 + R_{BC} + R_4$$
$$= 0.5 + 24 + 0.5 = 25 \text{ ohms}$$

Then
$$I = \frac{E}{R} = \frac{125}{25} = 5 \text{ amp}$$

The voltage across $R_1$ is

$$E = IR_1 = 5 \times 0.5 = 2.5 \text{ volts}$$

and the voltage across $R_4$ is

$$E_4 = IR_4 = 5 \times 0.5 = 2.5 \text{ volts}$$

The voltage across the parallel combination is then

$$E_{BC} = 125 - (2.5 + 2.5) = 120 \text{ volts}$$
or
$$E_{BC} = IR_{BC} = 5 \times 24 = 120 \text{ volts (check)}$$

**2-10. Wire Measurements**  Because of the fact that the diameter of wires used as conductors of electricity may be only a small fraction of an inch, it is convenient to express wire diameters in thousandths of an inch.  In order to avoid the use of decimals in expressing wire diameters, a unit of measurement known as the *mil* is in general use. *One mil is equal to one one-thousandth* (0.001) *of one inch.*  For example, instead of saying that a certain wire has a diameter of 0.051 or 51/1,000 in., it is said to have a diameter of 51 mils.

**Example 10**
$$1 \text{ in.} = 1 \times 1,000 = 1,000 \text{ mils}$$
$$0.5 \text{ in.} = 0.5 \times 1,000 = 500 \text{ mils}$$
$$0.253 \text{ in.} = 0.253 \times 1,000 = 253 \text{ mils}$$

The cross-sectional area of round conductors is expressed in units called *circular mils* (cir mil).  A conductor with a diameter of 1 mil has a cross-sectional area of 1 cir mil.

Since the area of a circle is proportional to the square of its diameter (area = $\pi D^2/4$), *the area of a circular conductor in circular mils is equal to the square of its diameter in mils.*

**Example 11**  What is the circular-mil area of a wire (a) 0.1 in., (b) 0.2 in., (c) 0.325 in. in diameter?
  (a) Diameter in mils = $0.1 \times 1,000 = 100$ mils
    Area = diameter in mils, squared
       $= 100 \times 100 = 10,000$ cir mils

(*b*) Diameter = 0.2 × 1,000 = 200 mils
    Area = 200 × 200 = 40,000 cir mils
(*c*) Diameter = 0.325 × 1,000 = 325 mils
    Area = 325 × 325 = 105,625 cir mils

**2-11. Wire Gauges**  It is common practice to indicate wire sizes by a gauge number. Although there are several gauges or systems of numbering wires, the commonly used gauge in this country is the American Wire Gauge. American Wire Gauge (AWG) sizes range from No. 0000, the largest size, to No. 40, the smallest size. This system is based on a constant ratio between any wire diameter and the diameter of the next smaller wire. Appendix 2 gives the dimensions and properties of the AWG sizes of solid copper wire.

Following are several approximate rules concerning the AWG tables. If these simple facts are remembered, approximate values concerning many wire sizes may be calculated without referring to the tables.

1. Easily remembered approximate data concerning No. 10 AWG solid copper wire are

$$\text{Diameter} = 0.1 \text{ in. or } 100 \text{ mils}$$
$$\text{Area} = 10,000 \text{ cir mils}$$
$$\text{Resistance} = 1 \text{ ohm per } 1,000 \text{ ft}$$
$$\text{Weight} = 32 \text{ lb per } 1,000 \text{ ft}$$

2. An increase of three gauge numbers doubles the area and weight and halves the resistance.

3. An increase of 10 gauge numbers increases the area and weight by a factor of 10 and decreases the resistance by a factor of 10.

**Example 12**  Find the approximate resistance of No. 0 AWG copper wire without referring to the tables.

Since No. 0 is 10 gauge numbers larger than No. 10, its resistance is 1.0/10 = 0.1 ohm per 1,000 ft.

**Example 13**  Find the approximate area of No. 4 AWG copper wire without referring to the tables.

Number 4 is six gauge sizes larger than No. 10; therefore its area is 10,000 × 2 × 2 = 40,000 cir mils.

**2-12. Stranded Wire**  To obtain the flexibility required for easy handling, the larger sizes of wire are made in the form of a cable consisting of several small strands. Standard numbers of strands commonly used in cable are 7, 19, 37, 61, 91, and 127 strands, since by using these numbers the strands may be laid in concentric layers about a single central wire. Wires larger than No. 0000 are nearly always stranded, and it is often desirable to use stranded wire in the smaller sizes.

The separate strands of a stranded wire are not necessarily standard wire sizes since the total circular-mil area is equal to an AWG size, the area of each strand being the total area divided by the number of strands.

Appendix 3 gives the dimensions and properties of standard stranded copper conductors. Note that conductors larger than AWG No. 0000 are listed by their circular-mil area.

## 2-13. Temperature Coefficient of Resistance

Nearly all conductors of electricity show a change in resistance with a change in temperature, as was mentioned in Art. 1-4. The resistance of a pure metal conductor increases with an increase in temperature and decreases with a decrease in temperature.

Conductor-resistance tables show resistances at a specific temperature. For example, Appendixes 2 and 3 list the resistance of copper wires and cables at 20°C (68°F). A true comparison of the resistance of conductors of different sizes or materials cannot be made unless the resistances are compared at the same temperature.

It has been found by experiment that for each degree of change in temperature above or below 20°C, the resistance changes by a given percentage of what it was at 20°C. This percentage change in resistance is called the *temperature coefficient of resistance*. This coefficient for copper at 20°C is 0.00393 and is nearly the same for other pure metals. Thus, for each degree that the temperature of a copper wire increases above 20°C, the resistance increases 0.393 of 1 per cent of its value at 20°C. Likewise, for each degree the temperature falls below 20°C, the resistance decreases 0.393 of 1 per cent of its value at 20°C.

The straight-line relationship between temperature and resistance holds throughout the range of temperatures normally encountered and may be expressed mathematically as follows:

$$R_2 = R[1 + a(t_2 - t)] \qquad (11)$$

where $R_2$ = resistance at temperature $t_2$

$R$ = resistance at 20°C

$t$ = 20°C

$a$ = temperature coefficient of resistance at 20°C

**Example 14**  The resistance of a length of copper wire is 3.60 ohms at 20°C. What is its resistance at 80°C?

$$
\begin{aligned}
R_2 &= R[1 + a(t_2 - t)] \\
&= 3.60[1 + 0.00393(80 - 20)] \\
&= 3.60 \times 1.236 = 4.45 \text{ ohms}
\end{aligned}
$$

**2-14. Line Drop**   Thus far in dealing with electric circuits, the resistance of the connecting-line wires between the source and the load has been neglected.   When connecting lines are short, this is permissible since the resistance is so small it can usually be neglected. However, a long line may have considerable resistance so that a certain amount of the applied voltage is used in overcoming this line resistance. This voltage is called *line drop*, and its value may be calculated by Ohm's law.   Since $E = IR$, the voltage drop in the line wires is also called the $IR$ *drop* in the lines.   Line drop or $IR$ drop is often expressed as a percentage of the voltage applied to the load.

While line resistance is distributed throughout the line wires, it is convenient when dealing with line resistance to consider the resistance of the line wires to be lumped into two resistances, one representing the resistance of each line, with these two resistances connected in series with the load resistance by connecting wires having negligible resistance.   The following example will illustrate the calculation of line drop.

**Example 15**   Figure 2-13 represents a simple lighting circuit with a source voltage of 120 volts.   Each lamp requires a current of 0.6 amp, and each connecting wire has a resistance of 1.5 ohms.   It is desired to find the line drop

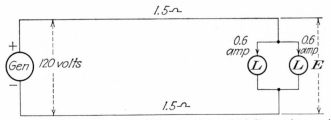

Fig. 2-13. Simple lighting circuit for Example 15, in which line resistance is taken into account.

in volts, the voltage at the lamps, and the percentage voltage drop.   Note that this problem is very similar to Example 9.

The line current is $0.6 \times 2 = 1.2$ amp.   Applying Ohm's law to each line wire

$$E = IR = 1.2 \times 1.5 = 1.8 \text{ volts}$$

The voltage at the lamps is equal to the source voltage minus the drop in both lines, or

$$E = 120 - (1.8 + 1.8)$$
$$= 120 - 3.6 = 116.4 \text{ volts}$$

The percentage voltage drop in the circuit is

$$\frac{3.6 \times 100}{116.4} = 3.09 \text{ per cent}$$

**Example 16** What is the voltage across each group of lamps in the lighting circuit of Fig. 2-14? Lines $AB$ and $EF$ have a resistance of 0.6 ohm each, and lines $BC$ and $ED$ have a resistance of 0.3 ohm each. Assume that each lamp takes a current of 1.5 amp.

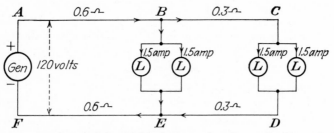

Fig. 2-14. Lighting circuit with lamps at two locations. See Example 16.

Current in lines $BC$ and $DE$ is $1.5 \times 2 = 3$ amp.
Current in lines $AB$ and $EF$ is 6 amp.
Line drop in $AB$ and $EF$ is

$$E = IR = 6 \times 0.6 = 3.6 \text{ volts}$$

Line drop in $BC$ and $DE$ is

$$E = IR = 3 \times 0.3 = 0.9 \text{ volts}$$

Voltage across lamps at $BE$ = voltage at source − line drop in $AB$ and $EF$

$$E_{BE} = 120 - (3.6 + 3.6)$$
$$= 120 - 7.2 = 112.8 \text{ volts}$$

Voltage across lamps at $CD$ = voltage at $BE$ − line drop in $BC$ and $DE$

$$E_{CD} = 112.8 - (0.9 + 0.9)$$
$$= 112.8 - 1.8 = 111 \text{ volts}$$

**2-15. Kirchhoff's Laws** Complex electric circuits may be solved with the aid of two simple rules known as Kirchhoff's laws.

*Kirchhoff's Current Law:* The sum of the currents flowing away from any point in an electric circuit must equal the sum of the currents flowing toward the point.

*Kirchhoff's Voltage Law:* Around any closedpath in an electric circuit, the sum of the potential drops is equal to the sum of the impressed emfs. This is equivalent to saying that the voltage drops must equal the voltage rises in any closed path.

The current law should be evident since this is the principle involved in the current rule for a parallel circuit; that is, the sum of the branch currents must equal the line current. Using Fig. 2-14 as an example, the current flowing into point $B$ is 6 amp. The current in line $BC$

is 3 amp and in $BE$ it is 3 amp, or a total of 6 amp flowing away from point $B$.

The voltage law may also be illustrated by Fig. 2-14. Considering the closed path $ABEFA$, the voltage rises must equal the voltage drops, or

$$\text{Rise through generator} = \text{drop in } AB + \text{drop in } BE + \text{drop in } EF$$
$$120 = 3.6 + 112.8 + 3.6$$
$$120 = 120 \text{ (check)}$$

Likewise in the closed path $ABCDEFA$

$$\text{Rises} = \text{drops}$$
$$120 = 3.6 + 0.9 + 111 + 0.9 + 3.6$$
$$120 = 120 \text{ (check)}$$

Kirchhoff's current and voltage laws restate, in concise and usable form, principles already discussed in connection with the rules for series and parallel circuits. By means of a systematic application of these laws, the current and voltage values of the various parts of complex circuits may be found. One simple application will be illustrated in the solution of three-wire circuit problems in Art. 2-23.

**2-16. Work**  Work is done when a force overcomes a resistance. In a mechanical sense, work is measured by the product of a force and the distance through which it acts. When a force of 1 lb acts through a distance of 1 ft, 1 ft-lb of work is done. If a force of 10 lb is required to lift a weight 6 ft, the work is 10 × 6 or 60 ft-lb. Thus

$$\text{Work} = \text{force} \times \text{distance}$$

Work is not done unless resistance is overcome. A building foundation exerts a tremendous force in holding up the building, but since there is no motion involved or no resistance being overcome, no work is done.

**2-17. Energy**  Energy is the ability to do work; energy is also stored work. A tank of air stored under pressure has energy; for, when released through an air hammer, it performs work. A coiled watch spring has energy since it is able to run the watch for an entire day. Water stored behind a dam also has energy since it may be used to operate turbines to generate electricity.

Since energy is stored work, energy is expended whenever work is done. The fact that 10,000 ft-lb of work is done in raising a 1,000-lb weight 10 ft means that 10,000 ft-lb of energy must be expended in raising the weight.    Thus the units of work and energy are the same.

Energy may exist in many forms—mechanical, electrical, chemical, heat, and light—and its form is readily changed.    For example, an electric generator changes mechanical energy to electrical energy; a storage battery changes chemical energy to electrical energy.    When a lump of coal is burned, chemical energy is changed to heat energy, and so on.    *However, it is a fundamental physical law that energy cannot be created, neither can it be destroyed.*    The electric generator does not create electrical energy, it merely changes mechanical energy to electrical energy.    Nor is the energy supplied to an electric lamp destroyed; it is merely converted to light and heat energy.

**2-18. Mechanical Power**    According to the definition of work, if 3,000 lb of cargo is lifted to a height of 40 ft, the work required is 3,000 × 40 or 120,000 ft-lb.    Nothing is said of the time required to raise the cargo, only that 120,000 ft-lb of work is required.

One motor driving the cargo winch may require 2 min to raise the load, while a second motor may accomplish the same result in ½ min. Work is done four times as fast by the second motor as by the first, or it is said that the second motor develops four times as much *power* as the first.    Thus, *power is the rate of doing work*, or

$$\text{Power} = \frac{\text{work}}{\text{time}}$$

When work is done at the rate of 33,000 ft-lb per min, the power is 1 *horsepower* (hp).    In the example of the cargo winch, the power required to raise the cargo in 2 min is

$$\frac{120,000}{2} = 60,000 \text{ ft-lb per min}$$

$$\frac{60,000}{33,000} = 1.82 \text{ hp}$$

The horsepower required in the second case is

$$\frac{120,000}{0.5} = 240,000 \text{ ft-lb per min}$$

$$\frac{240,000}{33,000} = 7.28 \text{ hp}$$

The distinctions between work, energy, and power are important. *Work is the overcoming of resistance.    Energy is the ability to do work. Power is the rate of doing work or the rate at which energy is expended.*

The commonly used mechanical units of energy, work, and power are summarized below:

The unit of energy: foot-pound (ft-lb)
The unit of work: foot-pound
The unit of power: horsepower (hp)

where 1 hp = 33,000 ft-lb per min.

**2-19. Electric Power**  The unit of electric power, the *watt*, is defined as the energy expended or the work done per second by an unvarying current of 1 ampere flowing under a pressure of 1 volt, or

$$P = IE \qquad (12)$$

where $P$ = power, watts
$I$ = current, amp
$E$ = voltage, volts

**Example 17**  What is the power used by an electric lamp that draws 2.5 amp from a 120-volt line?

$$P = IE$$
$$P = 2.5 \times 120 = 300 \text{ watts}$$

The fact that the watt is a unit of power or a unit of a rate of doing work cannot be emphasized too strongly.  It will be remembered that current in amperes is a rate of flow of electricity or is equal to the number of coulombs per second.  The power formula may then be written

$$\text{Power in watts} = \frac{\text{coulombs}}{\text{second}} \times \text{volts}$$

In other words, *the watt is a measure of how fast a quantity of electricity is being moved through a difference in potential.*

Since by Ohm's law, $E = IR$, this value of $E$ may be substituted in Eq. (12) to obtain another useful power formula:

$$P = IE = I \times IR$$
or $\qquad\qquad P = I^2R \qquad (13)$

**Example 18**  What is the power used in a 60-ohm generator field rheostat when the field current is 2 amp?

$$P = I^2R$$
$$P = (2)^2\, 60 = 4 \times 60 = 240 \text{ watts}$$

A third power formula may be derived from the fact that $I = E/R$ by Ohm's law.  Substituting in Eq. (12)

$$P = IE = \frac{E \times E}{R}$$

or
$$P = \frac{E^2}{R} \tag{14}$$

**Example 19** What is the power used by a 15-ohm electric heater when a voltage of 120 volts is applied?

$$P = \frac{E^2}{R}$$

$$P = \frac{(120)^2}{15} = \frac{14,400}{15} = 960 \text{ watts}$$

As illustrated in the above examples, Eq. (12) is used to find the power in a circuit when the current and voltage are known, Eq. (13) when the current and resistance are known, and Eq. (14) when the voltage and resistance are known.

Since the watt is a small unit, a larger unit, the kilowatt (kw), is often used instead. *One kilowatt is equal to 1,000 watts.*

Calculations concerning electrical machinery often involve both the electrical unit of power (watt) and the mechanical unit (horsepower). *One horsepower is equal to 746 watts.* Therefore, to change power in watts to power in horsepower, it is necessary to divide the number of watts by 746.

**Example 20** The input to a motor is 20 kw. What is the horsepower input?

$$20 \text{ kw} = 20 \times 1,000 = 20,000 \text{ watts}$$

$$\text{horsepower} = \frac{\text{watts}}{746} = \frac{20,000}{746} = 26.8 \text{ hp}$$

For most purposes, the relation between the horsepower and the kilowatt may be taken as

$$1 \text{ hp} = \frac{3}{4} \text{ kw (approximately)}$$

**2-20. Electrical Work and Energy** Power is a measure of how fast work is being done or of how fast energy is being expended, that is,

$$\text{Power} = \frac{\text{work or energy}}{\text{time}}$$

Thus, the energy used by an electrical device is the rate at which the energy is being used (the power) multiplied by the time during which the device is in use. When power is measured in watts and time in hours, then

$$\text{Power} \times \text{time} = \text{energy}$$

or
$$\text{Watts} \times \text{hours} = \text{watthours}$$

the *watthour* (whr) being the energy expended when 1 watt is used for 1 hour.

The watthour is a relatively small unit, the *kilowatthour* being used much more extensively in commercial measurements. One kilowatthour is equal to 1,000 watthours.

**Example 21**   How much energy is used by a 1,500-watt heater in 8 hr?

$$\text{Energy} = \text{power} \times \text{time}$$
$$= 1,500 \times 8 = 12,000 \text{ whr}$$
$$= \frac{12,000}{1,000} = 12 \text{ kwhr}$$

Power is a rate of expending energy just as speed is a rate of motion. If the average speed of an automobile is known for a given time, the distance traveled is the average speed multiplied by the time traveled. Likewise, if the average power required by an electric motor for a given time is known, the energy used by the motor is the average power multiplied by the time the motor is used.   The student should make sure that he understands the difference between power and energy. Power is the *rate* of expending energy or of doing work, just as speed is a *rate* of motion.

**2-21. Measurement of Electric Power and Energy**   The power being used by a lamp, motor, or other device on a d-c circuit may be determined by measuring both the current and the voltage and calculating

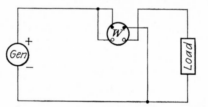

FIG. 2-15. Connection of a wattmeter to measure the power supplied to the load.

the power by means of the formula $P = IE$.   Power may also be measured directly by means of a *wattmeter*.   The wattmeter, which is described in Chap. 17, is an instrument with both a current and a voltage or potential element.   The current element is connected in series and the potential element in parallel with the circuit in which the power is being measured, as shown in Fig. 2-15.   The power in watts, being a product of current and voltage, is indicated directly on the scale of the wattmeter.

Electrical energy is measured by means of the *watthour meter*. This is the familiar type of meter used in the home to determine the monthly electric bill. The connections of the watthour meter are the same as those of the wattmeter, a current element being connected in series and a potential element being connected in parallel with the circuit. However, the watthour meter has a rotating element, the speed of which at any time is proportional to the power being used at that time. The total number of revolutions over a period of time is then proportional to the energy used in that time. The rotating element drives a gear train that records on a row of dials the number of kilo-watthours used. The amount of energy, in kilowatthours, used during a certain period is then the dial reading at the beginning of the period subtracted from the dial reading at the end of the period.

The user of electricity then pays for the amount of *energy* or *kilo-watthours* used and not the power in kilowatts. Power is the measure of how fast he is using energy at any given time as evidenced by the speed of the rotating element of his watthour meter at that time. The energy used, however, over a certain period of time is determined by the total number of revolutions made by the watthour meter in that time.

**2-22. Line Loss** Whenever a current flows through a resistance, the resistance becomes heated, or it is said that electrical energy is transformed into heat energy. The rate at which the electrical energy is transformed into heat is called power, and the common way of finding this power is by the formula $P = I^2R$. In other words, the rate at which energy is expended in a resistance is proportional to the square of the current.

Because the conductors of a transmission or distribution circuit have resistance, the conductors become heated whenever a current flows through them. Since this heat is lost to the surrounding air, it is called a *line loss*. This loss of power is proportional to the square of the current flowing, and for this reason it is desirable to transmit power with as low a current value as possible to keep the line losses from being excessive. Since the power supplied to a load is a product of current and voltage, the current required to transmit a given amount of power may be made smaller by using higher voltages; that is, the higher the voltage, the lower the current for a given amount of power. The advantages obtained by increasing the voltage used to transmit a given amount of power will be illustrated by the following example.

**Example 22**   A 12-kw load is supplied from a line that has a resistance of 0.1 ohm in each conductor.   Find the line loss in watts when the load is supplied at (*a*) 120 volts and (*b*) 240 volts.

(*a*)  $I = \dfrac{P}{E} = \dfrac{12,000}{120} = 100$ amp

Line loss (both lines) $P = I^2R$
$P = (100)^2 \times 0.2 = 2,000$ watts

(*b*)  $I = \dfrac{P}{E} = \dfrac{12,000}{240} = 50$ amp

Line loss (both lines) $P = I^2R$
$P = (50)^2 \times 0.2 = 500$ watts

Note in the above example that the same power may be transmitted at 240 volts with one-fourth the line loss as at 120 volts.  Or the power could be transmitted at the same loss with conductors one-fourth as large at 240 volts as at 120 volts.

**2-23. Three-wire Distribution Circuits**   To obtain the advantage of a higher voltage-distribution circuit and yet provide 120 volts for the operation of standard incandescent lights, Edison developed the 120/240-volt three-wire system of power distribution.   For a fixed

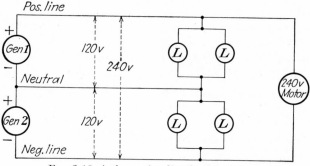

Fig. 2-16. A three-wire distribution circuit.

amount of line loss, power can be transmitted by means of the three-wire system with only three-eighths the line copper required for a two-wire 120-volt system.   The system has the further advantage of making available either 120 or 240 volts for the operation of electric equipment.

Figure 2-16 shows one method of connecting the supply for a three-wire system.   Two 120-volt generators are connected in series to supply the system, with three wires brought out, one from each outside terminal of the generators and the third, called the *neutral*, from the common connection between the generators.   With this arrangement, 120-volt lamps and appliances may be connected between either outside wire and the neutral, while 240-volt equipment, such as motors and electric heaters, may be connected between the two outside wires, as shown in Fig. 2-16.

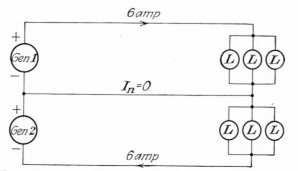

Fig. 2-17. Three-wire circuit with balanced loads.   The neutral carries no current.

When the 120-volt loads are balanced on each side of the neutral as in Fig. 2-17, the neutral carries no current.   If a heavier load is connected between the positive line and neutral as in Fig. 2-18, the neutral carries toward the generators the difference in current between the upper and lower lines.   If the heavier load is connected between

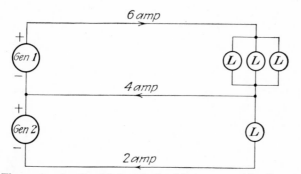

Fig. 2-18. Three-wire circuit with heavier load between positive line and neutral. Neutral carries current toward generators.

the negative line and neutral as in Fig. 2-19, the neutral carries the unbalanced current from the generators toward the load.   That is, the current flowing in the neutral wire is always the difference between the currents in the positive and negative lines.   It is desirable to keep the loads as nearly balanced as possible to keep the flow of neutral current to a minimum.

When load is connected to only one side of a three-wire system, the neutral carries the full-load current. For this reason, the neutral is usually of the same size as the positive and negative lines.

An accidental opening of the neutral wire when an unbalanced load is being supplied results in badly unbalanced voltages across the loads. For this reason, the neutral is not fused but is solidly connected from the generator to the load. For further protection against an open

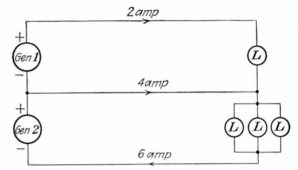

Fig. 2-19. Three-wire circuit with heavier load between negative line and neutral. Neutral carries current toward load.

neutral and for protection against damage by lightning, the neutral wire is grounded at several points.

It is often necessary to find the voltage across the loads connected to a three-wire system when the line resistance and the load currents are known. The following example will illustrate this calculation for the simple case of two loads connected to the system at the same point.

**Example 23** Two loads located 1,000 ft from a source are to be supplied from a three-wire system using three No. 0 AWG copper wires (resistance per 1,000 ft = 0.1 ohm). One load requires 30 amp and the other 20 amp. Find the voltage across each load. Generator voltages are 120 volts.

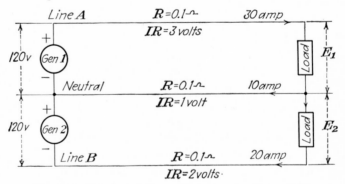

Fig. 2-20. Unbalanced three-wire system for Example 23.

*Solution:* When the loads are connected as shown in Fig. 2-20, the neutral carries 10 amp toward the source.   The voltage drop in each line is

| | |
|---|---|
| Line *A* | $IR = 30 \times 0.1 = 3$ volts |
| Neutral | $IR = 10 \times 0.1 = 1$ volt |
| Line *B* | $IR = 20 \times 0.1 = 2$ volts |

Writing an equation for the upper half of the circuit in accordance with Kirchhoff's voltage law,

$$\text{Voltage rises} = \text{voltage drops}$$
$$120 = 3 + E_1 + 1$$
$$E_1 = 120 - 3 - 1 = 116 \text{ volts}$$

Kirchhoff's voltage equation for the entire outside loop is

$$120 + 120 = 3 + 116 + E_2 + 2$$
$$240 = 121 + E_2$$
$$E_2 = 240 - 121 = 119 \text{ volts}$$

## REVIEW QUESTIONS

**1.** What are the two basic ways in which electric apparatus may be connected?

**2.** What is the relation between the values of current flowing in different parts of a series circuit?

**3.** If the voltages across the several parts of a series circuit are known, how may the total circuit voltage be determined?

**4.** A voltage of 20 volts is required to cause 2 amp to flow through a resistance of 10 ohms.   What voltage is necessary to cause the same current to flow through 40 ohms?

**5.** Give the rule for determining the voltage across parallel branches of a circuit when the applied voltage is known.

**6.** State Ohm's law in its three forms.   Which form is most convenient for finding (*a*) the resistance, (*b*) the current, or (*c*) the voltage of a circuit?

**7.** What precautions should be observed in applying Ohm's law to a part of a circuit?

**8.** Give the rule for finding the combined resistance of several resistances (*a*) in series and (*b*) in parallel.

**9.** Give the rule for finding the combined resistance of two resistances in parallel.

**10.** What is the general rule for finding the combined resistance of several equal resistances in parallel?

**11.** In reducing series-parallel circuits to simpler form, what is the general procedure?

**12.** One mil is equal to what part of 1 in.?

**13.** What unit of measurement is used for the cross-sectional area of conductors?

**14.** What is the relation between the cross-sectional area of No. 0 AWG and No. 6 AWG wire?

**15.** Why are large conductors stranded?

**16.** What is meant by line drop?   How is it calculated?

**17.** State Kirchhoff's current and voltage laws.

**18.** Define work.   What is the unit?

**19.** What is energy?   What is the unit?

**20.** How is power defined? One horsepower is equal to how many foot-pounds per minute?

**21.** What is the unit of electric power?

**22.** Give the power formula in three forms.

**23.** One kilowatt is equal to how many watts?

**24.** One horsepower is equal to how many watts?

**25.** One horsepower is equal to approximately how many kilowatts?

**26.** Give two ways in which power in a d-c circuit may be measured.

**27.** How is electrical energy measured? What is the unit of measurement?

**28.** What is meant by line loss?

**29.** What are some advantages of the three-wire distribution system?

**30.** What determines the neutral current in a three-wire distribution system?

## PROBLEMS

**1.** Two lamps are connected in series to a 120-volt line. The voltage across one lamp is 70 volts. What is the voltage across the second lamp?

**2.** Eight lamps of the same size are connected in series to a 120-volt circuit. What is the voltage across each lamp?

**3.** Three lamps of equal size are connected in parallel to a lighting circuit. Each lamp draws a current of 1.5 amp. What is the total line current?

**4.** Twenty lamps of equal size are connected in parallel to a 120-volt lighting circuit. If the total current drawn by the 20 lamps is 15 amp, what is the current through each lamp? If the lamps are reconnected in series in another circuit, so that the current through one of the lamps is 1 amp, what will be the current through the other 19 lamps?

**5.** A 220-ohm lamp is connected to a 110-volt circuit. What current does it take?

**6.** The field resistance of a shunt motor is 93 ohms. What will be the field current if 240 volts is applied to the field terminals?

**7.** An accidental short circuit is made on a 240-volt circuit by placing a 0.15-ohm resistance across the line. What will be the momentary short-circuit current?

**8.** A telephone receiver has a resistance of 1,200 ohms. If a current of 0.02 amp is to flow through the receiver, what voltage must be used?

**9.** What is the voltage drop across a rheostat if its resistance is 5 ohms and the current through it is 26 amp?

**10.** Find the voltage drop across an electric furnace that has a resistance of 5 ohms and draws 43 amp.

**11.** The voltage across the terminals of a motor field is 220 volts, and the field current is 1 amp. What is the field-circuit resistance?

**12.** A relay coil draws a current of 0.03 amp when connected to a 12-volt battery. What is its resistance?

**13.** Find the combined resistance of a 5-ohm rheostat in series with a 56-ohm shunt field.

**14.** What is the total resistance of a string of eight Christmas-tree lights connected in series, if the resistance of each lamp is 30 ohms?

**15.** How much voltage is required to cause a current of 0.4 amp to flow through a 70-ohm, a 90-ohm, and a 120-ohm lamp all connected in series?

**16.** Three lamps are connected in series across a 120-volt supply and take a current of 1.25 amp. If the resistance of two of the lamps is 25 ohms each, what is the resistance of the third?

**17.** How much resistance must be added in series with a 60-ohm generator field if the field current desired is 2 amp and the voltage applied to the field circuit is 230 volts?

**18.** A certain series street-lighting system of 60 lamps operates at a constant current of 6.6 amp. How much voltage must be applied to the circuit if each lamp has a resistance of 5 ohms and the total line resistance is 10 ohms?

**19.** Four lamps of equal resistance are connected in parallel across a 120-volt circuit. If the total current supplied the lamps is 3 amp, what is the resistance of each lamp?

**20.** Three resistances $A$, $B$, and $C$ are connected in parallel across a 120-volt line. If $A = 10$ ohms, $B = 30$ ohms, and $C = 40$ ohms, find (a) the voltage across each resistance, (b) the current through each resistance, (c) the total line current, and (d) the combined resistance of the circuit.

**21.** The combined resistance of two resistors connected in parallel is 8 ohms. The resistance of one resistor is 14 ohms. What would be their combined resistance if they were reconnected in series?

**22.** A trolley wire is paralleled for 3 miles by a heavy copper cable. The trolley-wire resistance is 0.3 ohm per mile, and the cable resistance is 0.10 ohm per mile. When the sum of the two currents through the lines is 150 amp, find the current in each conductor.

**23.** A parallel circuit has three branches of 12, 4, and 16 ohms, respectively. If a current of 4 amp flows in the branch containing 12 ohms, what current will flow in each of the others?

**24.** Three resistances of 3, 4, and 6 ohms are connected in parallel. In series with the group is an unknown resistance $R$. When the circuit is connected to a 12-volt battery, a current of 4 amp flows. What is the resistance of $R$?

**25.** A resistance of 12 ohms is connected in parallel with a series circuit of a 15-ohm and a 5-ohm resistance. A 40-ohm resistance is connected in series with the combination. What is the resistance of the entire circuit?

**26.** Three resistances of 4, 8, and 10 ohms are connected so that each resistance forms the side of a triangle. Point $A$ is the connection between the 4- and 8-ohm sides; point $B$, between the 8- and 10-ohm sides; point $C$, between the 4- and 10-ohm sides. Find the resistance between points $A$ and $B$, $B$ and $C$, and $C$ and $A$.

**27.** Four resistors of 6 ohms each form the sides of a diamond. A fifth resistor of 10 ohms forms the long diagonal of the diamond. What is the resistance of the combination between the ends of the long diagonal? What is the resistance between one end of the long diagonal and one end of the short diagonal?

**28.** What are the diameters in mils of wires that have diameters of 2.0, ¾, 0.675, 0.43, and ¼ in.?

**29.** What is the circular-mil area of each of the wires in Prob. 28?

**30.** What are the nearest AWG sizes of solid wires with areas of 5,000, 10,000, 40,000, and 100,000 cir mils?

**31.** What is the diameter in mils of a wire that has an area of 1,600 cir mils? What is the nearest AWG size?

**32.** A conductor of certain specifications can carry safely 1 amp for each 300 cir mils of its cross-sectional area. If the current to be carried is 20 amp, what is the AWG size of the wire required?

**33.** The resistance of a copper coil is 200 ohms at 20°C. What will be the resistance of the coil when it is heated to 90°C?

**34.** The resistance of a generator field coil wound with copper wire is 130 ohms at 80°C. What is its resistance at 20°C?

**35.** Find the temperature coefficient of resistance at 20°C of a conductor that increases resistance from 20 to 24 ohms when heated from 20 to 80°C.

**36.** A copper conductor has a resistance of 400 ohms at 40°C. What will its resistance be at 60°C? (HINT: First find its resistance at 20°C.)

**37.** The resistance of a copper generator coil is 0.10 ohm at 20°C. Following operation of the generator at full load, the same coil measures 0.114 ohm. What was the temperature increase in the coil?

**38.** A d-c motor is supplied by a d-c generator. Each line connecting the two machines has a resistance of 0.15 ohm. What is the terminal voltage across the motor when the motor current is 50 amp and the generator terminal voltage is 230 volts?

**39.** A d-c motor is located 2,000 ft from a d-c generator. The motor requires 30 amp to operate a given load. The generator voltage is 220 volts. Each line connecting the generator and motor is No. 0 cable which has a resistance of 0.1 ohm per 1,000 ft. Find the voltage at the motor.

**40.** A 240-volt generator supplies 10 amp to each of two motors connected in parallel. The resistance of each line wire between the generator and the first motor is 0.3 ohm, and the resistance of each line wire between the first and second motor is 0.4 ohm. What is the voltage across each motor?

**41.** Each wire of a two-wire distribution circuit has a resistance of 0.2 ohm per 1,000 ft. Connected to this circuit at a point 500 ft from the generator is a motor that requires a current of 15 amp and has a terminal voltage of 230 volts. A second motor that requires 10 amp is located on the same circuit but 750 ft from the generator. (*a*) What is the voltage at the second motor? (*b*) What is the generator voltage?

**42.** The voltage drop across an electric heater is 225 volts. If the voltage at the source is 230 volts and the heater draws 15 amp, what is the resistance of each connecting line wire?

**43.** A crane lifts a weight of 8,000 lb to a height of 20 ft. What is the work done by the crane?

**44.** If the crane in Prob. 43 raises the weight in 30 sec, what is the average power (*a*) in foot-pounds per minute; (*b*) in horsepower?

**45.** A 120-volt lamp draws 0.8 amp. What power does it consume?

**46.** A current of 8 amp flows through a resistance of 20 ohms. How much power is consumed (*a*) in watts; (*b*) in kilowatts?

**47.** A motor takes 11.2 kw when it is connected to 220-volt mains. What current does the motor take?

**48.** The output of a motor is 1.2 kw. What is the horsepower output?

**49.** A d-c motor is connected across 110-volt mains and draws 50 amp. What is the horsepower input to the motor?

**50.** A d-c shunt motor takes 60 amp at 550 volts. (*a*) Find the power consumed in kilowatts. (*b*) If the energy cost is $0.05 per kwhr, find the cost of operating this motor for 10 hr.

**51.** An electric heater uses 20 kwhr in 8 hr. If the voltage at the heater is 240 volts, what is the resistance of the heater?

**52.** Find the current taken by 40-, 60-, and 100-watt lamps when connected to a 120-volt power supply. Determine the time (in hours) needed for each of these lamps to consume 1 kwhr.

**53.** The load voltage of 12-kw load is 400 volts. The resistance of each line wire connecting the load to the source is 0.1 ohm. (*a*) What is the voltage at the source?  (b) What is the power dissipated as heat by the lines?   (c) How much energy is used by the load in 24 hr?   (d) How much energy is lost in the lines in 24 hr?

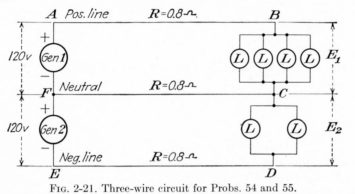

FIG. 2-21. Three-wire circuit for Probs. 54 and 55.

**54.** If each lamp in Fig. 2-21 requires a current of 1 amp, find (a) the current and its direction in each of the three lines, (b) the $IR$ drop in each line, and (c) the voltages $E_1$ and $E_2$.

**55.** Repeat the preceding problem if one lamp in the upper bank of lamps burns out.

# CHAPTER 3

# PRIMARY AND SECONDARY BATTERIES

Devices in which chemical energy is changed to electrical energy are called *electric cells*. When several cells are connected electrically (usually in series), they form a *battery*.

The essentials of any cell are two *dissimilar* metals or conductors that are immersed in a conducting liquid.

Cells or batteries may be classified into two general types: *primary* and *secondary*. In the primary cell it is necessary to renew the active materials from time to time or to discard the cell when electrical energy can no longer be obtained from it. In the secondary, or storage, cell the active materials may be restored by passing a current through the cell in a direction opposite to that of discharge.

**3-1. Primary Cells** When two dissimilar conductors are placed in a conducting solution that will act chemically on one of the conductors, an emf is developed between the two conductors. The conductors are called *plates* or *electrodes*, and the solution is called the *electrolyte*. When the electrodes are connected by a conductor, a current will flow from one electrode to the other through the conductor, the circuit being completed through the electrolyte. The electrode from which the current leaves the cell is called the *positive electrode*, and the other is called the *negative electrode*.

The emf developed in any cell depends on the materials used for electrodes and electrolyte. For example, if electrodes of zinc and lead are placed in a solution of sulfuric acid, the emf developed is about 0.5 volt; zinc and copper in sulfuric acid, about 1.0 volt; and zinc and silver in sulfuric acid, about 1.2 volts. The size and spacing of the electrodes does not affect the emf developed but does affect other characteristics of the cell.

Numerous combinations of materials have been used in the past for the electrodes and electrolytes of primary cells. Many of these combinations have found limited commercial application and others that were formerly used have been replaced by newer developments. The dry cell in several forms is now the most widely used primary cell, although some use is still made of the zinc–cupric oxide and the zinc-air cells in applications requiring moderately high currents at constant voltage for relatively long periods of time. Both of these cells have spillable electrolytes and are therefore not readily portable.

**3-2. Internal Resistance of a Cell** The entire resistance encountered by a current as it flows through a cell from the negative terminal to the positive terminal is called the internal resistance of the cell. As in any other conductor of electricity, the resistance of a cell depends on the materials, the cross-sectional area, the length of the current path, and the temperature. Thus the area and spacing of the electrodes both affect the internal resistance of a cell even though the emf developed is independent of these factors.

The current delivered by a cell depends not only on the emf of the cell and the load resistance, but on the internal resistance of the cell as well. By Ohm's law the current delivered by a cell is

$$I = \frac{E}{R_i + R_l} \tag{1}$$

where $I$ = current, amp
$E$ = emf, volts
$R_i$ = internal resistance of cell, ohms
$R_l$ = load resistance, ohms

On open circuit, the terminal voltage of a cell is equal to the emf developed. However, when a cell delivers current, some of the emf developed must be used in overcoming the resistance of the cell itself so that the terminal voltage is lower than the emf. The greater the current delivered, the greater the voltage drop, or $IR$ drop, in the cell and the lower the terminal voltage becomes. The terminal voltage in any case is

$$E_t = E - IR_i \tag{2}$$

where $E_t$ = terminal voltage, volts
$E$ = emf, volts
$I$ = current, amp
$R_i$ = internal resistance, ohms

By transposing Eq. (2), the following expression for internal resistance results:

$$R_i = \frac{E - E_t}{I} \tag{3}$$

The relation given in Eq. (3) suggests a method of measuring internal resistance. First the open-circuit voltage of the cell is measured to get the value of $E$. A high-resistance voltmeter should be used so that the current drawn by the voltmeter is negligible. Then with the cell delivering a current $I$, the terminal voltage $E_t$ is measured. The internal resistance $R_i$ may then be obtained by means of Eq. (3).

The following example will illustrate the effect of different values of internal resistance on the amount of current that a cell is able to deliver to a particular load.

**Example 1**    A coil that has a resistance of 0.05 ohm is connected to a cell that develops an emf of 1.5 volts. Find the current flowing if the internal resistance of the cell is (a) 0.1 ohm, and (b) 0.01 ohm.

$$(a) \quad I = \frac{E}{R_i + R_l} = \frac{1.5}{0.1 + 0.05} = 10 \text{ amp}$$

$$(b) \quad I = \frac{E}{R_i + R_l} = \frac{1.5}{0.01 + 0.05} = 25 \text{ amp}$$

**3-3. Dry Cells**    There are three types of dry cells being produced in quantity in the United States: the *Leclanché*, the *zinc–mercuric oxide*, and the *alkaline zinc–manganese dioxide* cells. Actually, these cells are not dry but the electrolyte is combined with an absorbent inactive material. The cells are, however, sealed into watertight containers so that they may be easily transported and operated in any position.

The most widely used and probably the most familiar type of dry cell is the Leclanché cell. A cross-sectional view of a cell of this type is shown in Fig. 3-1. The container, which also serves as the negative electrode, is zinc. Next to the zinc is a layer of blotting paper or starch paste which is saturated with the electrolyte, the electrolyte being composed of sal ammoniac and a small amount of zinc chloride. The positive electrode is a carbon rod set in the center of the cell. Between the carbon electrode and the electrolyte paste is a mixture of powdered coke, graphite, and manganese dioxide, the latter being called the depolarizer. The cell is sealed with a watertight gasket.

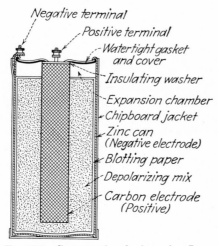

*Negative terminal*
*Positive terminal*
*Watertight gasket and cover*
*Insulating washer*
*Expansion chamber*
*Chipboard jacket*
*Zinc can (Negative electrode)*
*Blotting paper*
*Depolarizing mix*
*Carbon electrode (Positive)*

Fig. 3-1. Cross-sectional view of a Leclanché dry cell.

The open-circuit emf of a new Leclanché dry cell is about 1.5 volts. The capacity of the cell is dependent upon the size of the cell and the rate at which energy is withdrawn. The lower the rate, the more efficiently the cell is able to convert the available chemical energy into electrical energy. For this reason, the best application of this cell is for use in intermittent service, such as in flashlights, portable radios, or ignition systems.

The zinc–mercuric oxide cell has a negative electrode of zinc and a positive electrode consisting of a mixture of red mercuric oxide and graphite. The electrolyte is a potassium hydroxide solution containing zinc oxide. The cell has an open-circuit emf of 1.34 volts and has a relatively flat voltage-time discharge characteristic for most of its useful life. Because of its flat voltage characteristic and higher capacity for a given volume than the Leclanché cell, it is commonly applied in hearing aids, small portable radios, and scientific instruments. The mercuric oxide cell has not replaced the Leclanché cell in the larger sizes because of its higher cost.

Alkaline zinc–manganese dioxide cells, sometimes referred to as crown cells, are similar in construction to the mercuric oxide cells. These cells have an open-circuit emf of approximately 1.5 volts. However, they do not have as high a capacity as mercuric oxide cells of the same size. They are best suited to low-drain intermittent-duty applications.

**3-4. Secondary, or Storage, Cells**   A cell in which the physical state and chemical condition of the electrodes and electrolyte may be restored by charging is called a secondary, or storage, cell. Charging such a cell consists of passing current through the cell in a direction opposite to the direction of current flow on discharge. There are several types of storage cells in use, the more common ones being the *lead-acid*, the *nickel-cadmium-alkaline*, and the *nickel-iron-alkaline*, or *Edison*, cell.

As in the primary cell, the emf of a secondary cell depends on the materials used for electrodes and the electrolyte. The average terminal voltage of a lead-acid cell is approximately 2.0 volts, while that of the nickel-cadmium-alkaline and Edison cells is approximately 1.2 volts.

The capacity of a cell, for a given plate thickness, depends on the total plate area; the greater the plate area, the greater the capacity.

**3-5. Theory of the Lead-Acid Cell**   The positive plate of a lead-acid storage cell is lead peroxide, $PbO_2$, and the negative plate is pure sponge lead, $Pb$. Dilute sulfuric acid, $H_2SO_4$, is used as the electrolyte. When the cell supplies current to a load or is discharging, the chemical action that takes place forms lead sulfate, $PbSO_4$, on both plates with water being formed in the electrolyte. After a certain amount of energy has been withdrawn from the cell, both plates having been transformed into the same material, the cell is no longer able to develop an emf.

To charge the cell, a current is caused to flow through the cell in the opposite direction; this reverses the chemical process and again forms a lead peroxide positive plate and a pure lead negative plate, at the same time restoring the electrolyte to its original condition. The chemical reaction may be represented as follows:

| Positive plate | | Negative plate | | Electrolyte | | Positive plate | | Negative plate | | Electrolyte |
|---|---|---|---|---|---|---|---|---|---|---|

$$PbO_2 \ + \ Pb \ + \ 2H_2SO_4 \ \rightleftharpoons PbSO_4 \ + \ PbSO_4 \ + \ 2H_2O$$

Cell charged          Cell discharged

This equation represents the discharging action when read from left to right and the charging action when read from right to left.

### 3-6. Specific Gravity
The ratio of the weight of a volume of any liquid to the same volume of water is called the specific gravity of the liquid. For example, the specific gravity of sulfuric acid is 1.840, which means that sulfuric acid is 1.840 times as heavy as water.

The electrolyte of a lead-acid battery is a solution of sulfuric acid in water. In a battery used for stationary work, in which a large volume of electrolyte may be used, the specific gravity in the fully charged state is about 1.210 to 1.225. In a portable battery, such as those used in automobile and airplane service, and where space and weight are limited, a smaller volume of electrolyte is used. The specific gravity of the electrolyte in portable batteries is 1.275 to 1.300 when fully charged.

The climate or temperature at which batteries are to be operated is also a factor that is taken into account in determining the specific gravity to be used. Batteries used in extremely cold climates require electrolytes of higher specific gravity to prevent freezing. Batteries used in torrid climates require electrolytes of lower specific gravity to prevent their overheating while in operation.

The amount of decrease in specific gravity from the fully charged state to the discharged state varies with the volume of the electrolyte. For large volumes of electrolyte, the drop may be as small as 0.030, and for small volumes, as in automobile batteries, it may be as large as 0.180.

The specific gravity of a cell electrolyte varies with temperature, an increase in temperature of 3°F amounting to a drop of about 0.001 in specific gravity, or vice versa.

If the specific gravity of a cell electrolyte is known for the fully charged and discharged conditions, specific-gravity readings may be used as an indication of the state of charge of a battery. Temperature corrections should be used if widely varying temperatures are encountered.

For measuring specific gravity, an instrument called a *hydrometer* is used. In the syringe-type hydrometer shown in Fig. 3-2, a part of the electrolyte is drawn from the cell into the syringe. A weighted bulb floats in the electrolyte inside the syringe, the depth at which it floats being a measure of the specific gravity of the electrolyte being tested. The lower the bulb floats, the lower the specific gravity. The stem on the bulb is marked for different values of specific gravity so that the reading on the stem at the surface of the liquid is the gravity reading of the electrolyte in the syringe.

### 3-7. Battery Capacity
The capacity of a battery depends on the number, the design, and the dimensions of the plates and the quantity of electrolyte. The amount of energy that any given fully charged battery can deliver also depends on several variables such as the discharge rate, the temperature, and the age of the cell.

Because of the many variables involved, there are various methods of rating battery capacity. Since batteries are usually adapted to a particular kind of service, the rating of a battery is ordinarily based on the requirements for that service.

Fig. 3-2. A syringe-type hydrometer.

For example, automobile starting batteries are often given two ratings. One rating called the *twenty-hour* rate is an ampere-hour rating based on (1) a starting temperature of 80°F, (2) a constant current output for 20 hr, and (3) a final or limiting voltage of 1.75 volts per cell. For example, if under the above conditions, a battery can deliver 5 amp continuously for 20 hr, its ampere-hour rating is 5 × 20 or 100 amp-hr.

The second rating given automobile batteries is called the *cold rating* and indicates the number of minutes a battery can deliver 300 amp at 0°F.

For comparatively low-rate discharge service batteries, the *eight-hour rate* has been standard.   This is an ampere-hour rating based on a continuous discharge rate for 8 hr under specified conditions.

### 3-8. Construction of Lead-Acid Batteries

In the pasted-plate battery, which is used extensively, the plates are formed by applying special lead oxide pastes to a grid made of a lead-antimony alloy.   After charging, the lead oxides become the active material.   The grid serves to hold the active material in place and also to distribute the current evenly over the surface of the plate.

The plates are formed into positive and negative groups so that they may be nested together as shown in Fig. 3-3.   The number of negative

Fig. 3-3. A lead-acid cell element partly assembled.   (*Courtesy of Delco-Remy Division, General Motors Corporation.*)

plates is always one more than the number of positive plates so that both sides of each positive plate will be acted upon chemically.   This is necessary since the active material on the positive plate expands and contracts as the battery is charged and discharged, and this expansion and contraction must be kept the same on both sides of the plate to prevent buckling.

Separators of wood, rubber, or glass mat are placed between the positive and negative plates, as shown in Fig. 3-3, to prevent the plates from coming in contact with each other.   Separators are grooved vertically on one side and are smooth on the other.   The grooved side is placed against the positive plate to permit free circulation of the electrolyte around the positive plate where the greater chemical action takes place.

Figure 3-4 shows the element assembled with the cell cover in place
and with the positive and negative
terminals projecting through the
cover.   To provide a means for fill-
ing and testing, each cell cover has
a hole into which is fitted the filler
cap.   The filler cap has a venthole
to allow the gas that is formed in
the cell to escape.

In the 6-volt storage battery,
three cells are assembled, each in an
acidproof compartment, the cells
then being connected in series.   In
the battery shown in Fig. 3-5, six
cells are connected in series to form
a 12-volt battery.   The intercell
connections are of lead-alloy links
that are attached to the cell terminals by a lead-burning process.
The case and cell covers of portable
lead-acid batteries, similar to that
shown in Fig. 3-5, are usually of

FIG. 3-4. Assembled lead-acid cell ele-
ment with cell cover.   (*Courtesy of
Delco-Remy Division, General Motors
Corporation.*)

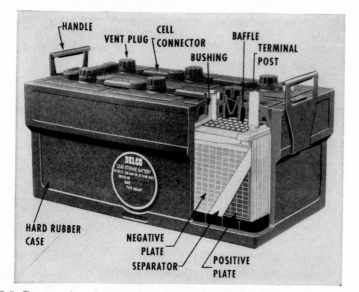

FIG. 3-5. Construction of a typical 12-volt lead-acid storage battery.   (*Courtesy of
Delco-Remy Division, General Motors Corporation.*)

hard rubber, the cell covers being sealed in place by an acidproof sealing compound.   Stationary-type batteries are usually contained in glass or plastic jars, the cell covers being made of hard rubber.

### 3-9. Operation and Maintenance of Lead-Acid Batteries   In the normal operation of a lead-acid storage battery, a certain amount of water is lost from the electrolyte by evaporation and because of gassing.   Gassing takes place during charging when the water in the electrolyte is decomposed to hydrogen and oxygen, each of which are given off in the form of gas.   The level of the electrolyte should never be allowed to fall below the tops of the plates, and it should be kept at the proper level by adding pure distilled water at regular intervals. Acid is not added to a battery unless the electrolyte has been spilled.

Lead-acid batteries should not be discharged further after a terminal voltage of about 1.75 volts per cell is reached and the specific gravity has dropped its normal amount.   Further discharge produces an excess of lead sulfate on the plates.

A battery should not be left in the discharged condition for any length of time since the lead sulfate on the plates crystallizes so that proper reforming of the plates becomes difficult if not impossible. If a battery is to be stored for any length of time, water should be added to the proper level, after which the battery should be fully charged.   At intervals of 4 to 6 weeks the battery should be given a freshening charge to keep it in the fully charged state.

Batteries may be charged at almost any rate provided the cell temperature does not exceed 110°F and that excessive gassing does not take place.   Usual practice is to charge at a tapered rate, that is, at a high rate at first but at a gradually reduced rate as the battery becomes nearly charged.   Charging should continue until all cells are gassing freely and until the specific gravity of the electrolyte and the terminal voltage of the battery are constant for a period of 1 hr.   Although violent gassing or gassing for long periods should be avoided, a small amount of gassing for a short time at the end of a charge is desirable to ensure that no lead sulfate remains on the plates.

### 3-10. The Nickel-Cadmium Battery   The nickel-cadmium-alkaline battery, usually referred to as the nickel-cadmium battery, has been used in Europe since about 1910 but did not find extensive acceptance in America until after about 1945.   Experience gained in Europe indicates that the nickel-cadmium battery is extremely reliable and has a life expectancy of 25 years or more.

In the nickel-cadmium cell, the principal active material in the positive plate is nickelous hydroxide; in the negative plate it is cadmium hydroxide. The electrolyte is potassium hydroxide. During charge or discharge there is practically no change in the specific gravity of the electrolyte. The sole function of the electrolyte is to act as a conductor for the transfer of hydroxyl ions (electrically charged particles) from one plate to the other depending on whether the cell is being charged or discharged.

**3-11. Construction of the Nickel-Cadmium Battery** Two different constructions are used in the nickel-cadmium cell: the pocket-plate and the sintered-plate construction.

Fig. 3-6. Sintered plate, nickel-cadmium battery. (*Courtesy of Nicad Division, Gould-National Batteries, Inc.*)

The pocket-plate construction was the type used when the nickel-cadmium cell was first introduced in America and which has since gained wide acceptance in heavy-duty applications. In this type of plate construction, the active materials are encased in finely perforated steel plates. Positive and negative plates are welded or bolted to steel bus bars and the plate groups are interleaved and separated by thin plastic rods. Plate groups of each cell are supported in nickel-plated steel cell containers. Cells are assembled into batteries in hardwood trays with spacers between cells to provide an insulating air space around each cell.

The sintered-plate construction is a later development, developed primarily to meet the military need for a rugged, lightweight battery suitable for operation over a wide range of temperatures. Plates are made from a nickel powder which is molded into shape and heated to a high temperature. The resulting plate is a highly porous structure the pores of which are impregnated with the active material, forming a plate with a large surface area. Plates are made up into groups and are separated by layers of thin synthetic fabric. Plate groups of each cell are supported in plastic containers and batteries are assembled in steel cases. This construction results in a lightweight vibration- and shock-resistant battery suitable for use in portable communication equipment, missile and rocket control, and other similar uses. A 6-volt battery of the sintered-plate type is shown in Fig. 3-6.

### 3-12. Characteristics of the Nickel-Cadmium Battery

The average discharge voltage per cell of the nickel-cadmium battery is 1.2 volts. However, the voltage per cell may be as high as 1.35 to 1.4 volts when the cell is being maintained in the fully charged state by a trickle charger. Five cells make up a nominal 6-volt battery which is normally trickle charged at about 6.75 volts. For the quite commonly used 125-volt supply used for control power in power plants and for emergency lighting systems, 92 cells are used and the battery is maintained at 129 volts by a continuous charge.

The nickel-cadmium battery is characterized by its low maintenance cost, long life, and reliability under severe operating conditions. The battery can be left idle for long periods of time in any state of charge without deteriorating. It will not freeze even in the completely discharged condition. Since the battery does not give off corrosive fumes, no special precautions need be used regarding its location.

### 3-13. Edison Cells

The Edison nickel-iron-alkaline cell consists of a positive plate of a nickel oxide, a negative plate of iron, and an electrolyte of 21 per cent solution of potassium hydroxide with a small amount of lithium hydroxide added. As the cell is discharged, the positive plate is reduced to a lower oxide of nickel and the negative plate is oxidized to iron oxide. When the cell is being charged, the process is reversed. The electrochemical actions then are merely a transfer of oxygen from one plate to the other. The specific gravity of the electrolyte does not change appreciably during charge or discharge as it does in the lead-acid cell and thus cannot be used as an indication of the state of charge of the cell.

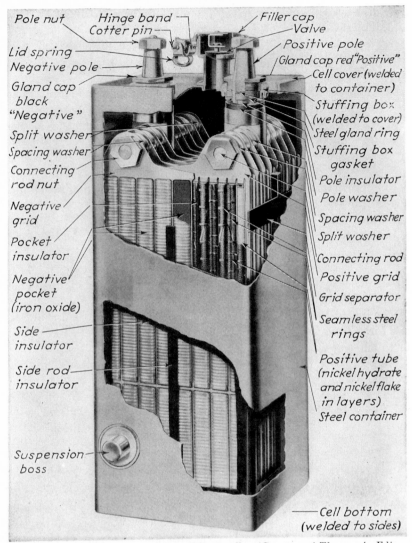

Pole nut
Hinge band
Cotter pin
Filler cap
Valve
Lid spring
Negative pole
Positive pole
Gland cap red "Positive"
Cell cover (welded to container)
Gland cap black "Negative"
Split washer
Spacing washer
Connecting rod nut
Negative grid
Pocket insulator
Negative pocket (iron oxide)
Side insulator
Side rod insulator
Suspension boss
Stuffing box (welded to cover)
Steel gland ring
Stuffing box gasket
Pole insulator
Pole washer
Spacing washer
Split washer
Connecting rod
Positive grid
Grid separator
Seamless steel rings
Positive tube (nickel hydrate and nickel flake in layers)
Steel container
Cell bottom (welded to sides)

FIG. 3-7. Cross-sectional view of the Edison cell.    (*Courtesy of Thomas A. Edison, Inc., Storage Battery Division.*)

### 3-14. Construction of the Edison Cell

The positive plate of the Edison cell consists of a nickel-plated steel grid upon which are mounted perforated steel tubes filled with alternate layers of nickel hydrate and pure nickel flakes. These tubes are strongly constructed and are securely attached to the grid so that the active material is not dislodged by chemical action or physical disturbance. Different cell capacities are obtained by using different numbers of tubes per plate and different numbers of plates per cell.

Edison-cell negative plates are also formed on nickel-plated steel grids in which are mounted steel pockets filled with finely divided iron oxide.

Plate assemblies are similar to those of the lead-acid cell. The assembled element is placed in a nickel-plated steel container with a liquidtight cover through which protrude the cell terminals. A filler opening is provided for each cell. An assembled Edison cell, cut away to show constructional details, is shown in Fig. 3-7.

**3-15. Characteristics of the Edison Cell**   At the beginning of discharge the terminal voltage of an Edison cell is about 1.4 volts and averages about 1.2 volts during a normal discharge period. The cell is ordinarily recharged after the terminal voltage drops to about 1.0 volt.

Unlike the lead-acid cell, the Edison cell may be repeatedly short-circuited without harm. It may also be left idle in a discharged condition indefinitely without harm.

The internal resistance is about five times that of the lead-acid cell, and for this reason it is able to deliver much less current at short circuit or to low-resistance loads.

As compared with the lead-acid cell, the Edison cell is lighter in weight and more rugged in construction. Its first cost is higher, but it has a much longer life than the lead-acid cell. The Edison cell is used extensively for the propulsion of industrial trucks and mine locomotives and for railway-car lighting and air conditioning, its rugged construction making it especially adaptable to service of this kind.

**3-16. Applications of Storage Batteries**   A very important use of storage batteries is in the providing of stand-by power for various electrical systems. In some electrical systems, storage batteries are connected in parallel with the generator and the load. When the generator is in operation, the battery draws enough current to keep it fully charged. When the generator is shut down, the battery supplies the load.

Railway-car lighting systems are supplied from axle-driven generators when the train is in motion, with batteries supplying the system when the train runs at slow speeds or is stopped.

Automobile electrical systems are similar to the above-mentioned system in that the generator, battery, and load are connected in parallel, the battery supplying power for starting and lighting when the generator is not in operation.

In a-c generating plants, storage batteries are used to energize control apparatus and, during emergency shutdowns of the generators, are used to supply emergency lights. Hospitals and other places where a continuous source of power is absolutely essential often use batteries as an emergency supply.

Applications in which storage batteries supply the primary or normal current are in industrial-truck or mine-locomotive propulsion, portable lighting equipment, portable radios, and other applications in which continuous connection to a generator is impracticable.

## REVIEW QUESTIONS

**1.** What is the function of an electric cell?

**2.** What are the essential parts of an electric cell?

**3.** Upon what does the emf of a cell depend?

**4.** How do primary and secondary cells differ?

**5.** Upon what factors does the internal resistance of a cell depend?

**6.** Why does the terminal voltage of a cell drop with increases in current output?

**7.** How can internal resistance be determined?

**8.** Name three types of dry cells.

**9.** Describe the construction of a Leclanché dry cell.

**10.** What materials are used for electrodes in the mercuric oxide cell?

**11.** Name three types of storage cells.

**12.** Describe briefly the chemical action that takes place in the lead-acid cell.

**13.** What is meant by the term *specific gravity*? Why is it valuable to know the specific gravity of the electrolyte of a lead-acid cell? How is it measured?

**14.** How are batteries rated as to capacity?

**15.** Describe briefly the construction of the lead-acid battery.

**16.** Why is it necessary to add water to the electrolyte of a lead-acid cell?

**17.** Why should lead-acid cells not be discharged below certain levels? Should a lead-acid battery be left standing in the discharged condition? Why?

**18.** What two things limit the charging rate of a lead-acid cell?

**19.** What are the active materials in the nickel-cadmium cell?

**20.** What are the two types of construction used in the nickel-cadmium cell?

**21.** Give some of the more important characteristics of the nickel-cadmium battery.

**22.** Briefly, what is the chemical action in an Edison cell? In what way does the chemical action differ from that of the lead-acid cell?

**23.** Why is Edison-cell construction considered to be more rugged than that of the lead-acid cell?

**24.** What are some characteristics of the Edison cell and how do they differ from those of the lead-acid cell?

**25.** Give several general applications of storage batteries.

# CHAPTER 4

## MAGNETISM

Magnetism is involved in the operation of a great number of electric devices, such as generators, motors, measuring instruments, and transformers. For this reason, a knowledge of the underlying principles of magnetism is essential before the operation of electrical machinery may be understood.

**4-1. Magnets and Magnetic Materials** It has been known for centuries that certain materials have the ability of attracting iron and steel. A body possessing this property is called a *magnet*. Magnets are found in a natural state in the form of the mineral called magnetite. However, natural magnets have no practical value and commercial magnets are made artificially from iron and steel or alloy materials.

Magnets may be classified as being *permanent* or *temporary*, depending on their ability to retain magnetism. Hardened steel and certain alloys of nickel and cobalt, when magnetized, retain their magnetism indefinitely and are called permanent magnets. However, when a piece of soft iron is magnetized, it retains but a small part of its magnetism after the magnetizing force is removed.

The amount of magnetism retained by a magnet after the magnetizing force is removed is called *residual magnetism*. The fact that temporary magnets are able to retain even a small amount of magnetism plays an important part in the operation of d-c generators, as will be shown in Chap. 6.

Permanent magnets are used extensively in electric instruments and in meters, telephone receivers, and magnetos. In electric generators and motors where it is desirable to control the amount of magnetism present in the magnet, soft-iron temporary magnets are used.

Materials that are attracted or repelled by a magnet are called *magnetic materials*. Iron and steel are by far the most common magnetic materials. Nickel and cobalt and some of their alloys are also magnetic, the alloys being used in high-grade, permanent magnets.

When a material is easy to magnetize, it is said to have a high *permeability*. Soft iron, being relatively easy to magnetize, has a high permeability. Steel is hard to magnetize and, therefore, has a much lower permeability than soft iron.

A straight bar of steel when magnetized is called a *bar magnet*. When a bar magnet is dipped into iron filings, it is found that the filings are attracted in great numbers at the ends of the bar while very few are attracted to the center of the magnet. The areas at the end of a magnet where the attractive force is the greatest are called the *poles* of the magnet.

**4-2. Magnetic Fields and Lines of Force**   It has been stated that magnets have an attractive force for certain materials. With the aid of a compass, which is merely a freely suspended magnetized steel needle, the direction of the magnetic force may be determined at various points near a magnet. As shown in Fig. 4-1, the marked end of

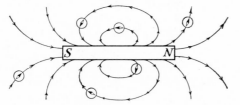

F*ig*. 4-1. The direction of the magnetic force around a bar magnet as indicated by a compass needle.

the compass needle always points away from one pole and toward the other. At the center of the magnet the needle points in a direction parallel to the magnet. The pole toward which the needle points is called the *south pole* of the magnet, and the other pole is called the *north pole*.

Another way of determining the polarity of a magnet is to suspend or pivot it at its center. The magnet will then come to rest in a north-south direction. The end of the magnet pointing north is called the *north pole* of the magnet, while the end pointing south is called the *south pole*.

When the directions to which the compass needle points as it is moved slowly from the north to the south pole of the magnet are plotted as in Fig. 4-1, the resulting figure shows that the magnetic force has definite direction at all points and acts along a curved line from north to south. Such a line is called a *line of force*. While lines of force are really imaginary lines surrounding a magnet, they are helpful in forming a picture of the nature of magnetism.

The space around a magnet or the space in which magnetic forces act is called a *magnetic field* and may be considered to be made up of many lines of force. The compass needle shows that the lines of force emerge from the north pole of a magnet, pass through the surrounding medium, and reenter the south pole. Inside the magnet, each line of force passes from the south pole to the north pole, thus forming a complete closed loop or magnetic circuit independently; that is, the lines do not cut across or merge into other magnetic lines.

An excellent graphical demonstration of the magnetic field pattern around a magnet may be made by placing a sheet of cardboard over a magnet and sifting fine iron filings over the cardboard. The filings,

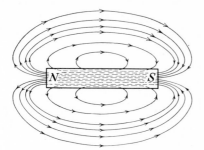

Fig. 4-2. The field around a bar magnet.

being magnetic bodies, arrange themselves in definite paths or lines between the poles. The pattern formed shows the shape of the field to be about as shown in Fig. 4-2.

To show that the magnetic field exists on all sides of the magnet, the magnet may be turned on edge. A pattern similar to that of Fig. 4-2 again results. The magnetic field exists in the entire space surrounding a magnet.

The magnetic field or entire quantity of magnetic lines surrounding a magnet taken as a whole is called *magnetic flux*. The number of lines of force per unit area is called the *flux density*. Common units of flux density are *lines per square inch* or *lines per square centimeter*.

The path in which magnetic lines of force are established is called a *magnetic circuit*. The magnetic circuit of a bar magnet consists of the path of magnetic lines through the magnet and the surrounding space. The opposition offered to the establishment of magnetic lines of force in a magnetic circuit is called the *reluctance* of the circuit. Air has a much higher reluctance than does iron or steel. For this reason, magnetic circuits such as are used in generators and motors are designed with very small air gaps, the greater part of the path followed by the lines of force being iron.

**4-3. Magnetic Attraction and Repulsion** When two magnets are suspended freely with their north poles toward each other, the two magnets push each other apart. The same happens when two south poles are placed near each other. However, when a north pole of one magnet and a south pole of the other are placed near each other, the two magnets attract each other.

The rule of magnetic attraction and repulsion is, then, that *like magnetic poles repel* and that *unlike magnetic poles attract* one another.

Upon this rule is based a more accurate picture of a magnetic line of force. If a small north pole were free to move in the field about a magnet, it would be repelled by the north pole of the magnet and attracted by the south pole. The path that this small north pole would follow in moving from north to south is called a line of force.

**4-4. Nature of Magnetism**   If a bar magnet is broken into two parts, each part is in itself a complete magnet with both a north and a south pole. If each part is again broken, the resulting parts are magnets. If the process is continued, it is found that the smaller and smaller particles retain their magnetism. If it were physically possible to break a magnet into so many pieces that each piece was a molecule, it would be logical to assume that each of these molecules would be a magnet.

Weber's theory of the nature of magnetism is based on the assumption that each of the molecules of a magnet is a tiny magnet. According to this theory, an unmagnetized bar of iron or steel is composed of these tiny molecular magnets haphazardly arranged so that the magnetism of each of the molecules is neutralized by an adjacent molecule. However, when a magnetizing force is applied to the iron or steel, the molecules become arranged in a definite pattern with their north and south poles pointing in opposite directions. The magnetism of each of the molecules acting in the same direction establishes the north and south poles of the magnet.

After a magnetizing force is removed from a piece of hardened steel, the molecules of the steel retain their positions indefinitely, while the molecules of a soft-iron bar tend to return to their original position.

**4-5. Field around a Current-carrying Conductor**   In 1819, Oersted found that a definite relation existed between electricity and magnetism. This discovery and later experiments by Henry and Faraday laid the foundation for the development of modern electrical machinery.

When a compass is brought into the vicinity of a current-carrying conductor, the needle sets itself at right angles to the conductor, thereby indicating the presence of a magnetic field. If a conductor is passed through a hole in a sheet of cardboard as shown in Fig. 4-3 and a current is passed through the conductor, the shape and direction of the field may be determined by setting the compass at various points on the cardboard and noting its deflection. This experiment shows that the magnetic field exists in concentric circles around the conductor. When the current is flowing downward as shown in Fig. 4-3, the field

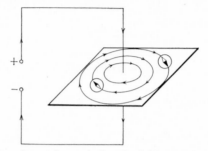

FIG. 4-3. Experiment for exploring the field around a conductor.

direction is clockwise. However, if the supply polarity is reversed so that current flows upward, the field is found to be counterclockwise. A simple rule, called the right-hand rule for a conductor, for relating the directions of current and field has been established.

*Grasp the conductor in the right hand with the thumb pointing in the direction of the current flow. The fingers then point in the direction of the field around the conductor.*

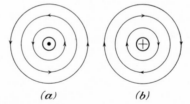

*(a)*                *(b)*

FIG. 4-4. Representation of the field around a conductor carrying current (*a*) toward the reader and (*b*) away from the reader.

The symbol ⊙ is used in diagrams to denote a cross-sectional view of a conductor carrying current toward the reader, while the symbol ⊕ is used to indicate current flowing away from the reader. These symbols may be thought of as views of an arrow pointing in the direction of current flow; in the former the arrow is approaching, and in the latter the arrow is going away from the reader. Figure 4-4 illustrates the use of these symbols.

**4-6. Field around a Coil**    The magnetism associated with a current-carrying conductor can be intensified by forming the conductor into a *coil* or *solenoid*.

It may be shown how the field is established around a coil by first considering two parallel conductors carrying current in the same direction as in Fig. 4-5. Lines of force pass around each conductor in the same direction, resulting in a field that entirely surrounds the two conductors. Likewise the field established by a belt of several con-

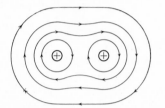

FIG. 4-5. Field around two parallel conductors.

ductors, all carrying current in the same direction, completely envelops the conductors as shown in Fig. 4-6a. When the current is reversed, the direction of the field is reversed as in Fig. 4-6b.

Figure 4-7a represents a coil formed by wrapping a conductor on a hollow, fiber or cardboard tube. Note that when current flows through the coil in the direction shown, current is flowing away from the

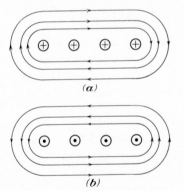

(a)

(b)

FIG. 4-6. Field around several conductors all carrying current (a) away from the reader and (b) toward the reader.

observer in the upper part of each turn (at points 1, 2, 3, 4, and 5) and toward the observer in the lower part of each turn (at points 6, 7, 8, and 9). This is further illustrated in the cross-sectional view of the coil in Fig. 4-7b. As indicated by the right-hand rule for a conductor, the field around conductors 1, 2, 3, 4, and 5 is in a clockwise direction and in a counterclockwise direction around conductors 6, 7, 8, and 9. Thus the field established by the coil is similar to that of a bar magnet, with flux emerging from one end of the coil and entering the other.

The end of the coil from which the flux emerges is called the north pole of the coil.

The polarity of any coil may be found by means of the right-hand rule for a coil, which may be stated as follows:

*Grasp the coil in the right hand with the fingers pointing in the direction of the current in the coil; the thumb then points toward the north pole of the coil.*

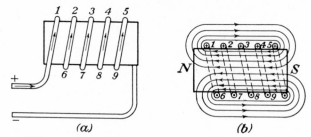

FIG. 4-7. (a) Coil wound on a hollow tube.   (b) Cross-sectional view showing the field produced by the coil.

### 4-7. Magnetomotive Force or MMF

A measure of the ability of a coil to produce flux is called *magnetomotive force* (abbreviated mmf). Magnetomotive force corresponds to emf in an electric circuit and may be considered to be a magnetic pressure, just as emf is considered an electric pressure.   The mmf of a coil varies directly with the current flowing in the coil and the number of turns on the coil.   The product of the current in amperes and the number of turns is called the *ampere-turns* of the coil.   The ampere-turn is taken as a practical unit of mmf.

### 4-8. Electromagnets

A coil with a given amount of mmf is able to produce a much greater amount of flux when an iron core is inserted into the coil, since the permeability of iron is so much greater than that of air.   Very powerful magnets called *electromagnets* may be made by placing a coil around an iron core.

The strength of an electromagnet depends on the number of ampere-turns of the exciting coil and on the permeability of the core.   Soft iron is the material usually used for the core of an electromagnet because of its high permeability.   The strength of an electromagnet with a given number of turns on the exciting coil may be varied by varying the amount of current through the coil.   This is the method of varying the amount of flux, and hence the amount of generated emf, in a generator.

Electromagnets have a multitude of applications in electrical machinery.   One important application, as mentioned above, is in the generator. The magnetic circuit of a two-pole d-c generator is shown in Fig. 4-8. A strong magnetic field is produced by the two field coils that are wound around the iron pole cores. As the armature is turned through the magnetic field, emf is generated in the armature conductors.

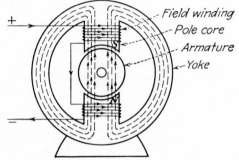

Fig. 4-8. The magnetic circuit of a two-pole generator.

Fig. 4-9. An electromagnet used for lifting scrap iron. (*Courtesy of Square D Company, EC&M Division.*)

Electromagnets are also used as lifting magnets to move scrap iron as shown in Fig. 4-9. Powerful magnets are formed by passing current through a coil that is placed around an iron core.

Other applications of electromagnets are in relays, motor controllers, circuit breakers, electrically operated valves, and motor brakes.

**4-9. Saturation**  In a coil with air as the core, the flux produced is directly proportional to the ampere-turns of the coil.  This is approximately true for an iron-cored coil up to a certain stage of magnetization of the core.  Above this point, increases in ampere-turns produce smaller and smaller increases in flux in the core, and the core is said to be *saturated*.

The saturation of iron may be explained by Weber's theory of magnetism.  As the ampere-turns of an exciting coil are increased from zero, molecules are moved into their magnetized position relatively easily since there are many haphazardly arranged molecules in the unmagnetized iron.  When the larger share of these molecules is arranged in a definite order, the iron is said to be saturated.  Further increases in ampere-turns produce smaller increases in magnetism of the iron since fewer molecules are left to bring into the magnetized position.

The effect of the saturation of iron on the operation of generators will be dealt with in Chap. 6.

### REVIEW QUESTIONS

**1.** What is a magnet?  Into what two classifications may magnets be divided?

**2.** What is the magnetism called that is retained by a magnet after its magnetizing force is removed?

**3.** What distinguishes magnetic materials from nonmagnetic materials?

**4.** How can the north and south poles of a magnet be identified?

**5.** What is a magnetic line of force?  What is a magnetic field?

**6.** What is meant by the term *flux density*?  What are units of flux density?

**7.** Give the rule of magnetic attraction and repulsion.

**8.** Describe, briefly, Weber's theory of magnetism.

**9.** How may it be shown that there is a magnetic field around a current-carrying conductor?  Give the rule that relates the current direction and the field direction.

**10.** What determines the polarity of a coil?  State the rule for finding the polarity of a coil.

**11.** Define magnetomotive force.  What is the unit?

**12.** In an electric circuit an emf causes a current to flow through a resistance in accordance with Ohm's law.  What are the corresponding quantities in a magnetic circuit?

**13.** Upon what does the strength of an air-cored coil depend? an iron-cored coil?  How is the strength of an electromagnet varied?

**14.** Give some applications of electromagnets.

**15.** When is a bar of iron said to be saturated?

# CHAPTER 5

## ELECTROMAGNETIC INDUCTION

It can be shown experimentally that an electromotive force can be produced in a conductor by moving the conductor through a magnetic field. The discovery of this principle was announced by Faraday in 1831; and it has been called the most important in the history of electricity, since it has led to the development of the electric generator, the transformer, the telephone, and numerous other electric devices.

**5-1. Induced EMF** If the ends of a conductor are connected to a low-reading voltmeter and the conductor is moved into the field of a magnet as shown in Fig. 5-1, a momentary reading will be noted on the voltmeter. As the conductor is withdrawn from the field, the meter will deflect momentarily in the opposite direction. If the conductor is held stationary and the magnet moved so that the field cuts the conductor, the same results are obtained. The voltage developed across the terminals of the voltmeter when the conductor is moved through the magnetic field (or when the field is moved across the conductor) is

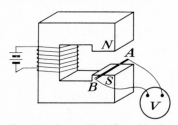

Fig. 5-1. An emf is induced in the conductor $AB$ when it is moved through the magnetic field.

known as an *induced electromotive force*. The current caused to flow in the conductor by the induced emf is sometimes called an *induced current*. The phenomenon whereby an emf is induced in a conductor when the conductor cuts or is cut by a magnetic field is called *electromagnetic induction*.

The principle of inducing an emf in a conductor by moving the conductor through a magnetic field is used in the d-c generator (Chap. 6). Stationary electromagnets establish the magnetic field through which conductors are moved, causing an emf to be induced in them.

In a-c generators, because of insulation and mechanical design problems, the conductors are stationary while the electromagnets are revolved (see Chap. 12). The principle is the same in both a-c and d-c generators, however, in that lines of force are being cut by a conductor in either case.

### 5-2. Factors Affecting the Amount of Induced EMF

When the conductor of Fig. 5-1 is replaced by a coil of several turns as in Fig. 5-2 and the experiment is repeated, it will be found that the voltmeter

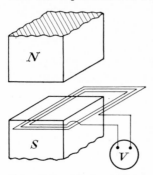

deflection is greater than when the single conductor was used, other conditions being the same. Each turn of the coil now has an emf induced in it, and since the turns are in series, the total emf of the coil is the sum of the emfs of each of the turns. If a coil of still more turns is used, correspondingly greater emfs will be induced, the amount of emf increasing directly with the number of turns on the coil.

When the speed at which a given coil is moved into the field is increased, the emf induced is increased, the emf being directly proportional to the speed at which the lines of force are cut.

FIG. 5-2. Electromotive force is induced in each turn of the coil as it is moved through the magnetic field.

The strength of the field is also a factor since, at a given speed, more lines of force are cut per second in a strong field than in a weak field. Other factors involved in inducing an emf are the angle at which the field is cut and the length of the section of conductor that is being moved through the field.

### 5-3. Faraday's Law of Induction

All the above-mentioned factors that are involved in the induction of an emf concern the *rate* at which the magnetic field is being cut by a conductor or the rate at which the number of lines of force through a coil is changing. In general:

*Whenever the number of lines of force threading through a coil is changed, an emf is induced in that coil. The amount of emf induced is proportional to the rate at which the number of lines of force through the coil is changing.*

This is known as Faraday's law of induction.

### 5-4. Numerical Value of Induced EMF

It has been shown that when flux is changing through a coil an emf is induced. When the flux through a one-turn coil is changing at the rate of 100 million lines per second, 1 volt is induced in the coil.

**5-5. Direction of Induced EMF**   As the conductor in Fig. 5-1 is moved into the magnetic field from right to left, the voltmeter indicates that an emf is induced from $A$ to $B$.   When the conductor is withdrawn from the field, the direction of the emf is reversed or is induced from $B$ to $A$.   If the polarity of the electromagnet is reversed, emf is induced from $B$ to $A$ as the conductor is moved into the field and from $A$ to $B$ when the conductor is withdrawn.   The relation between the directions of motion, field, and induced emf is given by *Fleming's right-hand rule:*

  *Extend the thumb, forefinger, and middle finger of the right hand at right angles to one another as in Fig. 5-3.   Point the forefinger in the*

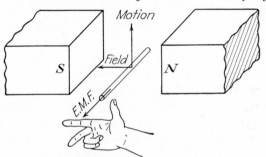

FIG. 5-3. Fleming's right-hand rule for determining the direction of an induced emf.

*direction of the magnetic field and the thumb in the direction of motion of the conductor.   The middle finger then points in the direction of the induced emf.*

  Fleming's right-hand rule is established for a *stationary field* and a *moving conductor.*   However, it may also be applied in the case of a moving field and a stationary conductor if the *relative* motion of the conductor is considered.   If the conductor $AB$ were stationary in Fig. 5-1 and the field moved toward the right, emf would be induced from $A$ to $B$ just as if the conductor were moved to the left into a stationary field.   That is, the motion of the conductor relative to the field is to the left in either case.   Therefore, it must be kept in mind when using Fleming's right-hand rule that the thumb must point in the direction of relative motion of the conductor.

**5-6. Lenz's Law of Induction**   According to Faraday's law, whenever the number of lines of force threading through or linking with a closed circuit is changed, an emf is induced which causes a current to flow in the circuit.   The direction of the induced current has a definite relation to the variation of the field that produces it.   This relation is stated by Lenz's law of induction, which may be stated as follows:

*An induced emf will cause a current to flow in a closed circuit in such a direction that its magnetic effect will oppose the change that produces it.*

This rule follows directly from the law of the conservation of energy; that is, to cause an induced current to flow requires the expenditure of energy.   In the case of a generator, for example, when the induced current is caused to flow through a load connected to the generator, electric energy is expended.   The field produced by the current is always in a direction so that it reacts with the main generator field, to oppose the turning action of the prime mover driving the generator. Thus, the greaterthe electric energy supplied to the load, the greater is the reaction and in turn the greater is the mechanical energy required from the prime mover.   Energy must be supplied to the generator at the same rate that it is being taken from the generator.

**5-7. Self-induced EMF: Inductance**   When a conductor is carrying a current, there is a magnetic field around the conductor.   When the current ceases to flow, the field ceases to exist.   When the current changes in intensity, the field likewise changes in intensity.   It has been shown that when the amount of flux threading through, or linking with, a circuit is changed, an emf is induced in that circuit.   When due to a change of current in a circuit itself, the induced emf is called the *emf of self-induction*.

Since, according to Lenz's law, any induced emf acts to oppose the change that produces it, a self-induced emf is always in such a direction as to oppose the *change* of current in the circuit in which it is induced.   When a coil or other electric circuit has the property of opposing any change of current in the circuit, it is said to possess *self-inductance* or simply *inductance*.

**5-8. Self-induction in a Coil**   A circuit consisting of a straight wire contains a certain amount of inductance; for a change of current in the wire produces a change in the flux enveloping or linking the circuit. However, a circuit containing a coil has a much higher value of inductance; for a change in current in such a circuit produces much more of a change in the flux linking the circuit.

Figure 5-4 represents a vertical cross section of a coil.   When the switch S is closed, current will flow from the battery into the coil at A. As the current increases in value, the magnetic lines expand from the center of each turn of the coil and cut across adjacent turns.   For example, the lines set up by the current in turn $A$ expand and cut across turn $B$, which is the equivalent of moving $B$ into the field of $A$. Fleming's right-hand rule shows the resulting induced emf to be toward the reader at $B$ or *against* the flow of current.   Other turns of the coil react in the same way.   The increase of current in the coil is thus opposed.

When the switch is opened, the collapsing field of the coil cuts across the coil in a direction opposite to that of the increasing flux.   This induces an emf in the reverse direction or in the *same* direction as the current flow, tending to maintain the current flow or to oppose its decrease.

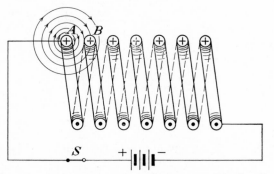

Fig. 5-4. As the current increases in the coil, the expanding flux lines from each turn of the coil move across adjacent turns, inducing an emf in them.

Thus, a circuit that has inductance opposes any *change* in current through the circuit.   In the coil of Fig. 5-4, the self-induced emf opposes the increase in current as the switch is closed and opposes the decrease in current as the switch is opened.   When a current is unchanging in value, the inductance of the circuit has no effect on its flow.   A steady current is opposed only by the resistance of the circuit.

When a highly inductive circuit (such as a generator field circuit) is opened, the self-induced emf may be high enough to damage the insulation of the coil or to endanger the life of the person opening the switch.   For this reason, a discharge resistor is often connected across the coil at the same instant that the switch blade is opened.   The induced emf then causes a current to flow through the resistor and permits the field to collapse gradually, thus limiting the value of the self-induced emf.

**5-9. Mutual Induction**  In Art. 5-1 it was shown how an emf may be induced by moving either a conductor or the magnets that produce the field, as in the case of electric generators.   Electromotive forces may also be induced by devices in which neither the conductor nor the magnets move but in which the magnetic field is made to vary in strength or direction.

If two coils are placed adjacent to one another as in Fig. 5-5, a part of the flux produced by coil *A* passes through or links with coil *B*. If the field strength of coil *A* is increased or decreased, there is a corresponding increase or decrease in the field strength inside coil *B*. Since, according to Faraday's law, an emf is induced whenever the number of lines of force is changing through a coil, each change of field strength through coil *B* causes an emf to be induced in that coil. Electromotive force is induced in one direction in coil *B* as the field

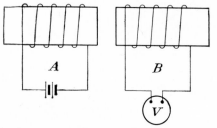

Fig. 5-5. A change in the amount of current flowing in coil *A* induces an emf in coil *B*.

expands and in the other direction as the field collapses, the direction in each case being that indicated by Fleming's right-hand rule or by Lenz's law.

Coil *A*, the coil that is connected to the supply and that produces the original flux, is called the *primary coil*. Coil *B* is called the *secondary coil*. If the two coils are wound on the same iron core, the flow established by the primary coil is not only greater, but a larger part of it is made to cut or link with the secondary coil as it expands or collapses. An emf induced in a secondary coil by a change of current in the primary coil is said to be induced by *mutual induction*.

The field established by the primary coil and which links with the secondary coil may be made to vary by one of three methods: by varying the intensity of the primary current, by periodically reversing the primary current, or by interrupting or "making and breaking" the primary current.

An example of the use of a varying primary current to induce an emf in a secondary circuit is in the telephone. A battery, the telephone transmitter, and the primary of an induction coil are connected in series as shown in Fig. 5-6. The sound waves of the speaker's voice cause the transmitter diaphragm to vibrate, which in turn varies the resistance of the transmitter. The primary current thus increases and decreases in value with the variations of the transmitter resistance, thereby causing a variation in the amount of flux linking the secondary coil of the induction coil. The alternating emf so induced in the secondary circuit causes an alternating current to flow over the line and through a distant receiver.

The transformer is a mutual-induction device used for changing the value of alternating voltages. It consists of two windings, a primary and a secondary, wound on the same iron core. When an alternating voltage is applied to the primary winding, an alternating current, or a current that flows back and forth, flows in the primary winding.

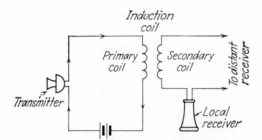

FIG. 5-6. Telephone-transmitter circuit.

The flux produced in the core increases, decreases, and reverses with the primary current. This induces an alternating emf in the secondary winding which is directly proportional to the number of turns on the secondary winding. Transformers are discussed in detail in Chap. 11.

**5-10. Ignition Systems** The method of interrupting the primary current to induce an emf is used extensively in ignition systems for internal-combustion engines. Figure 5-7 shows a circuit diagram of a six-cylinder automobile-engine ignition system, while the parts of the system are shown in schematic form in Fig. 5-8.

The ignition coil consists of a primary coil of a few turns of relatively heavy wire wound on an iron core and a secondary coil of many turns of fine wire wound directly around, but insulated from, the primary coil and the core. Primary current is supplied from a 6-volt storage battery. Breaker points that are connected in series with the primary coil and the battery are alternately opened and closed by a mechanically driven cam. When the points are closed, current from the battery flows through the primary coil, establishing a flux that links both primary and secondary coils. At the proper instant the cam "breaks" the points, opening the primary circuit. At the same time

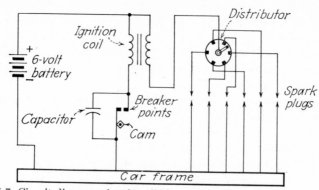

FIG. 5-7. Circuit diagram of a six-cylinder automobile-engine ignition system.

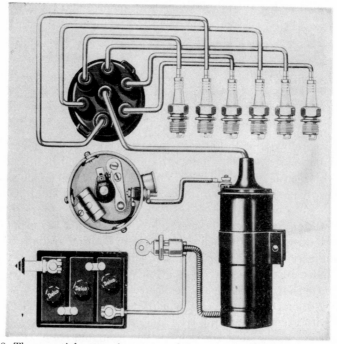

FIG. 5-8. The essential parts of an automobile-engine ignition system. (*Courtesy of Delco-Remy Division, General Motors Corporation.*)

the distributor arm connects the secondary coil to the proper spark plug. Thus as the field collapses around the secondary coil, the high voltage induced is applied across the spark-plug gap, causing an arc between the points which ignites the mixture in the combustion chamber.

The capacitor that is connected across the breaker points may be thought of as a storage tank for electricity. As the breaker points are separated, the capacitor momentarily provides a place for the current to flow. This causes the flow of primary current to come to a quick stop and prevents the forming of an arc across the breaker points. Since the primary current flow is brought to an abrupt stop, the flux collapses very fast and in so doing induces a high-voltage surge in the secondary circuit. The secondary voltage increases to a value high enough to establish the spark at the spark-plug gap. This sequence of events is then repeated as the next lobe on the cam again breaks the points and the distributor arm advances to fire the next spark plug.

## REVIEW QUESTIONS

1. What is an induced emf?
2. What factors affect the amount of emf induced in a coil?
3. State the general rule that covers all the variable factors involved in inducing an emf?
4. Numerically, what rate of change of flux is necessary to induce 1 volt?
5. State Fleming's right-hand rule. How may it be applied to a moving field and a stationary conductor?
6. State Lenz's law of induction. Upon what fundamental law is it based?
7. What is an emf of self-induction? Under what conditions of current flow is this emf induced? What is its direction in relation to any change in current?
8. In an inductive circuit, does the inductance have any effect on the flow of a steady current? Why?
9. Why is a coil said to have a higher value of inductance than a straight wire?
10. What is the purpose of a discharge resistor used in conjunction with opening a highly inductive circuit?
11. Show how a change of current may be made to induce an emf in an adjacent circuit. Using the relation given by Lenz's law, determine the direction of the flux established by an induced secondary-coil current in relation to an increasing primary flux.
12. Give three ways in which flux that mutually links two circuits may be varied. Which of these methods is used in (a) the telephone; (b) the transformer; (c) the ignition system?
13. What would be the effect of connecting a transformer to a d-c supply?
14. Describe briefly the action of the telephone-transmitter circuit.
15. Why is the secondary coil of an ignition coil wound with many turns of wire?
16. If a capacitor were not used in the ignition system, what would prevent the flux in the ignition coil from decreasing rapidly when the breaker points were opened?

# CHAPTER 6

## DIRECT-CURRENT GENERATORS

A *dynamo* is a machine that converts either mechanical energy to electric energy or electric energy to mechanical energy. When a dynamo is driven mechanically by a prime mover such as a steam turbine, water turbine, or diesel engine and delivers electric energy to electric lights or machines, it is called a *generator*. If electric energy is supplied to the dynamo and its output is used to drive mechanical devices such as line shafts and machine tools, it is called a *motor*. Generators are rated as to the *kilowatts* they can deliver without overheating at a rated voltage and speed. Motors are rated as to the *horsepower* they can deliver without overheating at their rated voltage and speed.

This chapter deals with dynamos used as generators, although much of what is said concerning generators is equally applicable to motors. Motors are discussed in Chap. 7.

**6-1. Dynamo Construction**  Flux produced by the field windings of a dynamo is established in the field yoke, pole cores, air gap, and armature core, all of which form what is known as the *magnetic circuit* of a dynamo. The magnetic circuit of a four-pole dynamo is shown in Fig. 6-1 and that of a six-pole dynamo in Fig. 6-2. The *field yoke*, or frame, being made of cast steel or rolled steel, serves as a mechanical support for the pole cores as well as serving as part of the magnetic circuit. *End bells*, which support the brush rigging and which in all but the very large machines also support the armature bearings, are also attached to the yoke.

Dynamo *pole cores* are made of sheet-steel laminations that are insulated from each other and riveted together, the core then being bolted to the field yoke as shown in Fig. 6-2. Note that the pole face, which is the surface of the core next to the air gap, is made larger than the main body of the core. This is to reduce the reluctance of the air gap and to provide a means of support for the field coils.

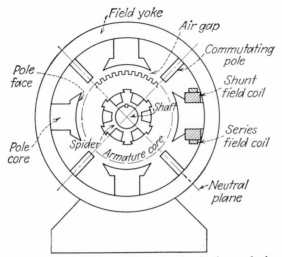

FIG. 6-1. The parts of the magnetic circuit of a four-pole dynamo.

FIG. 6-2. Partly assembled six-pole dynamo showing the parts of the magnetic circuit. (*Courtesy of Westinghouse Electric Corporation.*)

An assembled *armature core* and commutator, without the armature windings, are shown in Fig. 6-3. The core is made of sheet-steel laminations that are keyed to the shaft or, as is shown in Figs. 6-2 and 6-3, are keyed to a spider which in turn is keyed to the shaft. The outer surface of the core is slotted to provide a means of securing the armature coils.

The *air gap* is the space between the armature surface and the pole face and varies in length with the size of the machine but is of the order of $\frac{1}{16}$ to $\frac{1}{4}$ in.

The *electric circuits* of a dynamo are made up of the armature winding, commutator, brushes, and field windings. Except on small armatures, armature windings consist of coils that are wound to their correct shape and size on a form, after which they are completely

Fig. 6-3. An armature core with assembled commutator in the foreground. (*Courtesy of General Electric Company.*)

insulated. After the formed coils are slipped into their proper places in the armature slots, they are securely wedged into place and the coil ends are connected to the proper commutator segments. On small armatures, the windings are not form-wound but are wound by hand or by machine directly into the slots of the armature core.

The *commutator* consists of a number of copper segments that are assembled into a cylinder which is secured to, but insulated from, the shaft as shown in Fig. 6-3. The segments are well insulated from each other, mica being the insulating material commonly used. To these commutator segments are soldered the ends of the armature coils.

*Brushes* that rest on the face of the commutator form the sliding electrical connection between the armature coils and the external circuit. Brushes are made of carbon of varying degrees of hardness and in some cases are made of a mixture of carbon and metallic copper. The brushes are held in place under spring pressure by brush holders,

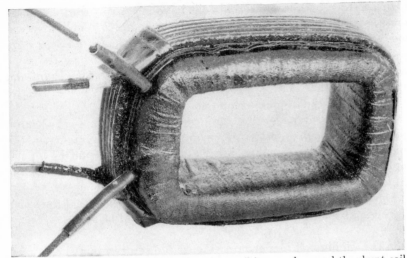

FIG. 6-4. Field coils of a dynamo. The series coil is wound around the shunt coil. (*Courtesy of General Electric Company.*)

FIG. 6-5. A dynamo, dismantled to show the various parts. (*Courtesy of Robbins & Myers, Inc.*)

the electrical connection between the brush and brush holder being made by a flexible copper cable called a *pigtail*.

The *field coils* are placed around the pole cores as shown in Fig. 6-1. The coils of each of the poles are connected in series to form the field circuit. Field circuits may be designed to be connected either in series or in parallel with the armature circuit. Parallel- or shunt-field coils have many turns of wire of small cross section and a relatively high resistance, while series-field coils have few turns of wire of large cross section and relatively low resistance. In order to obtain special operating characteristics, some dynamos (compound dynamos) are equipped with both shunt- and series-field coils placed on the same pole core. The field winding shown in Fig. 6-4 has both a shunt and a series coil, the series coil consisting of a few turns of heavy wire placed around the insulated shunt coil.

Most modern dynamos are equipped with small poles called *interpoles* or *commutating poles*, which are placed midway between the main poles, as shown in Fig. 6-1. Flux is established in these poles only when current flows in the armature circuit, the purpose of the flux being to improve commutation (Art. 6-10).

Figure 6-5 shows a dismantled small dynamo. Note that the brush rigging and the bearings are supported by the end bells.

**6-2. The Single-coil Generator**   Figure 6-6 represents a simple two-pole single-coil generator with the armature core and commutator

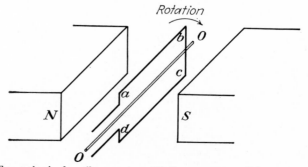

Fig. 6-6. Two-pole single-coil generator with the armature coil in the neutral plane.

omitted for the sake of simplicity. The single armature coil can be rotated about its axis *O-O* in the uniform magnetic field produced by the two poles. As the coil is rotated through the field by some mechanical means not shown, the number of lines of force through the coil changes continually. In Chap. 5 it was shown that when the number of lines of force through a coil is changed an emf is induced in that coil. The amount of emf induced depends on the rate at which the flux is changing through the coil, and its direction is determined by Fleming's right-hand rule. In a single-coil generator with a constant field strength, the amount of emf induced at any instant then depends upon how fast the coil is cutting across the field at that instant. An emf produced by the movement of a coil through a magnetic field, as in a generator, is called a *generated emf*.

When the coil is in the vertical position shown in Fig. 6-6, the coil edges are moving parallel to the lines of force so that the flux enclosed by the coil is not changing. Thus no emf is generated when the coil is in this position. When the coil is in this position, it is said to be in the *neutral plane*.

As the coil is turned in a clockwise direction at a constant speed, the coil edges begin to cut across the field, slowly at first but at a gradually increasing rate. Thus, the amount of emf generated gradually increases as the coil moves around to the position shown in Fig. 6-7,

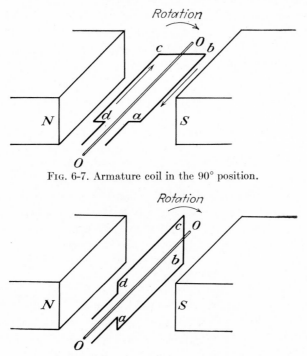

Fig. 6-7. Armature coil in the 90° position.

Fig. 6-8. Armature coil in the 180° position.

which is 90° from the position shown in Fig. 6-6. As determined by Fleming's right-hand rule, the direction of the emf generated as the coil moves through the 90° is from *b* to *a* and from *d* to *c*. In the 90° position, the coil edges are moving at right angles to the field and are therefore cutting across the field at a maximum rate; consequently, the emf generated at this point is at a maximum value.

As the coil is turned on past the 90° position, the rate at which the conductors cut across the field gradually decreases, causing the amount of generated emf to decrease gradually. When the coil reaches the position shown in Fig. 6-8, the coil is again in the neutral plane and the generated emf is again zero.

When the coil is moved in a clockwise direction from the 180° position in Fig. 6-8, the coil sides again begin to cut the field. However, the direction of the generated emf is now from $a$ to $b$ and from $c$ to $d$.

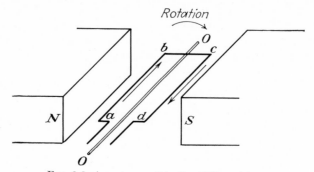

Fig. 6-9. Armature coil in the 270° position.

The amount of emf gradually increases until a maximum value is induced again at the 270° position shown in Fig. 6-9.

A comparison of Figs. 6-7 and 6-9 shows the directions of the generated emfs in the two coil sides to be reversed, but in each case the emf in the side $ab$ adds to that generated in the side $cd$.

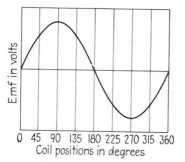

Fig. 6-10. Curve showing the variation of induced emf in a coil rotated in a uniform magnetic field.

As the coil is moved from the 270° position, the generated emf gradually decreases until the coil again reaches the neutral plane where the emf is zero. The cycle then repeats for each revolution of the armature.

Thus when a coil is rotated in a two-pole magnetic field, an emf is generated in one direction during the first half and in the opposite direction during the second half of each revolution. Such an emf is called an *alternating emf*. If the value of the generated emf is plotted for a number of the positions the coil passes through in one revolution, a curve similar to that shown in Fig. 6-10 results.

The single-coil generator may be connected to an external circuit by connecting the coil terminals to two continuous and insulated rings, called *slip rings*, or *collector rings*. These rings are mounted on the generator shaft and rotate with the coil and the shaft so that two stationary brushes, one bearing on each ring, connect the coil to the external circuit as shown in Fig. 6-11. When the coil is rotated, the generated alternating emf causes a current to flow first in one direction and then the other through the coil and external circuit. Such a current is called an *alternating current*.

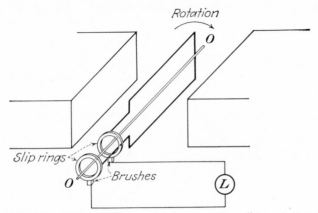

FIG. 6-11. Slip rings and brushes are used to connect the coil to an external circuit.

### 6-3. The Simple D-C Generator

It has been shown that the emf generated in a rotating armature coil is alternating. When this coil is connected to an external circuit by means of slip rings, an alternating

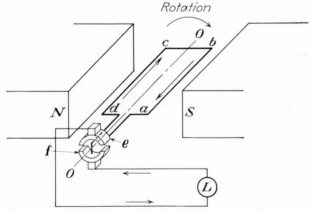

FIG. 6-12. Single-coil generator with a commutator.

current flows through the external circuit. Therefore slip rings cannot be used if direct current, which always flows in the same direction, is desired.

However, the alternating current in the armature coil may be converted into direct current for the external circuit by using a single split ring as shown in Figs. 6-12, 6-13, and 6-14. The two sections or segments that are insulated from each other and from the shaft form a simple *commutator*. Each end of the armature coil is connected to a segment. The action of the commutator is to reverse the armature coil connections to the external circuit at the same instant that the

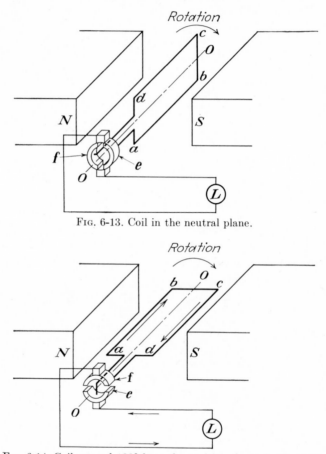

FIG. 6-13. Coil in the neutral plane.

FIG. 6-14. Coil rotated 180° from the position shown in Fig. 6-12.

current reverses in the armature coil. This action is described more fully in the following paragraphs.

When the armature coil is being turned in the clockwise direction, as in Fig. 6-12, emf is generated in the coil sides from *b* to *a* and from *d* to *c* as the arrows indicate. The circuit is completed by the lamp that is connected across the two brushes. The generated emf causes current to flow out through segment *e*, the upper brush, through the lamp, into the lower brush and segment $f$, and around the armature coil as indicated by the arrows.   When the coil is turned 90° into the neutral plane as shown in Fig. 6-13, the generated emf and, hence, the current drops to zero.   At this point the brushes make contact with both segments.   As the coil is moved on past the neutral plane through another 90° to the position shown in Fig. 6-14, emf is generated from $a$ to $b$ and from $c$ to $d$.   However, the upper brush now makes contact with segment $f$ and the lower brush with segment $e$.   A comparison of Figs. 6-12 and 6-14 shows that while the current has reversed in the armature coil it flows out of the upper brush, through the lamp, and into the lower brush in each case.   The emf and current drop to zero when the coil is moved another 90° into the neutral plane where the connections to the lamp are again reversed.

Although the current through the lamp is always in the same direction, it is not a steady current, since the emf, generated in the

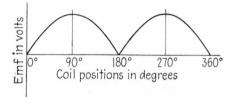

FIG. 6-15. The variation in brush voltage of a single-coil generator with a commutator.

armature coil and applied to the brushes, varies from zero to a maximum and back to zero twice each revolution.   The variation in brush voltage is shown in Fig. 6-15.

A pulsating direct current such as is produced by a single-coil generator is not suitable for most commercial uses.   However, by using a large number of coils and commutator segments, with the coils evenly distributed around the surface of the armature, the brush voltage may be made practically constant.

The voltage generated by a single-turn armature coil is small.   For this reason, the coils used in commercial generators consist of several turns in series, thereby increasing the amount of generated emf in direct proportion to the number of turns in the coil.

**6-4. Multicoil Armatures**   The method of connecting several armature coils to form a continuous or closed armature winding may be illustrated by the ring winding represented in Fig. 6-16a.   A ring winding is formed by winding the armature conductors around an iron ring or hollow iron cylinder as shown in the diagram.   This is an early form of armature winding which has been replaced by the more efficient, drum type of winding. However, the principle of the two windings is fundamentally the same, and the action of the ring winding is much more clearly represented by a diagram than is the drum winding. Hence the ring winding is used here as an illustration.

Figure 6-16a represents a two-pole ring winding with 16 coils of one turn each. By starting at the bottom brush and tracing through the winding to the upper brush, it may be seen that there are two separate paths through the winding. Coils 8 to 1 form one path, and coils 9 to 16 form the other. When the armature is turned in a clockwise direction, emf is generated away from the reader in the conductors under the face of the north pole and toward the reader in the conductors

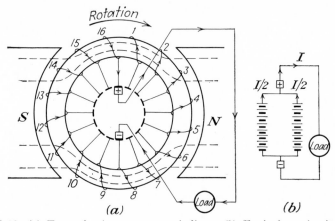

FIG. 6-16. (a) Two-pole ring-armature winding. (b) Equivalent circuit of the ring winding.

under the face of the south pole, causing currents to flow in the directions indicated by the arrows. The emf generated in each path is additive; that is, the emf generated in the path 8 to 1 is the sum of the emfs generated in each of the eight coils. Likewise the emf in the path 9 to 16 is the sum of the emfs generated in coils 9 to 16. However, since the two paths are connected in parallel, the voltage between the two brushes is equal to the emf generated in either of the two parallel paths. For example, if the average emf generated in each of the 16 coils is 5 volts, then the average emf generated in each path is 40 volts and the brush voltage is 40 volts.

Since the two paths through the armature winding are in parallel, any current supplied to the load divides equally between the two paths. For example, if the load current is 30 amp, then 15 amp is supplied by each of the two halves of the armature winding.

The armature winding of Fig. 6-16a may be represented by the equivalent circuit of Fig. 6-16b, in which each of the 16 coils is represented by a battery cell. The emf generated in each path is the sum of the emfs generated in the eight coils in that path, and the brush voltage is equal to the voltage of either path.

Since current is assumed to flow from the positive terminal of a source through a circuit and back into the negative terminal, the upper brush in Fig. 6-16 is called the positive brush and the lower brush the negative brush.

The drum-type armature winding used in modern d-c machines has the advantages of being easier to build and repair and of being more efficient than the ring winding. It is formed by placing the armature conductors, usually in the form of coils, in slots on the surface of a

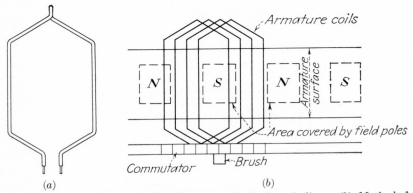

FIG. 6-17. (a) Single-turn winding element used in the lap winding. (b) Method of connecting the winding elements of a lap winding together and to the commutator.

drum-shaped or cylindrical iron core. Armature cores designed for drum winding are shown in Figs. 6-2 and 6-3, and a completed drum-wound armature is shown in Fig. 6-5.

In general there are two types of drum-armature winding: the *lap* and the *wave* windings. Each type of winding may be further classified as being a *simplex* (single) or a *multiplex* (double or triple) winding. Both lap and wave windings are closed-circuit windings; that is, they close upon themselves to form a closed electric circuit, just as does the ring winding shown in Fig. 6-16. Both windings are formed by interconnecting a number of separately insulated winding elements or coils, which have been laid in place in the armature core slots.

A winding element used in forming a lap winding is shown in Fig. 6-17a. The lap winding is so named because of the lapping back of one coil on the adjacent coil as shown in Fig. 6-17b. Figure 6-17b represents a developed view of part of a simplex lap winding; that is, the armature surface, windings, and commutator are represented as a flat surface. Note that ends of each coil are attached to adjacent commutator segments and that the finish end of one coil is attached to the start end of the adjacent coil.

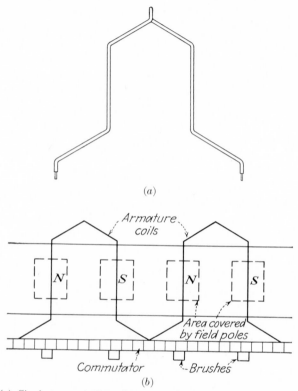

*(a)*

*(b)*

FIG. 6-18. *(a)* Single-turn winding element of a wave winding. *(b)* Two winding elements of a wave winding showing the method of connection.

The lap and wave windings differ essentially in the manner in which the ends of the coils are attached to the commutator. In the lap winding the coil ends are attached to adjacent commutator segments, while the ends of the wave-winding coils are attached to the commutator at points separated by approximately twice the distance between two adjacent field poles. Figure 6-18a shows a one-turn coil of the type used in a wave winding. Two coils of a simplex wave winding are shown in developed form in Fig. 6-18b.

Double and triple windings are used on armatures that must supply large currents. A double winding consists of two similar simplex windings placed in alternate slots on the armature and connected to alternate commutator segments. Each winding carries half the armature current. Likewise, a triple winding has three similar windings occupying every third slot and connected to every third commutator segment.

In the simplex lap winding there are as many parallel paths or circuits through the winding as there are field poles on the machine. Therefore, in the double lap winding the number of parallel circuits is twice the number of poles and in the triple winding, three times the number of poles. For this reason the lap winding is sometimes called the multiple or parallel winding and is suited for generators that operate at relatively low voltages but with high current outputs.

The simplex wave winding is sometimes called the two-circuit or series winding, since regardless of the number of field poles on the dynamo, there are two parallel paths or circuits through the winding. The double and triple wave windings have four and six parallel circuits, respectively. Only two brushes are necessary on a wave-wound machine, although more are often used to provide better commutation. The wave winding is used on medium-voltage machines up to about 50 kw in size and on large high-voltage machines.

A complete treatment of the many variations of the two basic types of armature windings is beyond the scope of this book. For further reading on the subject, the reader is referred to the many excellent books on armature windings.

**6-5. Methods of Field Excitation**   The general types of d-c generators take their names from the type of field excitation used. When a generator is excited from a storage battery or from a separate d-c source, it is called a *separately excited* generator. When a generator supplies its own excitation, it is called a *self-excited* generator. If the field of a self-excited generator is connected in parallel with the armature circuit, it is called a *shunt* generator. When the field is in series with the armature, the generator is called a *series* generator. If both shunt and series fields are used, the generator is called a *compound* generator. Compound generators may be connected *short-shunt* with the shunt field in parallel with the armature only or *long-shunt* with the shunt field in parallel with both the armature and series field. The circuit diagrams of the various types of generators are shown in Fig. 6-19. Field rheostats, as shown in this figure, are adjustable resistances placed in the field circuits to provide a means of varying the field flux and thereby the amount of emf generated by the generator.

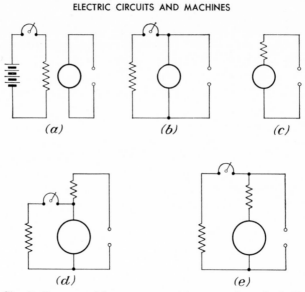

FIG. 6-19. Circuit diagrams of d-c generators: (a) separately excited, (b) shunt, (c) series, (d) short-shunt compound, and (e) long-shunt compound generators.

**6-6. Generator Voltage Equations**   The average generated emf $E_g$ of a generator may be calculated from the formula

$$E_g = \frac{pZ\phi n}{10^8 \times 60b} \qquad \text{volts} \tag{1}$$

where $p$ = number of poles

$Z$ = total number of conductors on armature (sometimes called *inductors*)

$\phi$ = flux per pole

$n$ = the speed of the armature in rpm

$b$ = number of parallel paths through armature, depending on type of armature winding

For any given generator, all the factors in Eq. (1) are fixed values except the flux per pole $\phi$ and the speed $n$.   Therefore Eq. (1) may be simplified to the form

$$E_g = K\phi n \tag{2}$$

where $K$ is equal numerically to all the fixed values or constants for a given generator.

Equation (2) is merely a restatement of Faraday's law of induction: the value of an induced emf in any circuit is proportional to the rate at which flux is being cut by the circuit.   Thus, if the flux per pole of a generator is doubled with the speed remaining constant, the generated emf will be doubled; or if the speed is doubled, the flux remaining constant, the generated emf will be doubled.

In practice, generators are usually operated at nearly constant speed, with the generated emf being adjusted to the desired value by adjusting the field flux. The field flux, being established by the field current, is controlled by the field rheostat.

**Example 1** When a generator is being driven at 1,200 rpm, the generated emf is 125 volts. What will be the generated emf (a) if the field flux is decreased by 10 per cent with the speed remaining unchanged, and (b) if the speed is reduced to 1,100 rpm, the field flux remaining unchanged?

(a) $E_{g2} = 125 \times 0.90 = 112.5$ volts

(b) $\dfrac{E_{g1}}{E_{g2}} = \dfrac{n_1}{n_2}$   or   $\dfrac{125}{E_{g2}} = \dfrac{1,200}{1,100}$

$E_{g2} = \dfrac{1,100 \times 125}{1,200} = 114.6$ volts

The terminal voltage $E_t$ differs from the generated emf of a generator by the voltage drop in the armature series circuit. The armature-circuit resistance consists of the resistance of the armature windings, the series field and commutating pole windings, if used, and the brushes; in other words, the entire resistance between the positive and negative terminals of the generator. At no load, the terminal voltage is equal to the generated emf since there is no $IR$ drop in the armature circuit. However, load current flowing through the armature circuit produces an $IR$ drop which of course increases as the load current increases.

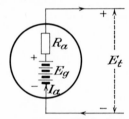

Fig. 6-20. Equivalent circuit of a generator armature.

A convenient way of representing the relationship between the generated emf, the $IR$ drop in the armature circuit, and the terminal voltage is shown in the equivalent circuit of Fig. 6-20. The generated emf $E_g$ is represented as a storage battery with zero internal resistance and the entire armature-circuit resistance by the resistor $R_a$ in series with the battery.

From this circuit, then,

$$E_t = E_g - I_a R_a \tag{3}$$

where $I_a$ is the armature current. Substituting the value of $E_g$ from Eq. (2) in Eq. (3) results in the equation

$$E_t = K\phi n - I_a R_a \tag{4}$$

This equation is called the *fundamental generator equation* because it contains all the factors that govern the value of the terminal voltage. Note that there are three factors that may affect the generator terminal voltage: (1) $\phi$, the flux per pole; (2) $n$, the speed in rpm; and (3) $I_aR_a$, the voltage drop in the armature circuit.

### 6-7. The Magnetization Curve

According to the molecular theory of magnetism (Chap. 4), the molecules of an unmagnetized piece of iron are not arranged in any definite order. When the iron is magnetized by passing current through a coil placed around the iron, the molecules become arranged in a definite order. To arrange the greater part of the molecules in a definite order or to magnetize the iron up to a certain point requires relatively few ampere turns of applied mmf.

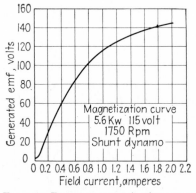

FIG. 6-21. Dynamo magnetization curve.

In this stage of magnetization, the amount of flux established in the iron increases almost directly with increases in the ampere turns applied. However, above this point, which is called the *saturation point*, it becomes increasingly difficult to magnetize the iron further, since the unmagnetized molecules become fewer and fewer. Above the saturation point, when much larger increases in ampere turns are required for corresponding increases in flux in the iron, the iron is said to be *saturated*. The fact that the iron has become saturated does not mean that a further increase in magnetism is impossible; the increases in magnetism merely require very much larger increases in applied ampere turns than before the iron became saturated.

It was shown in Art. 6-6 that the generated emf is proportional to both the flux per pole and the speed of the generator. If the speed is held constant, the generated emf then depends directly on the flux per pole. Since the flux is produced by the ampere turns of the field coils, and since the number of turns on field coils is constant, the flux must depend on the amount of field current flowing. However, the flux is not directly proportional to the field current at all times, owing to the fact that the magnetic circuit of the generator becomes saturated. The variation of the generated emf with the field current for a given generator driven at a constant speed and at no load may be shown by a curve called the *magnetization curve*. This curve is sometimes called the generator-saturation curve or the no-load characteristic.

The magnetization curve of a shunt dynamo is shown in Fig. 6-21. With zero field current, that is, with the field circuit open, the generated emf is equal to about 2 volts. This is because of the weak flux produced by the residual magnetism in the poles. As the field current is increased, the generated emf increases in a nearly straight line up to about 102 volts when the field current is 0.8 amp. At this point, the magnetic circuit of the generator approaches saturation. Beyond this point, larger increases in field current are necessary to produce proportionate increases in generated emf. For example, before the field becomes saturated, an increase in field current from 0.4 to 0.6 amp increases the generated emf from 60 to 84 volts. However, after the field becomes saturated, an increase of field current from 1.2 to 1.4 amp raises the generated emf from 125 to 132 volts. An increase of 0.2 amp in field current in the first case causes an increase of 24 volts, but the same increase in field current in the second case causes an increase in generated emf of only 7 volts.

**6-8. Armature Reaction** When the field winding of a two-pole generator is energized and the generator is supplying no load, the field flux is distributed as shown in Fig. 6-22a. The plane through $XY$ is called the neutral plane; the armature conductors in this plane are cutting no flux and therefore have no emf generated in them.

Current flowing in the armature windings creates a magnetizing effect or an mmf that acts at right angles to the main field flux. This magnetizing action of the armature current is called *cross magnetization*. Figure 6-22b shows the flux that would be produced by an armature current flowing in the directions shown when the field coils are not excited. Treating the armature as a solenoid and applying the right-hand rule shows the direction of the flux to be downward through the armature. Cross magnetization is present only when armature current is flowing, and the amount of magnetization so produced is proportional to the amount of armature current flowing.

Figure 6-22c represents the resultant field formed by the simultaneous action of the main field windings (Fig. 6-22a) and the field produced by the cross-magnetizing action of the armature current (Fig. 6-22b) when the armature is rotated in a clockwise direction. Flux is crowded into the upper or trailing north pole tip and into the lower or trailing south pole tip, and the field is distorted in the direction of rotation. Thus the neutral plane is shifted around to the new position $X'Y'$. It should be pointed out that the flux is not pulled around by the mechanical rotation of the armature but is distorted by the action of the main field and armature mmfs acting at right angles to each other.

To secure good commutation, the brushes of a generator must be set on or slightly ahead of the neutral plane.   Thus, in a generator carrying its load with the neutral plane moved considerably forward owing to the action of the armature mmf, the brushes must be shifted forward. If, for instance, the brushes were left in position $XY$ (Fig. 6-22c), the

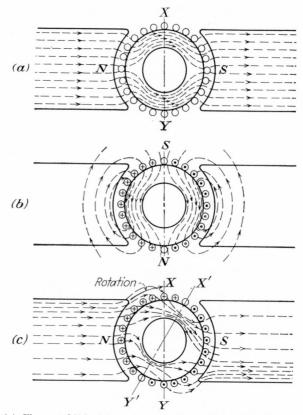

FIG. 6-22. (a) Flux established by current in the field windings.   (b) Flux established by armature currents.   (c) Resultant flux from simultaneous action of field and armature currents.

coils being short-circuited by the brushes would be cutting flux and would therefore have an emf generated in them causing an arc to be formed as the commutator segments move from under the brushes. However, as the load on the generator changes, the amount of distortion of the field or shifting of the neutral plane varies.   Therefore, the effect of the action of the armature mmf makes necessary a shifting of the brushes with changes in load to secure sparkless commutation.

When the brushes are set on the line $XY$ (Fig. 6-22c), the armature mmf acts along the line $XY$ or at right angles to the main field. If the brushes are moved to the new position $X'Y'$, to reduce sparking, the armature mmf then acts along the line $X'Y'$ and is no longer at right angles to the main field. The armature mmf then is no longer all cross-magnetizing in its effect but is partly demagnetizing in its action since it is partly directed *against* the main field. This results in a weakened field flux, which in turn results in a lowered generated emf in the generator. The action of the armature currents in establishing an mmf that distorts and weakens the field flux is called *armature reaction*.

A reduction in the effects resulting from armature reaction may be obtained by the use of a compensating, or pole-face, winding. This winding consists of conductors embedded in the pole faces that are parallel to the armature conductors. The winding is so connected that it carries full armature current or a definite proportion of it but in a direction opposite to that of the adjacent armature conductors. The flux produced by the compensating winding thus neutralizes the flux produced by the armature current. Because of their high cost, however, compensating windings are ordinarily used only on the larger capacity machines.

**6-9. Commutation** The process of reversing the direction of the current in an armature coil as the commutator segments to which the coil is connected pass under a brush is called *commutation*. During the short time that the commutator segments to which a coil is connected are passing under the brush, the current must be completely reversed so that an arc is not formed as the commutator segments move from under the brush. Sparking at the brushes causes the commutator to pit which, in turn, increases the brush-contact resistance and also causes the brushes and commutator to wear excessively. Sparking at the brushes, then, must be avoided.

Since an armature coil is partially surrounded by iron, it has a considerable amount of inductance. It was shown in Chap. 5 that in an inductive circuit each change in current is opposed by an emf of self-induction. The emf of self-induction in an armature coil, then, opposes the reversal of the coil current while the coil is short-circuited by the brush and maintains a current flow around the short-circuited coil, thereby producing a spark as the commutator segments leave the brush.

Since the emf of self-induction in the armature coils is due to a property of the coil, namely, its inductance, it cannot be prevented. However, it may be neutralized by causing an emf to be induced in the coil *opposite* to the self-induced emf.   This can be done in one of two ways: by shifting the brushes or by using interpoles.

If the brushes of a generator are shifted in the direction of rotation so that the coil undergoing commutation is cutting flux from the following main pole, enough emf can be induced to neutralize the effect of the self-induced emf, thereby permitting the current in the coil to reverse fast enough to prevent sparking.   The flux necessary to generate the emf needed to overcome the emf of self-induction is called the *commutating flux*.   This method of reducing sparking at the brushes is satisfactory for generators that carry constant loads.   However, the amount of commutating flux required and, hence, the amount of brush shift necessary varies with the load on the generator.   For proper commutation at light loads, the brushes need be shifted but a small amount.   However, for larger armature currents, the self-induced emf is larger so that the brushes must be shifted farther away from the neutral plane.   Thus, a disadvantage of this method of improving commutation is that the brushes must be shifted with each change in load.

**6-10. Interpoles**   The results obtained in improving commutation by brush shifting may be accomplished in a much more satisfactory manner by introducing small poles called *interpoles*, sometimes called *commutating poles*, between the main poles.   It was shown in Art. 6-9 that a commutating flux is necessary to generate an emf to overcome the emf of self-induction in a coil undergoing commutation.   An interpole in a generator has the same polarity as the following main pole in the direction of rotation.   The interpole, then, does the same thing that is done by shifting the brushes forward into the flux of the next main pole; that is, it provides a commutating flux to generate an emf opposite to the emf of self-induction.

Since the amount of emf of self-induction present in the armature coils varies with the amount of armature current flowing, the amount of commutating flux necessary also varies.   To make the commutating flux produced by the interpoles proportional to the armature current, interpole windings are connected in series with the armature circuit.

The interpole mmf must be great enough to provide the commutating flux and also to neutralize the flux that is shifted into the neutral plane by the effect of the armature reaction.   It is not necessary, then, to shift the brushes of a generator that is equipped with interpoles in order to secure good commutation.   This means that the demagnetizing effect of the armature currents will not be appreciable, their effect being largely distorting.

**6-11. Motor Action of a Generator**   The action of the armature mmf affords an excellent illustration of the fact that energy is not created by a generator.   It is true that a generator supplies energy to a load, but at the same time energy must be supplied to the generator at the same rate, assuming no loss.   It will be noted in Fig. 6-22b that the action of the armature as a solenoid establishes a north pole below the armature and a south pole above the armature.   As the armature must be driven in a clockwise direction by its prime mover to cause the armature current to flow in the directions indicated, the north pole of the armature flux is being forced toward the north main pole and the armature south pole toward the south main pole.   Since like poles repel, this means that power must be supplied from the prime mover to overcome the repulsion of the poles.   The more current the generator supplies, the stronger are the poles established by the armature mmf, and the more power the generator requires from the prime mover to overcome the repulsion of the poles.   Thus, the power input must vary directly with the power output.

The reaction of the armature field with the main field of a generator is in effect a turning action in a direction opposite to the rotation of the generator.   This action is referred to as the countertorque or as the motor action of the generator.   In Chap. 7 it will be shown that there is also a generator action present in a motor.

**6-12. The External Characteristic: Voltage Regulation**   As load is added to a generator, the terminal voltage will change unless some provision is made to keep it constant.   A curve that shows the value of the terminal voltage for different values of load current is called the *external characteristic* or the *regulation curve*.   The values of voltage for various load currents may be calculated or may be obtained from an actual test.   Readings of current and voltage obtained from a test are taken at a constant speed and with the field excitation so adjusted that rated voltage is obtained at full load.

Voltage regulation is defined as the difference between the no-load and full-load terminal voltage of a generator and is expressed as a percentage of the full-load value, the full-load voltage being the rated or normal voltage of the generator.   Thus

$$\text{Per cent regulation} = \frac{\text{no-load voltage} - \text{full-load voltage}}{\text{full-load voltage}} \times 100$$

It is important to know how the terminal voltage of a generator varies with different amounts of load in order to determine the suitability of the generator for a specific use.   For example, a generator to be used to supply a lighting circuit should have a very low percentage regulation; that is, its terminal voltage should be very nearly the same at full load as it is at no load.   The characteristics of the various types of generators are discussed in the following articles.

**6-13. The Separately Excited Generator** The separately excited generator is supplied field excitation from an independent d-c source such as a storage battery or separate d-c generator.   The connection diagram is shown in Fig. 6-19a.   A field rheostat is connected in series with the field to provide a means of varying the field excitation.

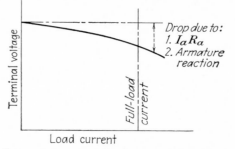

Fig. 6-23. External characteristic of a separately excited generator.

Figure 6-23 shows an external characteristic of a typical separately excited generator.   It will be noted that as the load current increases the terminal voltage decreases.   There are two important reasons for this decrease in terminal voltage:

1. Armature reaction reduces the amount of effective field flux so that the generated emf $E_g$ is decreased.   This is especially true in noninterpole machines.

2. There is a voltage drop due to the armature-circuit resistance. These two factors affecting the terminal voltage are indicated on the drawing in Fig. 6-23.

The separately excited generator has a decided advantage over the self-excited generator in that it will operate in a stable condition with any field excitation.   Thus, a wide range of output voltages may be obtained.

The main disadvantage of a separately excited generator lies in the inconvenience and expense of providing the separate excitation source. For this reason, the use of this type of generator is largely confined to experimental and testing laboratories where such a source is available and a wide variation of output voltage is desirable.

**6-14. The Self-excited Shunt Generator** A self-excited generator depends on the residual magnetism of its field poles for its operation.

Ordinarily there is some residual magnetism in the field poles if the poles have at a previous time been magnetized. If, then, a shunt generator is brought up to speed, the armature conductors will cut the small amount of flux present and a small amount of emf will be generated. As the shunt field is connected directly across the brushes (Fig. 6-19b), a current will flow in this winding. If the field resistance is sufficiently low and if the current is in such a direction so that it increases the field strength, a higher emf is generated, which in turn causes more current to flow through the field windings. This again increases the field flux and generated emf. At first it would appear that this building-up process would go on indefinitely, but a limit is reached owing to the saturation of the magnetic circuit. As the generator magnetic circuit approaches saturation, smaller and smaller increases in generated emf produce smaller and smaller increases in field current until the building-up process stops. At this point of equilibrium, the field current produces just enough flux to generate the emf that causes the field current to flow. After the voltage has been built up, it may be adjusted to the desired value by an adjustment of the field rheostat.

The voltage of a shunt generator may fail to build up for several reasons. If the field poles have for some reason or other lost their residual magnetism, the generator may fail to build up. If this is the case, the magnetism of the poles may be restored by passing current from a separate source through the field windings in the proper direction. A 6-volt storage battery will usually supply enough current for this purpose.

If the field connections are such that when the current caused by the residual voltage flows through the field the field strength is decreased instead of being increased, the voltage will not build up. Of course the remedy for this condition is the reversal of the field windings.

Other conditions that may prevent a generator from building up are too low an armature speed, too much field resistance, dirty brushes or commutator, an open- or short-circuited field circuit, or loose brush connections.

An external characteristic of a shunt generator is shown in Fig. 6-24. This curve shows the performance of a shunt generator to be similar to that of the separately excited generator, except that the voltage of the shunt generator falls off more rapidly with the addition of load. As in the separately excited generator, armature reaction and $IR$ drop in the armature circuit cause the terminal voltage to decrease. Since the field excitation is obtained from the generator itself, the decrease in terminal voltage, because of the above-mentioned effects, also decreases the voltage applied to the field circuit. This causes a decrease in field current and field flux, which in turn causes a further decrease in the terminal voltage. These three important components of voltage drop are indicated in Fig. 6-24.

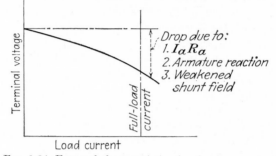

FIG. 6-24. External characteristic of a shunt generator.

The shunt generator may be used for supplying excitation to a-c generators or in other applications where the distance from the generator to its load is short. It is also used for charging storage batteries.

**6-15. The Series Generator** The series generator is a self-excited generator with armature, field windings, and load all connected in series. Thus, the field current and field flux are proportional to the load current. When the generator is running without load, there is a

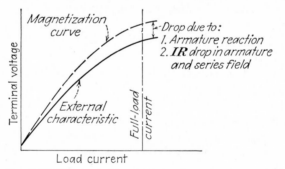

FIG. 6-25. External characteristic of a series generator.

small emf generated owing to the residual magnetism. As an external load is applied and current begins to flow in the field windings, the terminal voltage of the generator is increased. The terminal voltage continues to increase until the magnetic circuit becomes saturated. An external characteristic is shown in Fig. 6-25.

The series generator has very few practical applications. An under-

standing of the action of the series field is desirable, however, in the
study of the compound generator.

**6-16. The Compound Generator** It was pointed out in Art. 6-14 that
the terminal voltage of a shunt generator drops considerably with the
addition of load. Many applications, such as lighting circuits, require
a practically constant source of voltage, and for such applications the
shunt generator is unsuitable, especially if the amount of load is
variable.

The decrease in terminal voltage of a shunt generator is due mainly
to armature reaction and $IR$ drop in the armature circuit. Both of
these factors are proportional to the armature current. A generator
may be made to supply automatically a constant terminal voltage by
the use of a series field winding placed on the same poles as the shunt
field winding. The series field, which carries full armature current,
supplies an mmf to compensate for the decrease in terminal voltage
due to armature reaction and armature-circuit $IR$ drop. A generator
with both a series and a shunt field winding is called a *compound
generator*. When the series field is so connected that its ampere turns
act in the same direction as those of the shunt field, the generator is
said to be a *cumulative-compound generator*.

The cumulative-compound generator combines the characteristics
of the shunt and the series generators. At no load the shunt winding
provides all the field flux, since there is no current in the series field
winding. As load is increased on the generator, the series field adds
an increasing amount of field flux to that of the shunt field. The
terminal voltage of the loaded generator will depend on the relative
strength of the two fields. If the full-load terminal voltage is equal
to the no-load terminal voltage, the generator is said to be *flat-compounded*. If the series ampere turns at full load are more than enough
to compensate for armature reaction and armature-circuit $IR$ drop,
the terminal voltage is higher than at no load and the generator is said
to be *overcompounded*. Similarly, a generator is said to be *undercom-
pounded* when the full-load terminal voltage is less than the no-load
terminal voltage. The external characteristics for over-, under-, and
flat-compounded generators are shown in Fig. 6-26.

The compound generator is used more extensively than other types
of generators because it may be designed to have a wide variety of
characteristics. Overcompounded generators are commonly used in
generating stations that are some distance from the loads that they
supply. The increase in generator terminal voltage compensates for
the voltage drop in the load feeder circuits.

If the series field of a generator is connected so that its ampere turns oppose those of the shunt field, the generator is called a *differential-compound generator*. This type of generator has an extremely limited field of practical application.

When the shunt field of a compound generator is connected in parallel with the armature only, the connection is called a *short-shunt connection*. If the shunt field is connected in parallel with the circuit

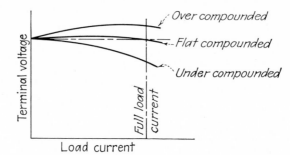

FIG. 6-26. External characteristics of compound generators.

containing the armature and the series field, the connection is called a *long-shunt connection*. These connections are shown in Figs. 6-19*d* and 6-19*e*. The operating characteristics are practically the same with either connection.

**6-17. Efficiency** The efficiency of any machine is the ratio of the useful power output to the total power input. A part of the energy delivered to a generator or a motor is converted into heat and is therefore wasted. Thus, the useful output is never as large as the total input. There are always unavoidable losses even in the most perfectly constructed machines. Efficiency is usually expressed as a percentage. Thus the ratio of output to input expressed as a decimal must be multiplied by 100 to change it to a percentage. Of course, output and input must be expressed in the same units. Thus, the definition of efficiency stated as a formula is

$$\text{Per cent efficiency} = \frac{\text{output}}{\text{input}} \times 100$$

Suppose it is desired to find the efficiency of a generator whose input is 20 hp and whose terminal voltage is 240 volts when it is supplying 50 amp to a load. The output of the generator is

$$P = EI = 240 \times 50 = 12,000 \text{ watts}$$

The input to the generator in watts is

$$\text{Input} = 20 \times 746 = 14{,}920 \text{ watts}$$

The per cent efficiency is

$$\frac{\text{output}}{\text{input}} \times 100 = \frac{12{,}000}{14{,}920} \times 100 = 80.4 \text{ per cent}$$

**6-18. Losses and Efficiency of a Dynamo**  The losses of a dynamo consist of the copper losses in the electric circuits of the machine and the mechanical losses due to the rotation of the machine.  The important losses may be outlined as follows:

I. Copper losses
    A. Armature $I^2R$ losses
    B. Field losses
        1. Shunt field $I^2R$
        2. Series field $I^2R$
        3. Interpole field $I^2R$
II. Mechanical or rotational losses
    A. Iron losses
        1. Eddy-current loss
        2. Hysteresis loss
    B. Friction losses
        1. Bearing friction
        2. Brush friction
        3. Windage or air friction loss

The copper losses are present because power is used whenever a current is made to flow through a resistance.  When an armature current $I_a$ flows through the armature-winding resistance $R_a$ the power used is $I_a^2 R_a$.  Likewise the power used in overcoming the resistances of the series field winding and the interpole winding is expressed as $I_a^2 R_s$ and $I_a^2 R_i$, where $R_s$ and $R_i$ are series-field and interpole-field resistances, respectively.

The shunt-field loss is equal to $EI_f$ where $E$ is the terminal voltage of the dynamo and $I_f$ is the shunt-field current.  This includes the shunt-field rheostat loss.

As the armature rotates in a magnetic field, the iron parts of the armature cut lines of force as do the armature conductors.  Since iron is a conductor of electricity, the emf induced in the iron parts causes currents to flow through these iron parts.  These circulating currents are called *eddy currents*, and their flow causes the iron through which they flow to become heated. This heat is dissipated to the air and represents energy wasted.

To increase the resistance of the paths followed by eddy currents, armature cores are made of laminated steel sheets, stacked and secured in a position perpendicular to the shaft and parallel to the direction of the magnetic field. A thin layer of insulation is placed between the laminations. This insulation may be a type of insulating varnish or merely the oxide that is allowed to form on the surfaces of each lamination. The eddy currents are therefore confined to the individual laminations, and their heating effect is greatly reduced. Laminating the armature core does not increase its reluctance, for the laminations are parallel to the magnetic field.

When a magnetic material is magnetized, first in one direction and then the other, an energy loss takes place owing to the molecular friction in the material. That is, the molecules of the material resist being turned first in one direction and then the other. Energy is thus expended in the material in overcoming this resistance. This loss is in the form of heat and is called *hysteresis loss*. Hysteresis loss is present in a rotating armature core, for the magnetism of the core is continually being reversed as the armature moves through the stationary magnetic field.

Other rotational losses are bearing friction, the friction of the brushes riding on the commutator, and air friction or windage.

Since it is wasteful and sometimes difficult to measure directly the input and output of dynamos, especially in the larger sizes, their efficiencies are often determined by determining their losses and calculating their efficiency.

### 6-19. Parallel Operation of Shunt Generators

It is generally more desirable in a generating station to have several small generators that may be paralleled than to have one large generator to supply all the load. The load supplied by a generating station is usually variable. As machines operate at greatest efficiency at or near full load, it is possible with several machines to keep each machine either fully loaded or shut down entirely. Greater reliability is realized from this arrangement also, since in case of a breakdown of one machine other machines are available to carry the load.

Generators to be operated in parallel are connected through circuit breakers and switches to heavy copper *bus bars*. The load-feeder circuits are then connected to the same bus bars by means of suitable switches and protective devices.

There are two main requirements to be met when generators are to be paralleled:

1. All polarities must be correct. The positive terminals of all machines must be connected to the positive bus bar, and the negative terminals must be connected to the negative bus bar.

2. The terminal voltages of machines being paralleled must be the same.

Figure 6-27 shows two shunt generators arranged for parallel operation with generator 1 supplying all the load. Suppose that it is desired to parallel the two generators so that the load may be divided between the two machines. Generator 2 is brought up to speed by its prime mover, its voltage built up, and its field excitation adjusted until its terminal voltage, as read by voltmeter $V_2$, is the same as the terminal voltage of generator 1, as read by voltmeter $V_1$. The polarity

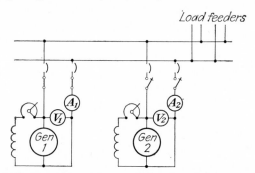

Fig. 6-27. Arrangement for paralleling two shunt generators.

of generator 2 must be such that its positive terminal will be connected to the positive bus and its negative terminal to the negative bus. With voltages and polarities correct, the circuit breakers and switches are closed.

Under these conditions, generator 2 is "floating" on the line, its generated emf being equal to the bus voltage. If, however, its generated emf is raised above the bus voltage by increasing its field excitation, it will deliver current to the load. To maintain a constant bus voltage, the field of generator 1 is weakened at the same time that the field of generator 2 is strengthened. The load may thus be shifted between the two machines in any desired amount at a constant bus voltage by the manipulation of the two field rheostats. Usual practice is to divide the load on generators in parallel in proportion to their kilowatt ratings.

If it is desired to disconnect one of two generators operating in parallel, the load is first removed from the generator being shut down by decreasing its field excitation. At the same time the bus voltage is maintained by increasing the field excitation of the other machine. When the generated emf is lowered to the value of the bus voltage, the current output is zero and the machine can be disconnected and shut down.

**6-20. Parallel Operation of Compound Generators** When two compound generators are paralleled as in Fig. 6-28, their operation is not stable. If two generators were being operated as shown and for some reason the speed of one machine were increased momentarily, thereby momentarily increasing its generated emf, this machine would attempt to supply more than its share of the load. This increase in armature current, in turn, increases its series-field strength which

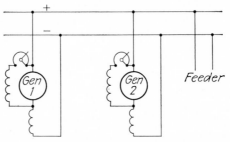

Fig. 6-28. Improper connection for parallel operation of compound generators.

further increases its generated emf, causing the generator to supply a still greater portion of the load current. At the same time the armature current being supplied by the other generator is decreased, thereby decreasing its series-field strength and causing it to supply a smaller and smaller portion of the load current. The process continues until one generator is supplying all the load and is attempting to operate the other machine as a motor. This causes the circuit breakers to open, disconnecting the generators from the load.

The instability of compound generators in parallel is overcome by the use of an *equalizer* connection as shown in Fig. 6-29. This connection is usually in the form of another bus bar on the switchboard. The equalizer connects the two series fields in parallel. This causes the load current to be divided between the series fields in inverse ratio to the resistances of the two fields. As long as the combined load current remains constant, the series-field currents of the two machines remain constant regardless of the distribution of the current in the two armatures. Thus the flux produced by the two series fields remains the same for a given load on the bus.

In addition to the requirements of correct polarity and equal terminal voltages, compound generators require an equalizer connection before they may be paralleled. Furthermore, the series fields of both machines must be either on the positive or on the negative side of the armature. If they are not, the armature of each machine will be short-circuited by the series field of the other.

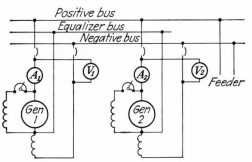

Fig. 6-29. Parallel connection of compound generators using an equalizer bus. Correct connection.

Compound generators are put in service and taken out of service in the same manner as shunt generators. Load is shifted from one compound generator to the other by adjustments of the shunt-field rheostats.

**6-21. Three-wire Generators** When a three-wire d-c distribution system is used, some method must be provided for connecting the

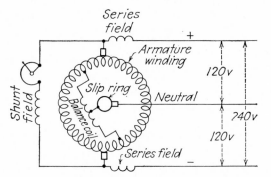

Fig. 6-30. Three-wire generator connections.

neutral wire to the source. One common way of doing this is by the use of the three-wire generator.

The three-wire generator is an ordinary 240-volt generator with special provision being made for connecting the neutral wire to the armature windings. The positive and negative line wires are connected to the positive and negative brushes as in a 240-volt two-wire system. Internal taps are made 180 electrical degrees apart directly to the armature winding. Connected between these taps is a balance coil of low-resistance wire that is wound around an iron core. The neutral wire is connected to the mid-point of the balance coil so that at all times the voltage between the neutral and either line wire is one-half the generator voltage.

The balance coil may be mounted directly on the armature, in which case the neutral point is brought out of the generator by means of a single slip ring and brush as shown in Fig. 6-30. In some three-wire generators, the taps from the armature winding are brought out through two slip rings and brushes and are connected to an external stationary balance coil.

Series fields, when used on three-wire generators, are divided with one-half of the winding connected on the positive side and the other on the negative side of the generator. This is necessary so that compounding is provided even though the load on the generator is unbalanced. Since two series fields are used on each machine, compound three-wire generators operating in parallel must have two equalizer connections to connect all series fields in parallel.

## REVIEW QUESTIONS

**1.** What is (a) a dynamo; (b) a generator; (c) a motor?

**2.** Name the parts of the magnetic circuit of a dynamo.

**3.** Name the parts that make up the electric circuits of a dynamo.

**4.** What are the neutral planes of a generator?

**5.** Explain why an alternating emf is generated in a coil that is rotated in a magnetic field.

**6.** If it is desired to bring alternating current out of a generator, what kind of a "take-off" system is used?

**7.** Describe the action of a commutator.

**8.** In the single-coil d-c generator is the brush voltage constant? Why?

**9.** Why is more than one coil used on a generator armature?

**10.** Give three methods of providing field excitation for a d-c generator.

**11.** What is the purpose of the field rheostat?

**12.** Name the factors that determine the amount of emf generated. Which are variable?

**13.** When a generator supplies load, the terminal voltage is not the same as the generated emf. Why?

**14.** Draw an equivalent circuit of a generator armature.

**15.** What is the fundamental generator equation?

**16.** The magnetization curve shows the relation between what two things?

**17.** Explain why the generator magnetization curve is not a straight line.

**18.** What is meant by cross magnetization? What is its effect on commutation?

**19.** What are two effects of armature reaction?

**20.** Why is a commutating flux necessary? How may it be obtained?

**21.** What is an interpole? What is its purpose? How is its winding connected?

**22.** Explain why more power must be supplied to a generator when the power output is increased.

**23.** The external characteristic shows the relation between what two factors?

**24.** Give the formula for finding the voltage regulation of a generator.

**25.** Give two reasons for the drop in terminal voltage of a separately excited generator as load is increased.

**26.** Explain the "building-up" process of a self-excited shunt generator.

**27.** Why may a shunt generator fail to build up?

**28.** A certain generator may be connected for either separate or self-excitation. Which of the two connections should be used to obtain the better voltage regulation?

**29.** Why is a small emf generated in a series generator at no load? What happens to the generated emf as load is added?

**30.** What is a compound generator? What is a cumulative-compound generator?

**31.** When is a generator said to be (a) flat-compounded; (b) overcompounded?

**32.** When might it be desirable to use an overcompounded generator?

**33.** In what type of generator do the series- and shunt-field ampere turns oppose each other?

**34.** Define efficiency. How is it usually expressed?

**35.** Name three classes of dynamo losses.

**36.** How are eddy-current losses reduced in dynamos?

**37.** Why is it necessary to operate generators in parallel? Why are generators connected in parallel and not in series?

**38.** Give the two requirements to be met in paralleling shunt generators.

**39.** Is it possible to parallel two generators with similar characteristics but with different capacity ratings?

**40.** How can load be shifted from one generator to another without changing the bus voltage?

**41.** If two generators are operating in parallel, how is it possible to raise the bus voltage without changing the load division between the two machines?

**42.** What would happen if when two shunt generators were operating in parallel the prime mover of one generator were disconnected?

**43.** Why is an equalizer connection necessary for successful parallel operation of two compound generators?

**44.** What requirements must be met in paralleling compound generators?

**45.** How is the neutral connection made in a three-wire generator?

**46.** Why must the series fields of three-wire generators be divided?

## PROBLEMS

**1.** How many amperes will a 50-kw 240-volt d-c generator deliver at full load?

**2.** What is the full-load kilowatt output of a d-c generator if the full-load line current is 30 amp and the terminal voltage is 115 volts?

**3.** A shunt generator generates 100 volts when its speed is 900 rpm. What emf does it generate if the speed is increased to 1,200 rpm, the field flux remaining unchanged?

**4.** A generator generates an emf of 520 volts, has 2,000 armature conductors or inductors, a flux per pole of 1,300,000 lines, a speed of 1,200 rpm, and the armature winding has four paths. Find the number of poles.

**5.** If the generated emf of a generator is 125 volts and the $IR$ drop in the armature circuit is 5 volts, what is the terminal voltage?

**6.** A self-excited shunt generator delivers 20 amp to a load. Its field current is 1.5 amp. What is the armature current?

**7.** A 240-volt shunt generator has a field-circuit resistance of 150 ohms. What is the field current when the generator operates at rated voltage?

**8.** A shunt field winding of a 240-volt generator has a resistance of 60 ohms. How much field-rheostat resistance must be added to limit the field current to 3 amp when the generator is operating at rated voltage?

**9.** A 120-volt shunt generator has a field-circuit resistance of 90 ohms. What is the armature current when the generator supplies 25 amp to a load?

**10.** A shunt generator is rated 200 kw at 240 volts. (*a*) What is the full-load current? (*b*) If the field-circuit resistance is 100 ohms, what is the field current? (*c*) What is the full-load armature current?

**11.** The terminal voltage of a shunt generator is 115 volts when the generated emf is 119 volts and the armature current is 20 amp. What is the armature-circuit resistance?

**12.** The terminal voltage of a 75-kw shunt generator is 600 volts at rated load. The resistance of the shunt-field circuit is 150 ohms, and the armature-circuit resistance is 0.1 ohm. Find the generated emf.

**13.** In a 50-kw 250-volt shunt generator, 258 volts are generated in the armature when the generator delivers rated load at rated voltage. The shunt-field current is 4 amp. Find the resistance of the armature.

**14.** A load that has a resistance of 8 ohms is connected to a separately excited generator that has an armature-circuit resistance of 0.5 ohm. (*a*) What is the armature current when the generated emf is 130 volts? (*b*) What is the generator terminal voltage?

**15.** A shunt generator has a full-load terminal voltage of 120 volts. When the load is removed, the voltage increases to 150 volts. What is the percentage voltage regulation?

**16.** A shunt generator has a field resistance of 50 ohms. When the terminal voltage of the generator is 120 volts, the field current is 2 amp. How much resistance is cut in on the shunt-field rheostat?

**17.** The no-load terminal voltage of a separately excited generator is 130 volts. When the generator is supplying 50 amp to a load, the speed and field excitation remaining unchanged, the terminal voltage is 115 volts. If the armature-circuit resistance is 0.25 ohm, how much of the 15-volt drop is due to the effect of armature reaction?

**18.** A shunt generator has an armature-circuit resistance of 0.4 ohm, a field-circuit resistance of 60 ohms, and a terminal voltage of 120 volts when it is supplying a load current of 30 amp. (*a*) Find the field current. (*b*) Find the armature current. (*c*) Find the copper losses at the above load. (*d*) If the rotational losses are 350 watts, what is the efficiency at the above load?

**19.** Find the efficiency at full load of a 50-kw generator when the input is 80 hp.

**20.** The losses of a 20-kw generator at full load are 4,500 watts. (*a*) What is the efficiency at full load? (*b*) at no load?

**21.** A shunt generator requires 53-hp input from its prime mover when it delivers 150 amp at 240 volts. Find the efficiency of the generator.

**22.** The full-load losses of a 20-kw 230-volt shunt generator are as follows:

| | |
|---|---|
| Field $I^2R$ loss..................... | 180 watts |
| Armature $I^2R$ loss................. | 1,200 watts |
| Windage and friction losses........ | 550 watts |
| Iron loss........................ | 500 watts |

Find the efficiency at full load.

**23.** A shunt generator supplies a load with 106 amp at 125 volts. The shunt-field resistance is 31.2 ohms, and the armature resistance is 0.11 ohm. Find (*a*) the shunt-field copper loss and (*b*) the armature copper loss.

**24.** From the following data concerning a shunt generator, calculate the efficiency at full load.

| | |
|---|---|
| Rated kilowatt output............... | 10 kw |
| Rated voltage..................... | 230 volts |
| Armature-circuit resistance.......... | 0.4 ohm |
| Field-circuit resistance.............. | 192 ohms |
| Rotational losses at full load........ | 750 watts |

**25.** A short-shunt connected compound generator delivers 216 amp to a load at 250 volts. Its shunt-field resistance is 26.8 ohms, its shunt-field rheostat resistance is 6.2 ohms, its series-field resistance is 0.042 ohm and its armature resistance is 0.096 ohm. Find the copper losses in (*a*) the shunt-field winding, (*b*) the shunt-field rheostat, (*c*) the series field, and (*d*) the armature winding.

**26.** A compound generator, short-shunt connected, has a terminal voltage of 230 volts when the line current is 50 amp. The series-field resistance is 0.04 ohm. (*a*) Find the voltage drop across the series field. (*b*) Find the voltage across the armature. (*c*) Find the armature current if the shunt-field current is 2 amp. (*d*) If the losses are 1,950 watts, what is the efficiency?

# CHAPTER 7

## DIRECT-CURRENT MOTORS AND CONTROLS

A motor is a machine that converts electric energy into mechanical energy. The d-c motor is very similar to a d-c generator in construction. In fact, a machine that runs well as a generator will operate satisfactorily as a motor.

One common constructional difference between motors and generators should be noted, however. As motors often operate in locations in which they are exposed to mechanical damage, dust, moisture, or corrosive fumes, they are often of the *semiguarded, dripproof,* or *totally enclosed* types. Semiguarded types have screens or grills over ventilating openings to limit access to and prevent damage to rotating or live parts. A semiguarded-type motor is shown in Fig. 7-1. A drip-

Fig. 7-1. A d-c motor rated 50 hp, 250 volts. (*Courtesy of Allis-Chalmers Manufacturing Company.*)

proof-type motor has ventilating openings so placed as to protect the motor against falling liquids. Totally enclosed motors, as the name implies, are completely sealed so that no ventilating air can enter the motor. The heat developed must be entirely dissipated by radiation from the enclosing case. As generators operate in more protected locations, their construction is generally of the *open* type.

Although the mechanical construction of d-c motors and generators is very similar, their functions are different. The function of a generator is to *generate a voltage* when conductors are moved through a field, while the function of a motor is to develop a *twisting effort* or a *torque*.

**7-1. Motor Principle**  Every conductor carrying current has a magnetic field around it, the direction of which may be established by the right-hand rule. The strength of the field depends on the amount of current flowing in the conductor.

If a wire carrying current away from the reader is placed in a uniform magnetic field, the combined fields will be similar to that shown in Fig. 7-2. Above the conductor, the field due to the conductor is from left to right, or in the same direction as the main field. Below the conductor, the magnetic lines from the conductor and the main field

magnetic lines are in opposite directions. The result is to strengthen the field or increase the flux density above the conductor and to weaken the field or decrease the flux density below the conductor.

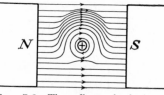

FIG. 7-2. The effect of placing a current-carrying conductor in a magnetic field.

It is convenient to think of magnetic lines as elastic bands under tension that are always trying to shorten themselves. Thus, the lines of force above the conductor exert a downward force on the conductor. Likewise, if the current in the conductor is reversed, the increased number of magnetic lines below the conductor will exert an upward force on the conductor.

While the above explanation of how a force is developed on a conductor is convenient, it is somewhat artificial. However, it is based on a fundamental principle of physics which may be proved experimentally and which may be stated as follows:

*A conductor carrying current in a magnetic field tends to move at right angles to the field.*

**7-2. Torque Development in a Motor**  *Torque* is defined as the action of a force on a body that tends to cause that body to rotate. Thus, the measure of the tendency of a motor armature to rotate is called the *torque* of the motor.

Motor-armature windings are wound in the same manner as are generator windings. When a voltage is applied to the brushes of a motor, current flows into the positive brush, through the commutator and armature windings, and out the negative brush. Armature conductors are wound so that all conductors under the south field poles carry current in one direction, while all the conductors under the north field poles carry current in the opposite direction. Figure 7-3 shows the distribution of armature currents in a four-pole motor for a given polarity of applied terminal voltage.

When voltage is applied to a motor, such as is shown in Fig. 7-3, current flows through the field winding, establishing the magnetic field. Current also flows through the armature winding from the positive brushes to the negative brushes. Since each armature conductor under the four pole faces is carrying current in a magnetic field, each of these conductors has a force exerted on it, tending to move it at right angles to that field.

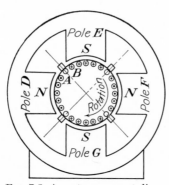

FIG. 7-3. Armature-current directions in a four-pole motor for clockwise rotation.

An application of the right-hand rule to the armature conductors under the north pole *D* in Fig. 7-3 shows the magnetic field to be strengthened under the conductors, resulting in an upward force on the conductors. Similarly, force is exerted to the right on the conductors under south pole *E*, downward on the conductors under north pole *F*, and to the left on the conductors under south pole *G*. Thus, there is a force developed on all the active armature conductors tending to turn the armature in a clockwise direction. The sum of these forces in pounds multiplied by the radius of the armature in feet is equal to the total torque developed by the motor in *pound-feet*. If the armature is free to turn, that is, if the connected load is not too great, the armature will begin to rotate in a clockwise direction.

As the armature rotates and the conductors move from under a pole into the neutral plane, the current is reversed in them by the action of the commutator. For example, in Fig. 7-3, as the conductor at *A* moves from under the north pole and approaches the neutral plane, the current is outward. At the neutral plane the current is reversed so that as it moves under the south pole as at *B* it carries current inward.    Thus, the conductors under a given pole carry current in the same direction at all times.

It should be evident from Fig. 7-3 that if the armature current were reversed by reversing the armature leads, but leaving the field polarity the same, torque would be developed in a counterclockwise direction. Likewise, if the field polarity were reversed leaving the armature current as shown, torque would be developed in a counterclockwise direction.    However, if both armature-current direction and field polarity were changed, torque would be developed in a clockwise direction.    *The direction of rotation of a d-c motor may be reversed by reversing either the field or the armature connections.    If both are reversed, the direction of rotation remains unchanged.*

The force developed on each conductor of a motor armature is due to the combined action of the main field and the field around the conductor.    It follows, then, that the force developed is directly proportional to the strength of the main field flux and to the strength of the field around each conductor.    The field around each armature conductor depends on the amount of armature current flowing in that conductor.    Therefore, the torque developed by a motor may be shown to be

$$T = K'\phi I_a \tag{1}$$

where $T$ = torque, lb-ft
$\quad K'$ = a constant depending on physical dimensions of motor
$\quad \phi$ = total number of lines of force per pole
$\quad I_a$ = armature current, amp
This important equation is of use in analyzing a motor's performance under various operating conditions.

**7-3. Measurement of Torque**    The torque developed by a motor may be measured by means of a *prony brake* attached to the motor pulley as shown in Fig. 7-4.    Any desired load may be placed on the motor by adjusting the pressure of the wooden-block brake shoes.    The

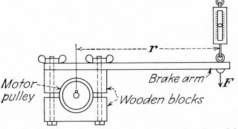

FIG. 7-4. Prony brake for measuring the torque developed by a motor.

energy output of the motor is dissipated as heat which is produced as the pulley turns in the brake shoes. For any given load, the torque output of the motor is the length of the brake arm $r$ in feet multiplied by the force $F$ in pounds as registered on the spring scales.

**Example 1** A prony brake arm is 42 in. long. The pressure on the motor pulley is adjusted so that a net force of 18 lb is measured on the scale. What torque is the motor developing?

$$\text{Torque} = \text{force} \times \text{brake arm}$$
$$T = Fr = 18 \times \frac{42}{12} = 63 \text{ lb-ft}$$

The turning or twisting effort that a motor develops at the instant of starting is called its *starting torque*. It may be measured with a prony brake by clamping the brake arm securely so that the pulley cannot turn. With the motor connected to the supply lines and the armature remaining stationary, the force in pounds is measured with the scale. The starting torque is then equal to the force multiplied by the brake-arm length.

**7-4. Generator Action of a Motor** It was shown in the study of generators that a motor action was developed in every generator. Likewise, a generator action is developed in every motor. Whenever a conductor cuts lines of force, an emf is induced in that conductor. The driving force is immaterial; if a conductor is moved through a magnetic field, an emf will be induced in that conductor. The direction of that emf is in accordance with *Fleming's right-hand rule* for generator action.

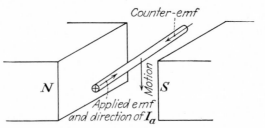

FIG. 7-5. The counter emf is induced in a direction opposite to the flow of armature current.

The conductor of Fig. 7-5 represents one of many current-carrying conductors of a motor armature. For the field polarity shown, the current in the conductor is such that by motor action it will be moved downward. As the conductor is moved downward, it cuts lines of force and an emf is induced in it. The direction of this emf by Fleming's right-hand rule for a generated emf is found to be toward the reader. Since this emf is in a direction opposite to the flow of current in the conductor, it is called a *counter electromotive force.*

Since the counter emf of a motor is generated by the action of armature conductors cutting lines of force, its value will depend on the field strength and the armature speed. The value of the counter emf $E_g$ that is generated in a motor is given by the relation

$$E_g = K\phi n \tag{2}$$

where $K$ is a constant depending on the physical properties of the motor. It will be remembered that Eq. (2) was used to determine the generated emf of a generator.

The effective voltage acting in the armature circuit of a motor is the applied or terminal voltage minus the counter emf. The armature current by Ohm's law is

$$I_a = \frac{E_t - E_g}{R_a} \tag{3}$$

where $I_a$ = armature current
$E_t$ = motor terminal voltage
$E_g$ = counter emf
$R_a$ = armature-circuit resistance

Multiplying both sides of Eq. (3) by $R_a$ and transposing results in

$$E_t = E_g + I_a R_a \tag{4}$$

which is the fundamental motor equation. Note that this is the same as the generator equation with the sign of the $I_a R_a$ term changed. The counter emf of a motor is always less than its terminal voltage.

**Example 2**   Find the counter emf of a motor when the terminal voltage is 240 volts and the armature current is 60 amp. The armature resistance is 0.08 ohm.

$$E_t = E_g + I_a R_a$$
or
$$E_g = E_t - I_a R_a$$
$$= 240 - (60 \times 0.08) = 240 - 4.8 = 235.2 \text{ volts}$$

**7-5. Equivalent Circuit of a Motor**   It is convenient when dealing with d-c motors to represent the armature as an equivalent circuit. As in the generator, the armature circuit is equivalent to a source of emf in series with a resistance as shown in Fig. 7-6. However, in the motor, current flows from the line into the armature against the generated emf. It is evident from Fig. 7-6 that the terminal voltage must be balanced by both the $IR$ drop in the armature circuit and the counter emf at all times. This is apparent also from Eq. (4).

A comparison of the equivalent circuit of a generator (Fig. 6-20) and the equivalent circuit of a motor (Fig. 7-6) shows that the only difference is the direction of flow of armature current. In the generator, the generated emf is larger than the terminal voltage, resulting in a flow of current *from* the generator. In the motor, the generated emf is smaller than the terminal voltage, resulting in a flow of current *into* the motor. This again brings out the fact that the dynamo is a reversible machine. When it is supplied with mechanical energy, it delivers electric energy; when it is supplied with electric energy, it delivers mechanical energy.

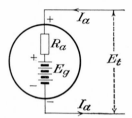

Fig. 7-6. Equivalent circuit of a motor armature.

### 7-6. Power Relationships in a Motor

If each term of the fundamental motor equation is multiplied by $I_a$, the resulting equation is

$$E_t I_a = E_g I_a + I_a^2 R_a$$

The term $E_t I_a$ is the power supplied to the armature of the motor. The power lost as heat in the armature circuit is represented by the term $I_a^2 R_a$. Thus, the term $E_g I_a$ must represent the power developed by the armature. This power is not all available at the pulley since some of this developed power must be used to overcome the mechanical or rotational losses of the motor.

**Example 3**  What is the power developed by the motor in the preceding example (*a*) in watts and (*b*) in horsepower?

(*a*) Developed power = $E_g I_a$ watts

= 235.2 × 60 = 14,112 watts

(*b*) Horsepower = $\dfrac{\text{watts}}{746}$

= $\dfrac{14,112}{746}$ = 18.92 hp

It may also be shown that the horsepower output of a motor is

$$\text{Horsepower output} = \frac{2\pi n T}{33,000} = \frac{nT}{5,252} \tag{5}$$

where $n$ = speed of motor, rpm

$T$ = torque at motor pulley, lb-ft

Thus, the horsepower output of a motor may be readily obtained by measuring its useful torque with a prony brake and measuring its speed with a tachometer. The horsepower output may then be calculated by means of Eq. (5).

**Example 4** The measured speed of a motor is 1,100 rpm. The net force registered on the scale used with a prony brake is 16 lb. If the brake arm measures 28 in., what is the horsepower output of the motor?

$$T = Fr$$

$$= 16 \times \frac{28}{12} = 37.3 \text{ lb-ft}$$

$$\text{Horsepower output} = \frac{nT}{5,252}$$

$$= \frac{1,100 \times 37.3}{5,252} = 7.82 \text{ hp}$$

**7-7. Armature Reaction in a Motor; Interpoles** The effect of armature reaction in a motor is similar to its effect in a generator, that is, it both distorts and weakens the main field flux.

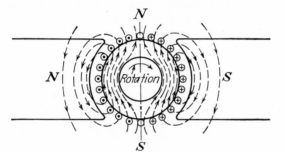

FIG. 7-7. Flux established by the flow of armature current in a motor.

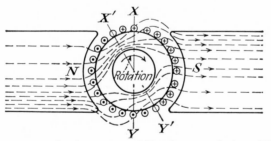

FIG. 7-8. Armature reaction in a motor shifts the neutral plane $XY$ to the new position $X'Y'$.

Figure 7-7 shows the action of the armature mmf when the armature currents are in a direction that causes the motor to rotate in a clockwise direction. The combined action of this armature mmf and the main field mmf is illustrated in Fig. 7-8, which shows that the resulting field is strengthened at the leading pole tips and weakened at the trailing pole tips. This causes the neutral plane to be shifted *against* the direction of rotation to the new position $X'Y'$. Thus, in a motor without interpoles, it is necessary to shift the brushes to secure good commutation. However, in a motor, the brushes must be shifted from the mechanical neutral in a direction *opposite* to the rotation of the armature.

Interpoles perform the same function in a motor as they do in a generator; that is, they provide a commutating flux that generates the emf necessary to neutralize the emf of self-induction in the armature coils undergoing commutation. Since the motor field flux is distorted in a direction opposite the field distortion in a generator, it follows that motor interpoles must be of a polarity opposite that of generator interpoles; that is, *motor interpoles must have a polarity opposite that of the following main pole in the direction of armature rotation.* It should be noted that for given external connections, a d-c machine that has correct interpole polarity when operated as a generator will have the correct interpole polarity when operated as a motor, since a reversal of armature current changes the polarity of the interpoles.

### 7-8. Speed of a Motor

A reduction of the field flux of a motor causes the motor speed to increase. The reduction of field strength reduces the counter emf of the motor, since fewer lines of force are being cut by the armature conductors. A reduction of the counter emf permits more armature current to flow. This increase in current causes a larger torque to be developed, for the increase in armature current much more than offsets the decrease in field flux. The increased torque causes the motor speed to increase, thereby increasing the counter emf in proportion. The speed and counter emf increase until the armature current and the torque are reduced to values just large enough to supply the load at a new constant speed.

**Example 5** A 220-volt shunt motor has an armature resistance of 0.2 ohm. For a given load on the motor, the armature current is 30 amp. What is the immediate effect on the torque developed by the motor if the field flux is reduced by 3 per cent?

The torque developed when the armature current is 30 amp is

$$T_1 = K'\phi I_a = K'\phi(30) \qquad \text{lb-ft}$$

and the counter emf is

$$E_{g1} = E_t - I_a R_a = 220 - (30 \times 0.2) = 214 \text{ volts}$$

If $\phi$ is reduced by 3 per cent, the value of $E_g$ is also reduced by 3 per cent, since $E_g = K\phi n$, and the speed $n$ cannot change instantly. Thus, the new counter emf is

$$E_{g2} = 0.97 \times 214 = 207.58 \text{ volts}$$

The new armature current is

$$I_{a2} = \frac{E_t - E_g}{R_a} = \frac{220 - 207.58}{0.2} = 62.1 \text{ amp}$$

and the new value of torque developed is

$$T_2 = K'(0.97)\phi(62.1)$$
$$= K'\phi 60.24 \quad \text{lb-ft}$$

The torque increase is

$$\frac{T_2}{T_1} = \frac{K'\phi 60.24}{K'\phi 30} = 2.008 \text{ times}$$

Thus, a 3 per cent decrease in field flux more than doubles the torque developed by the motor. This increased torque causes the armature speed to increase to a higher value at which the increased counter emf limits the armature current to a value just large enough to carry the load at the higher speed.

An increase in the field strength causes the motor speed to be decreased for similar reasons. A greater counter emf reduces the armature current and the torque, and the motor speed decreases. Thus, the motor slows down until the counter emf and the armature current reach values such that the load is again carried at a constant speed.

The fact that the speed of a motor varies with the field excitation provides a convenient means for controlling the speed of shunt and compound motors. The shunt-field current and, therefore, the field flux may be varied by a field rheostat. Cutting in resistance in the field circuit causes a decrease in field flux and, therefore, an increase in speed. Likewise, a decrease in resistance causes a decrease in speed. This is the most common method of motor-speed control.

If a motor is able to maintain a nearly constant speed for varying loads, the motor is said to have a good *speed regulation*. Speed regulation is usually expressed in per cent and is found as follows:

$$\text{Per cent regulation} = \frac{\text{no-load speed} - \text{full-load speed}}{\text{full-load speed}} \times 100 \quad (6)$$

**Example 6**  The no-load speed of a d-c shunt motor is 1,200 rpm. When the motor carries its rated load, the speed drops to 1,120 rpm. What is the speed regulation in per cent?

$$\text{Per cent regulation} = \frac{NL \text{ speed} - FL \text{ speed}}{FL \text{ speed}} \times 100$$

$$= \frac{1,200 - 1,120}{1,120} \times 100 = 7.14 \text{ per cent}$$

**7-9. The Shunt Motor**    This is the most common type of d-c motor. It is connected in the same way as the shunt generator, that is, with the shunt field directly across the terminals in parallel with the armature circuit.    A field rheostat is usually connected in series with the field.

A shunt motor has good speed regulation and is classed as a constant-speed motor even though its speed does decrease slightly with an increase in load.

As load is added to a shunt motor, the motor immediately tends to slow down.    The counter emf immediately decreases since it is dependent on the speed and the practically constant field flux.    The decrease in the counter emf permits the flow of an increased armature current, thus providing more torque for the increased load.    The increased armature current causes a larger $I_aR_a$ drop, which means that the counter emf does not return to its former value but remains at some lower value.    This is shown to be true by the fundamental motor equation

$$E_t = E_g + I_aR_a \tag{4}$$

Since $E_t$ is constant, the sum of the counter emf and the $I_aR_a$ drop must remain constant.    If $I_aR_a$ becomes larger owing to an increase in load, $E_g$ must decrease, thus causing a corresponding decrease in speed.

The basic speed of a shunt motor is the full-load full-field speed. Usual speed adjustment is made by inserting resistance in the field circuit with a field rheostat, thereby weakening the field flux.    This method of speed control provides a smooth and efficient means of varying the motor speed from basic speed to a maximum speed which is set by both electrical and mechanical limitations of the motor. *Care must be taken never to open the field circuit of a shunt motor that is running unloaded.*    The loss of the field flux causes the motor speed to increase to dangerously high values.

The speed of a shunt motor may also be changed by means of an adjustable resistance in the armature circuit, but this method is less efficient than the shunt-field control.    The method is also objectionable because it causes the motor to have a very poor speed regulation.

The field flux of a shunt motor is very nearly constant.    Since the torque of a motor is equal to $K'\phi I_a$, the torque is directly proportional to the armature current.    Figure 7-9 shows both the torque-load and the speed-load characteristics of a typical shunt motor.    Note that the torque increases in a practically straight-line relationship with an increase in armature current, while the speed drops slightly as armature current is increased.

Starters used with d-c motors are usually designed to limit the armature starting current to 125 to 200 per cent of full-load current. Since the torque of a shunt motor is proportional to the armature current, the starting torque will be 125 to 200 per cent of full-load torque, depending on the value of the starting resistance. For example, if the starting current of a given shunt motor is 150 per cent of full-load current, then the starting torque is 150 per cent of full-load value (note Fig. 7-9).

Since the speed of a shunt motor may be fixed at any value between a maximum and minimum value, it is often used for driving such loads as machine tools. The operator may select any speed within

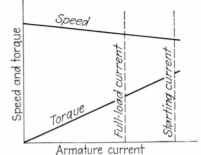

Fig. 7-9. Speed-load and torque-load curves of a shunt motor.

the rating of the motor by adjusting the field rheostat. But at any one setting of the rheostat the motor speed remains practically constant for all loads.

**7-10. The Series Motor**    In the series motor, the field is connected in series with the armature. As the series field must carry full armature current, it is wound with a few turns of comparatively large wire. Any change in load causes a change in armature current and also a change in field flux. Therefore as the load changes, the speed changes.

It was shown that the speed of a shunt motor is inversely proportional to the field flux. This is true also in a series motor. The armature-circuit $IR$ drop also varies with the load, but its effect is very small compared with the effect of the field flux. Therefore, the speed of a series motor depends almost entirely on the flux; the stronger the field flux, the lower the speed. Likewise, a decrease in load current and therefore in field current and field flux causes an increase in speed. Thus, the speed varies from a very high speed at light load to a low speed at full load.

A series motor does not have a definite no-load speed. As load is removed from the motor, the field flux decreases. If all the load is removed, the flux drops to practically zero and the motor speed may become dangerously high. For this reason, *the load should never be removed completely from a series motor.* A series motor is used only where load is directly connected to the shaft or geared to the shaft. Very small series motors usually have enough friction and other losses to keep the no-load speed down to a safe limit.    The speed-load curve of a typical series motor is shown in Fig. 7-10.

In a shunt motor, the torque is practically proportional to the armature current since the field flux is almost constant.    In the series motor, the field flux varies with the armature current, and for small loads the field flux is almost directly proportional to the armature current.    Since torque is equal to $K'\phi I_a$, this means that for small loads the torque is proportional to $I_a{}^2$.    However, as the armature current approaches full-load value, the saturation of the magnetic circuit and armature reaction both prevent the torque from increasing as rapidly as the square of the current.    This causes the torque-load curve to straighten out for the heavier loads as shown in Fig. 7-10.

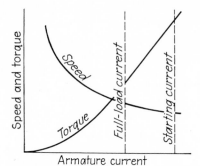

FIG. 7-10. Speed-load and torque-load curves of a series motor.

It has been pointed out that the series motor develops a large torque for large armature currents and also operates at low speed for large armature currents.    It is therefore a suitable motor for starting heavy loads.    It is often used for driving cranes and winches where heavy loads must be moved slowly but where the lighter loads may be moved with greater speed.    Another common application of the series motor is in electric-railway service.

**7-11. The Compound Motor**    The cumulative-compound motor combines the operating characteristics of the shunt and series motors. It has a definite no-load speed and may be safely operated at no load. As load is added, the increased amount of field flux causes the speed to decrease more than does the speed of a shunt motor.    Thus, the speed regulation of a cumulative-compound motor is poorer than that of a shunt motor.

The torque of the cumulative-compound motor is greater than that of the shunt motor for a given armature current owing to the series field flux.    The torque-load and speed-load curves are shown in Fig. 7-11.

Cumulative-compound motors are used where a fairly constant speed is required with irregular loads or suddenly applied heavy loads. Such loads as presses, shears, and reciprocating machines are often driven by compound motors.

The differential-compound motor has a nearly constant speed at all loads but has poor torque characteristics at heavy loads. The shunt motor has a sufficiently constant speed for most applications and a much better torque characteristic than the differential-compound motor. The differential-compound motor is little used for this reason.

Figure 7-12 shows a comparison of the characteristics of series, shunt, and cumulative-compound motors with the same full-load horsepower output and the same light-load speed. A representative value of starting current is shown, being 150 per cent of full-load current.

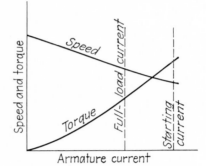

The speed regulation of the shunt motor is much better than that of the series or compound motor. Thus the shunt motor is suitable for constant-speed applications. The compound and series motors are used where good speed regulation is not essential or where a varying speed may be desirable.

FIG. 7-11. Speed-load and torque-load curves of a cumulative-compound motor.

The exceptionally high starting torque of the series motor makes it an ideal motor for starting heavy loads at a reduced speed. It will be noted from Fig. 7-12 that the series motor develops much more torque than the compound or shunt motors for a given armature current, at all but the lighter loads.

Thus, the different types of d-c motors have widely varying characteristics. The character of the load, of course, determines the type of motor to be used in each case.

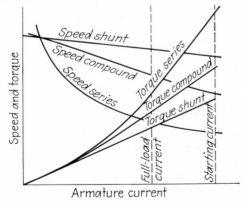

FIG. 7-12. Comparative speed-load and torque-load curves for series, shunt, and compound motors.

**7-12. Motor-starting Requirements**   Two requirements must be met in starting d-c motors, especially if they are to be started under load:

1. Both the motor and the supply lines must be protected from the flow of excessive current during the starting period.

2. The motor-starting torque should be made as large as possible, to bring the motor up to full speed in a minimum period of time.

At starting, when a motor armature is stationary, no counter emf is being generated.   This means that the only thing to limit the amount of current being drawn from the supply is the armature-circuit resistance, which in most motors is very low, being of the order of 1 ohm or less.   To meet the first starting requirement, an external resistance is placed in series with the motor-armature circuit during the starting period.   To show why this is necessary, consider a 10-hp motor with an armature resistance of 0.5 ohm.   If this motor were connected directly to a 230-volt supply line, the resulting current would be

$$I = \frac{E}{R} = \frac{230}{0.5} = 460 \text{ amp}$$

which is roughly twelve times normal full-load armature current for a motor of this size.   This large inrush of current would in all probability damage the brushes, commutator, or windings.   Starting resistances are usually designed to limit the starting current of a motor to 125 to 200 per cent of the full-load current.

The amount of starting resistance required to limit the armature starting current to the desired value is

$$R_s = \frac{E_t}{I_s} - R_a \tag{7}$$

where $R_s$ = starting resistance, ohms
$E_t$ = motor terminal voltage, volts
$I_s$ = desired armature starting current, amp
$R_a$ = armature-circuit resistance, ohms

**Example 7**   If the full-load armature current of the above motor is 40 amp and it is desired to limit the starting current to 150 per cent of this value, find the starting resistance that must be added in series with the armature.

$$R_s = \frac{E_t}{I_s} - R_a$$

$$= \frac{230}{40 \times 1.5} - 0.5$$

$$= \frac{230}{60} - 0.5 = 3.33 \text{ ohms}$$

Starting resistors are variable resistances, with the value of the resistance in the circuit at any time being manually or automatically controlled. The maximum value of the resistance is inserted in the armature circuit when the motor is first connected to the supply. As the motor speed increases, the counter emf increases, thereby decreasing the armature current. The starting resistance may then be cut out by successive steps until the motor has reached its full speed.

The second motor starting requirement is met by providing a maximum value of field flux and by allowing a maximum safe value of armature current to flow during the starting period. In shunt and compound motors, a maximum field flux is obtained by cutting out the shunt-field rheostat. In the series motor, the field flux is at a maximum by virtue of the heavy starting current flowing through the field winding. With a maximum field flux and a maximum allowable armature current, the starting torque (equal to $K'\phi I_a$) developed is at a maximum value, thereby bringing the motor to full speed in a short time.

**7-13. Controllers and Starters**  A controller is a device for regulating the operation of the apparatus to which it is connected. A d-c motor controller performs the basic functions of starting, controlling speed, reversing, stopping, and providing some measure of protection for the motor that it governs. The more common types of controllers are the faceplate, the drum, and the magnetic controller.

A starter is a controller whose main function is to start and accelerate a motor.

**7-14. Faceplate Starters**  Faceplate starters are manually operated controllers used mainly with shunt and compound motors that do not require frequent starting or stopping. A connection diagram of this type of starter is shown in Fig. 7-13, and the general appearance of an enclosed-type faceplate starter is shown in Fig. 7-14.

The starting resistance of the faceplate starter is tapped at several points to contact segments or buttons. These buttons are arranged in an arc so that a movable contact on the starting arm may come in contact successively with each button as the arm is advanced along the arc. The starting arm is normally held in the OFF position by a strong spring.

As the starting arm is moved to the START position, the starting resistance is connected in series with the motor armature, thereby completing the armature circuit. At the same time, the motor field circuit is completed in parallel with the holding magnet.

The starting resistance is gradually cut out as the starting arm is advanced successively from contact to contact while the motor speed (and hence the counter emf) increases. When the motor has reached its full speed and all the starting resistance is cut out, the starting arm comes in contact with the small electromagnet or holding coil $M$ and the arm is held in the RUN position.

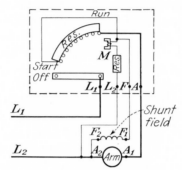

FIG. 7-13. Connection diagram of a faceplate starter.

FIG. 7-14. A faceplate starter for a d-c motor. (*Courtesy of General Electric Company.*)

If, while the motor is running, the supply voltage falls below a pre-determined value or fails completely, the holding magnet becomes deenergized, thereby releasing the starting arm, which then is pulled back to the OFF position by the spring. The action of the holding coil in releasing the starting arm for voltage failure or for low voltage is called *undervoltage protection* of the motor. Without this protection, the supply voltage might be restored with the starting arm in the RUN position, thereby applying full line voltage directly to the motor armature with a resulting excessive current flow.

In some starters, the starting arm consists of two sections that are advanced together over two rows of contact buttons as the motor is being started. When contact is made with the holding magnet, one section of the starting arm, called the field-control section, is released and resistance is connected in series with the field. Moving the field-control section of the arm back toward the OFF position cuts in additional field resistance, thereby increasing the motor speed. Upon failure of the voltage, the holding magnet is released and the starting arm is returned to the OFF position.

**7-15. Drum Controllers**  The drum controller is commonly used for starting and controlling series motors such as electric-train drive motors. Drum controllers are also used with shunt and compound motors that require frequent starting, stopping, and reversing.

A drum controller consists essentially of a cylinder, insulated from a central shaft on which is mounted a series of copper segments. As the cylinder is rotated by a handle, which is keyed to the shaft, the various contact segments come in contact with contact fingers. The contact fingers are held in place by adjusting screws and by springs strong enough to ensure a good electrical connection with the contact segments. By designing the controller with different sequences for the making and breaking of the contacts as the drum is rotated, a great variety of switching operations may be performed.

When the operating handle of a drum controller, used with a shunt or compound motor, is advanced to the START position, contacts are made to connect the field circuit across the line and also to complete the armature circuit through a starting resistance. As the drum is moved to succeeding contacts, the starting resistance is gradually cut out until the armature is connected directly across the line. Additional contacts may be arranged so that, after the starting resistance is cut out, speed control may be provided by inserting resistance into the field circuit.

Reversing may be accomplished by rotating the drum in the opposite direction from the neutral, or OFF, position. This operation reverses the armature connections, which in turn reverses the direction of rotation of the motor.

In some types of drum controllers, such as the crane-hoist controller shown in Fig. 7-15, the central shaft has mounted on it a series of projecting cams which, as the operating handle is rotated, move movable contacts against stationary contacts in a predetermined order. In the controller in Fig. 7-15, the movable contacts may be seen on the right and the stationary contacts on the left. A great many switching sequences may be performed with this type of controller.

Drum controllers are commonly used for starting, controlling speed, and reversing series motors. Starting a series motor consists of inserting a resistance in series with the armature and gradually cutting

FIG. 7-15. Cam-type drum controller with cover removed. (*Courtesy of General Electric Company.*)

out that resistance as the motor gains speed. Speed control is accomplished by varying the amount of starting resistance that may be left in the armature circuit. Of course any resistor used for this purpose must be capable of withstanding full-load currents continuously. Resistors used for both starting and speed control are often built in units separate from the controller.

Series motors may be reversed by reversing either the field or armature connections.

In order to prevent the contacts of controllers from being damaged by the arc formed when the contacts are opened, *magnetic blowouts* are often used to extinguish the arc.  A magnetic blowout is an electromagnet so constructed that its field is set up across the arc.  When the contacts open, the arc is moved at right angles to the field in the same way that a current carrying conductor is acted upon.  The field and contacts are so arranged that the arc is drawn away from the contacts, breaking it in a short time.  To make the field strength proportional to the current being interrupted, the blowout coil is connected in series with the circuit being opened.

**7-16. Automatic Control of D-C Motors**   Automatic starting, stopping, and reversing of d-c motors is commonly accomplished by means of magnetically operated switches called *magnetic contactors*.  Controllers using magnetic contactors to control the operation of the motor to which they are connected are called *magnetic controllers*.

Magnetic controllers may be actuated by means of a push button which is often located at some point remote from the motor and controller.  Controllers are also made entirely automatic by actuating them by various automatic devices.  If, for example, a motor drives an air compressor that supplies air to a storage tank, the starting and stopping "signals" to the motor may be given by a pressure switch connected to the tank.  When the pressure falls below a certain value, the motor is started; it is stopped again when the pressure has risen to the desired value.

**7-17. Magnetic Contactors**   The basic part of all magnetic controllers is the magnetic contactor.  An operating coil is placed on an iron core so that when current flows through the coil the iron core becomes magnetized.  This attracts a movable iron armature that carries one or more insulated electric contacts.  As the armature is moved toward the core, the moving contacts are moved against stationary contacts.  The contacts are connected in series with the controlled device, such as a motor-armature circuit, thereby completing the circuit when the operating coil is energized.  When the circuit of the operating coil is opened, the iron core becomes demagnetized and the armature is released, being returned to its open position by means of a spring or by gravity.  Since the contacts of a magnetic contactor may be designed to carry heavy currents, a means is provided whereby large amounts of current can be controlled by means of the relatively feeble current needed for energizing the operating coil.  To extinguish the arc formed when heavy currents are interrupted, magnetic blowout coils are often used.  A single-pole magnetic contactor equipped with a blowout coil is shown in Fig. 7-16.

FIG. 7-16. Sectional view of a one-pole magnetic contactor equipped with magnetic blowout coil.   (*Courtesy of the Square D Company, EC&M Division.*)

Magnetic contactors are used when it is desired to control a motor or other device from a remote point.   It is not necessary to run the main supply lines to the point of control.   Only small control wires need be used.

If a switch is to be opened and closed frequently, magnetic control is also desirable.   An operator is easily able to operate a push button to actuate a contactor several times a minute, whereas the operation of heavy manual controls might cause undue fatigue.

Undervoltage release, undervoltage protection, and overload protection are easily provided by the use of magnetic contactors as is described in the following articles.

**7-18. Control of Magnetic Contactors: Motor Protection** Figure 7-17 shows a two-wire control circuit using a magnetic contactor for connecting a motor to the line. When the switch $S$ is closed, the operating coil is connected directly across the supply lines from $L_1$ to $L_2$. This causes the contacts $C$ to close, connecting the motor to the supply. The method for cutting out the starting resistance is not shown as this will be considered in Art. 7-19. When the switch $S$ is opened, the contacts $C$ are opened, which disconnects the motor from the line.

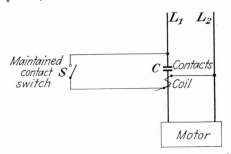

FIG. 7-17. Undervoltage release provided by two-wire control of the magnetic contactor.

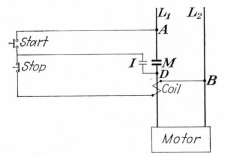

FIG. 7-18. Three-wire push-button control circuit providing undervoltage protection for the motor.

If, while the motor in Fig. 7-17 is in operation, the supply voltage falls below a certain value or fails completely, the contactor disconnects the motor from the line. This type of control is said to provide the motor with *undervoltage release*. This is desirable where it is necessary that the motor be restarted automatically after a voltage failure.

The switch $S$ in Fig. 7-17 may be replaced by any of a number of automatic devices such as a thermostat, float switch, photoelectric cell, or limit switch.

A three-wire push-button control circuit for a contactor is shown in Fig. 7-18. The START button is a momentary contact switch that is held normally open by a spring. The STOP button is held normally closed by a spring.   When the operator pushes the START button, the operating-coil circuit is completed from point $A$ on line 1, through the START button, the STOP button, and the coil to point $B$ on line 2.   This closes the main contacts $M$ that connect the motor to the supply. At the same time a set of auxiliary or maintaining contacts $I$ are closed.

When the maintaining contacts close, a new circuit is established from the point $D$ on line 1, through the contacts $I$, the STOP button, and the coil, to point $B$ on line 2.   Since the operating-coil circuit is now maintained by the $I$ contacts, the operator may release the START button.   When the STOP button is depressed, the coil is deenergized, thereby opening both sets of contacts.

If the supply voltage drops below a certain value, or fails, the main contacts and the maintaining contacts are both opened.   Upon return of the supply voltage, the contactor cannot close until the START button is again closed.   Because a contactor that is controlled by a three-wire control circuit maintains the interruption of the circuit even after the line voltage is restored, it is said to provide *undervoltage protection* for the motor.   This protection is used when it is desired to prevent the unexpected starting of a motor.

*Overload protection* for motors is used to protect the motor and control apparatus from excessive heating due to motor overloads. *Thermal-overload* relays are commonly used for motor-overload protection.   There are two principal types of thermal-overload relays. Both types are operated from the heat generated in a heating element through which the motor current passes.   In one type the heat bends a bimetallic strip, and in the other the heat melts a film of solder. Both act to open the motor-control circuit.

A bimetallic strip is made of two different metals whose surfaces have been welded together.   One of the metals expands rapidly when heated, while the other is not affected greatly by the heat.   When heat is applied, the strip is caused to deflect or curl up due to the different expansion of the two metals.   When the motor current reaches a predetermined value, the heat generated deflects the strip far enough to trip a latch that opens the motor-control circuit.   When the strip cools sufficiently, the relay may be reset and the motor restarted.

In the solder-film type of overload relay the heat generated at a given overload current melts the film, which releases a latch arrangement and opens the motor-control circuit.   When the solder has cooled enough to hold the latch, the relay may be reset.

In either type of thermal relay, the time required to operate is determined by the amount of current flowing in the heater.   Thus, the relay operates slowly for light overloads but disconnects the motor in a short time for dangerously heavy overloads. Relays in which the time of operation is inversely proportional to the amount of current flowing are called *inverse-time relays*.

**7-19. Magnetic Controllers for Starting D-C Motors**   It was shown in Art. 7-12 that a resistance must be connected in series with a d-c motor-armature circuit during the starting period. If magnetic control is to be used for starting a motor, some method must be used for inserting this resistance at starting and removing it as the motor speed increases. This is commonly done by using contactors to short-circuit sections of the starting resistance as the motor comes up to speed. In general, the contactors are actuated by one of three methods: the *counter emf method*, the *definite-time method*, and the *current-limit method*.

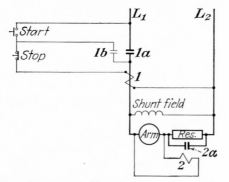

Fig. 7-19. Elementary diagram of a counter emf starter.

Figure 7-19 shows an elementary diagram of a *counter emf starter* in which the starting resistance is cut out in one step. Contactor 1, with its contacts 1*a* and 1*b*, is operated by means of a three-wire push-button station. The coil of contactor 2, called the accelerating contactor, is connected directly across the armature, while the accelerating contacts 2*a* are connected across the starting resistance. Depressing the START button closes contactor 1, connecting the motor to the supply lines with the starting resistance in series with the motor armature. Because the counter emf of the motor is zero at starting, the voltage across the armature is low, being due to the armature $IR$ drop only. As the motor speed and counter emf increase, the voltage across the armature increases. When the voltage across the armature and the coil of contactor 2 reaches approximately 80 per cent of line voltage, contactor 2 closes, thereby short-circuiting the starting resistance. This connects the armature directly across the lines.

To obtain smoother acceleration, several contactors may be arranged to close on different amounts of voltage so that the starting resistance is cut out in several steps. Counter emf starting is quite simple but is usually limited to small d-c motors that always start approximately the same load. If a different load is started each time, the accelerating contactors may close too soon or too late.

In *definite-time starting*, the starting resistor is cut out in steps by contactors that operate successively at definite intervals. When the

Fig. 7-20. An enclosed definite-time magnetic starter with cover removed. The escapement mechanism is shown in the lower left-hand corner. (*Courtesy of General Electric Company.*)

START button is depressed, the armature circuit is completed with the starting resistance in series. A timing device is automatically started at the same time. The timer then causes the contactors to close at predetermined intervals regardless of the motor speed until the entire starting resistance is short-circuited. Common timing devices are mechanical escapement mechanisms, motor-driven timers, and magnetic time-delay relays. Definite-time acceleration is perhaps more widely used than other methods in d-c motor-control equipment. A definite-time starter using a mechanical escapement timer is shown in Fig. 7-20.

*Current-limit acceleration* of d-c motors makes use of current-limit contactors that remain open while the current through them exceeds a certain value but that close when the current falls below that value. Operating coils for these contactors are series coils, that is, they are designed to be connected in series with the armature circuit of the motor. Therefore, the time required to operate the contactor, the contacts of which cut out the starting resistance, depends on the rate at which the motor accelerates and builds up its counter emf to lower the current it draws from the line.

**7-20. Dynamic Braking** Often it is desirable to have a means of stopping a motor quickly. One method of bringing a motor to a quick stop is by means of *dynamic braking*. If a running motor is disconnected from its supply lines and a resistance load (often the starting resistance) is placed across the armature terminals, the motor then acts as a generator, sending a current through the resistance. This causes the energy possessed by the rotating armature to be expended quickly in the form of heat in the resistance which brings the motor to a standstill quickly. The amount of braking effort available depends on the motor speed, the motor-field strength, and the value of the resistance. This type of braking is used extensively in connection with the control of elevators and hoists and in other applications in which motors must be started, stopped, and reversed frequently.

**7-21. Ward Leonard System of Speed Control** Some applications of d-c motors require a wide and finely graduated range of speed control. The Ward Leonard, or adjustable-voltage, system provides

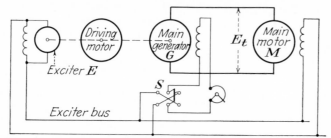
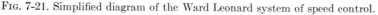

Fig. 7-21. Simplified diagram of the Ward Leonard system of speed control.

such control and involves a separate generator that drives an adjustable-speed motor. By varying the field excitation of the generator, the voltage applied to the motor may be varied over a wide range, resulting in a wide speed range on the motor.

A simplified diagram of the system is shown in Fig. 7-21. The driving motor is usually a constant-speed a-c motor. Directly connected to the prime mover is the separately excited d-c main generator $G$ that drives the main motor $M$. To supply the field excitation of both $G$ and $M$, a small self-excited d-c generator or exciter $E$ is connected also directly to the driving motor.

To start the motor $M$, the field excitation of $G$ is raised so that the voltage $E_t$ is gradually increased across $M$, which causes the motor to accelerate. No starting resistance is needed since the voltage $E_t$ is raised from a very low value, allowing the counter emf of the motor to increase with the applied voltage. The motor speed may be set at any speed between zero and its maximum speed by adjusting the field excitation of the generator $G$ to the desired value. Since the field flux of motor $M$ is constant, it has the speed-load characteristics of a shunt motor and the speed regulation is good at a given armature voltage.

The motor $M$ may be reversed by dropping $E_t$ to zero and reversing the generator-field current by means of the double-throw reversing switch. As the voltage $E_t$ is increased with the opposite polarity, the motor accelerates in the opposite direction.

If, while the motor $M$ is operating, the voltage $E_t$ is suddenly decreased to a value below the counter emf of the motor, the armature current is reversed with the motor acting as a generator, driving $G$ as a motor. Dynamic braking is thus established, which brings the motor to a quick stop.

An important requirement in many industrial motor-control applications is the maintenance of a constant speed of a drive motor or the maintenance of a variable speed which is a function of some operating quantity. For example, the speed of the individual sections of a paper-making machine must be maintained within an accuracy of a fraction of one per cent. Special control systems, called *closed-cycle feedback control systems,* have been developed for use with the conventional Ward Leonard system to obtain extremely accurate speed control. The subject of feedback control is beyond the scope of this book and the reader is referred to one of the many books available on this subject.

Some common applications of the Ward Leonard system are in steel mills for reversing rolling mills, elevators for tall buildings, gun turrets, and special hoist motors.

The first cost of the Ward Leonard system is high, and it is relatively inefficient since several energy transformations are involved. However, the speed control provided is very effective; that is, the response to changes in speed is fast, a wide range of speeds is available, and reversing and dynamic braking are provided. In applications where these factors are important, the advantages gained in using the Ward Leonard system justify the increased cost and low efficiency.

## Table 4. Summary of D-C Generator and Motor Characteristics

| Characteristic | Generator | Motor |
|---|---|---|
| Purpose...................... | To generate an emf | To develop a torque |
| Capacity rating.............. | Kilowatts | Horsepower |
| Output...................... | Electrical $P = EI$ | Mechanical $P = \dfrac{nT}{5{,}252}$ |
| Input....................... | Mechanical $P = \dfrac{nT}{5{,}252}$ | Electrical $P = EI$ |
| Opposing action.............. | Countertorque | Counter emf |
| Fundamental equation......... | $E_t = E_g - I_a R_a$ | $E_t = E_g + I_a R_a$ |
| Variation in field excitation results in.................... | Change in voltage | Change in speed |
| Armature reaction............ | Shifts field in direction of rotation | Shifts field against direction of rotation |
| Interpoles................... | Same polarity as following main pole | Opposite polarity from following main pole |
| Effect of increase in load: | | |
|   Shunt dynamo.............. | Voltage decreases | Small decrease in speed |
|   Series dynamo............. | Voltage increases | Large decrease in speed |
|   Cumulative-compound dynamo | Voltage may remain constant, increase, or decrease depending on compounding | Large or small decrease in speed depending on compounding |
|   Differential-compound dynamo | Voltage decreases large amount | Speed constant or may increase |
| | Generators and motors | |
| Generated emf................ | $E_g = K\phi n$ | |
| Methods of field excitation..... | Separately excited, shunt, series, compound | |
| Losses...................... | Copper, iron, friction | |
| Efficiency................... | Per cent efficiency $= \dfrac{\text{output}}{\text{input}} \times 100$ | |

## REVIEW QUESTIONS

**1.** What is the function of a motor?

**2.** Upon what fundamental principle does motor operation depend?

**3.** Define torque.  What is the unit?

**4.** Describe how torque is developed in a motor.

**5.** How may the direction of rotation of a d-c motor be reversed?

**6.** What two things determine the amount of force developed on an armature conductor?

**7.** Give the torque equation of a motor.

**8.** If the mechanical output of a motor is increased, what must happen to the electrical input?

**9.** Explain how the torque of a motor may be measured.

**10.** What is starting torque?

**11.** When a motor is in operation, why is the armature current *not* equal to the line voltage divided by the armature resistance? Give the correct equation for armature current.

**12.** What is the fundamental motor equation? How does it differ from the generator equation?

**13.** Given a prony brake and a tachometer, explain how the horsepower output of a motor may be measured. What other instruments would be needed to obtain data for finding the efficiency of a motor?

**14.** What is the effect of armature reaction in a motor?

**15.** What is the purpose of interpoles?

**16.** If the resistance of a motor shunt-field rheostat is increased, what happens to the speed of the motor?

**17.** What is a common method of controlling the speed of a shunt motor?

**18.** Define speed regulation.

**19.** Explain how a motor automatically adjusts its input to take care of changes in mechanical load.

**20.** What happens to the speed of a shunt motor as load is increased?

**21.** What effect might armature reaction have on the speed of a shunt motor?

**22.** How is the basic speed of a shunt motor defined?

**23.** Is it possible to lower the speed below the basic speed by varying the shunt-field-rheostat resistance?

**24.** Why is it dangerous to open the field of a shunt motor running at no load?

**25.** If the torque of a shunt motor is doubled, what happens to the armature current, assuming a constant field flux?

**26.** Why is the speed regulation of a series motor poorer than that of a shunt motor?

**27.** Why should a series motor never be operated without load?

**28.** Why does a series motor have a higher starting torque than a shunt motor of similar capacity?

**29.** What are some common applications of (*a*) shunt motors, (*b*) series motors?

**30.** How does the speed regulation of a compound motor compare with that of (*a*) a series motor, (*b*) a shunt motor?

**31.** How does the starting torque of a compound motor compare with that of (*a*) a series motor, (*b*) a shunt motor?

**32.** Give some applications of compound motors.

**33.** What two requirements must be met in starting d-c motors?

**34.** What is the purpose of the starting resistance used with d-c motors?

**35.** Give some of the functions of a controller.

**36.** Explain the operation of a faceplate starter.

**37.** Explain what is meant by undervoltage protection of a motor.

**38.** Where is the drum controller used?

**39.** What is a magnetic blowout? How does it operate?

**40.** What are some advantages of using magnetic contactors to control the operation of electric motors?

**41.** What is meant by undervoltage release? In what applications would it be desirable?

**42.** What kind of protection is provided for a motor by the three-wire push-button control of a magnetic contactor?

**43.** How is overload protection commonly provided for a motor?

**44.** What are three types of magnetic starters for d-c motors?

**45.** How is the accelerating contactor coil connected in the counter emf starter?

**46.** How is time delay obtained for operation of the accelerating contacts in a definite-time starter?

**47.** What is current-limit acceleration?

**48.** Describe what is meant by dynamic braking.

**49.** What are some advantages of the Ward Leonard system of speed control? What are some disadvantages?

## PROBLEMS

**1.** A 120-volt shunt motor develops a torque of 20 lb-ft when the armature current is 12 amp. Assuming a constant value of field flux, what torque will the motor develop when the armature current is 20 amp?

**2.** When developing a torque of 18 lb-ft, a 110-volt shunt motor draws a current of 10 amp from the source. The field current is 1.5 amp. What current will the motor draw from the line when it is developing a torque of 60 lb-ft, assuming that the field flux does not change in value?

**3.** A prony brake attached to a motor pulley has a brake-arm length of 20 in. If, when the motor runs at 1,150 rpm, the scale indicates a net force of 28 lb, what horsepower is being delivered?

**4.** A prony brake is to be built to measure the torque output of a 10-hp motor that operates at a speed of 1,200 rpm. If the scale available has a maximum capacity of 15 lb, what is the length of the shortest brake arm that could be used to measure any torque output of the motor up to 125 per cent of its rated value?

**5.** A shunt motor on a 230-volt line has an armature current of 75 amp. If the field-circuit resistance is 100 ohms, find the field current, the line current, and the kilowatt input to the motor.

**6.** A shunt motor draws 6 kw from a 240-volt line. If the field resistance is 96 ohms, find the line current, the field current, and the armature current of the motor.

**7.** A shunt motor connected to a 110-volt line runs at a speed of 1,200 rpm when the armature current is 20 amp. The armature resistance is 0.1 ohm. Assuming constant field flux, what is the speed when the armature current is 50 amp? (HINT: Speed is directly proportional to counter emf.)

**8.** Find the armature current of a shunt motor when the terminal voltage is 112 volts, the counter emf is 107 volts, and the armature-circuit resistance is 0.3 ohm.

**9.** The armature resistance of a 240-volt shunt motor is 0.16 ohm. At no load, the line current is 6.4 amp at rated voltage. The field current is 2.2 amp, and the speed is 1,280 rpm. Find the motor speed when the line current increases to 75 amp, the field current remaining the same. Assume that armature reaction does not affect the field flux.

**10.** The counter emf of a shunt motor is 227 volts, the field resistance is 160 ohms, and the field current is 1.5 amp. The line current is 36.5 amp. (a) Find the armature resistance. (b) If the line current during starting must be limited to 60 amp, how much starter resistance must be added in series with the armature?

**11.** A shunt motor draws a current of 38 amp from a 120-volt source. The field-circuit resistance is 50 ohms, and the armature-circuit resistance is 0.25 ohm. Find (a) the field current, (b) the armature current, (c) the counter emf, and (d) the counter emf at starting (armature at a standstill).

**12.** Find the horsepower developed by the motor in the preceding problem. If the mechanical and iron losses total 550 watts, what is the horsepower output?

**13.** What is the horsepower output of a motor that is running at 1,200 rpm and is supplying a torque of 24 lb-ft to the load?

**14.** What horsepower is developed by a motor when the armature current is 20 amp, the applied voltage is 115 volts, and the counter emf is 110 volts?

**15.** A 10-hp motor has a shunt-field resistance of 115 ohms and a field current of 2 amp. What is the applied voltage?

**16.** A certain shunt motor is connected to a 240-volt line. The armature-circuit resistance is 0.05 ohm. When the armature current is 60 amp, what is the counter emf?

**17.** A motor has a no-load speed of 900 rpm and a full-load speed of 850 rpm. What is the speed regulation?

**18.** The armature resistance of a shunt motor is 0.048 ohm. When the motor is connected across 120 volts, it develops a counter emf of 113 volts. Find (a) the $IR$ drop in the armature circuit, (b) the armature current, (c) the armature current if the armature were stationary, and (d) the counter emf when the armature current is 160 amp.

**19.** The efficiency, at rated load, of a 100-hp 600-volt shunt motor is 85 per cent. The field resistance is 190 ohms, and the armature resistance is 0.22 ohm. The full-load speed is 1,200 rpm. Find (a) the rated line current, (b) the armature current at full load, (c) the counter emf at full load, and (d) the field current.

**20.** The power input to a shunt motor is 5,600 watts for a given load on the motor. The terminal voltage is 220 volts, the $I_aR_a$ drop is 6.4 volts, and the armature resistance is 0.27 ohms. Find (a) the counter emf, (b) the power taken by the field, and (c) the field current.

**21.** At full load a 15-hp motor draws 58.9 amp from a 220-volt line. (a) What is the motor efficiency? (b) What is the motor efficiency at no load?

**22.** At rated load the rotational losses (iron losses plus mechanical losses) of a 240-volt shunt motor are 865 watts. The field resistance is 92 ohms, and the armature-circuit resistance is 0.12 ohm. The rated motor current is 140 amp. Find (a) the field copper losses, (b) the armature copper losses, (c) the rated horsepower output, and (d) the efficiency.

**23.** A long-shunt compound motor requires an armature current of 12 amp to carry a certain load. The armature resistance is 0.05 ohm, and the series-field resistance is 0.15 ohm. The motor is connected to a 115-volt source. Find (a) the counter emf, and (b) the developed horsepower.

**24.** A 10-hp compound motor connected short shunt is supplied by a 115-volt source. The full-load current is 90 amp. The shunt-field resistance is 90 ohms, the armature resistance is 0.08 ohm, and the series-field resistance is 0.04 ohm. Find (a) the shunt-field current, (b) the armature current, (c) the counter emf, (d) the efficiency at full load, (e) the full-load copper losses, and (f) the rotational losses (iron losses plus mechanical losses).

# CHAPTER 8

## ALTERNATING CURRENT

Over 90 per cent of the electric energy used in the United States is generated, distributed, and used as alternating current. Perhaps the greatest single reason for this widespread use of alternating current is the fact that an alternating voltage may be easily raised or lowered in value. Because of this, a-c energy may be generated and distributed efficiently at a relatively high voltage and then reduced to a lower usable voltage at the load.

Direct-current voltages are not easily changed in value; hence d-c energy is usually generated at the voltage at which it is to be used.

In addition to the fact that alternating voltages are easily changed in value, there are other reasons for the use of alternating currents. Alternating-current generators require no commutators with their accompanying troubles and maintenance. This means that commutation need not limit the size and speed of a-c generators as it does d-c generators. In general, a-c motors and controls are simpler, lighter in weight, and more reliable than d-c equipment of similar rating. The more extensive commercial development and the prospects of still further development of a-c equipment is still another reason for its use.

Although alternating current is used predominantly, there are some types of work for which direct current must be used or where it has a definite advantage. In mills and factories and in electric-railway service, where efficient speed control of motors is important, direct current has a definite advantage. Direct current is also commonly used for high-intensity light sources in searchlights and projectors, for charging storage batteries, for field excitation of a-c generators and synchronous motors, and for many electrochemical processes.

**8-1. Generation of an Alternating EMF**　It was explained in connection with d-c generators (Chap. 6) that when a coil is rotated in a uniform magnetic field an emf is generated in that coil. This emf reverses its direction at regular intervals and is continually varying in strength.  Such an emf is called an *alternating emf*.  The value of the emf at any given time is called the *instantaneous value of emf*, and the symbol is *e*.

The manner in which an alternating emf may be generated is illustrated in Fig. 8-1, which represents a two-pole generator with the armature rotating in a counterclockwise direction through a uniform magnetic field.  For convenience, positions 30° apart are marked off on the armature surface.  These are the positions through which a given armature conductor passes as the armature makes a complete revolution.  Position 0 will be used as a starting point.  At position 1 the conductor will have moved 30°, at position 2 it will have moved 60°, etc.

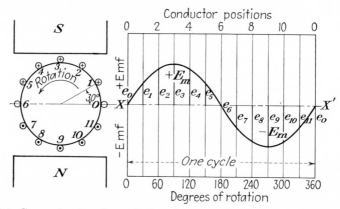

FIG. 8-1. Curve showing the variation of generated emf in a conductor as it is rotated through a uniform magnetic field.

A graph showing the instantaneous values of emf generated in a conductor as the armature rotates is also shown in Fig. 8-1.  Twelve equally spaced points are marked off on the horizontal line $XX'$ to correspond to the conductor positions on the armature.  The vertical lines at each point ($e_1$, $e_2$, $e_3$, etc.) represent the amount of emf generated at each conductor position as the armature rotates.

The amount of emf generated when the conductor moves through position 0 is zero since this point lies in the neutral plane of the generator and no lines of force are being cut.  As the conductor moves through points 1 and 2, it cuts across the field generating an emf, the direction of which is away from the reader.  Lines $e_1$ and $e_2$ represent the values of the emf generated at points 1 and 2, respectively.  At position 3, or 90°, the conductor moves at right angles to the field, generating a *maximum value of emf* (symbol $E_m$) which is represented by the line $e_3$.

As the conductor moves from position 3 around to position 6 the direction of the emf remains unchanged, but its value is diminishing, as shown by $e_4$ and $e_5$ on the graph.   At position 6, or 180°, the emf is again zero.   As soon as the conductor passes point 6, it begins to cut across the field in the opposite direction, reversing the direction of the generated emf.   The values of emf generated in this direction are represented below the horizontal line on the graph.

At position 9, or 270°, the conductor is again cutting the field at a maximum rate and the emf, $e_9$ or $-E_m$, is at a maximum.   From position 9 to position 0 the emf gradually decreases until it again becomes zero at 360° or the starting point.   The cycle of events then repeats as the armature completes each successive revolution.

The curve plotted from the values of the emf generated at the various points represents the variation of the generated emf in a conductor for a complete revolution in a two-pole generator.   It is customary to speak of the values of emf above the horizontal line as being in the positive direction and those below the line as being in the negative direction.   Most modern generators generate values of emf whose positive values are exactly like the negative values, and when these values are plotted, as in Fig. 8-1, the curve is of the same shape as a curve showing the values of the sine of the various angles of rotation. Therefore the curve is called a *sine wave.*

All a-c circuit problems discussed in this text are based on the assumption that the emfs and currents are sine waves.

### 8-2. Alternating Current
When an alternating emf is applied to a circuit, an alternating current is caused to flow.   In general, if a sine-wave emf is applied, the resulting current varies as does a sine wave (transient state ignored).   An alternating current may be defined as a current that flows back and forth through a circuit at regular intervals. An alternating current varies in intensity as does an alternating emf. The value at any given time is called the instantaneous value (symbol $i$), and the greatest value reached by the current is called its maximum value (symbol $I_m$).

### 8-3. Cycle; Frequency
When the value of an alternating emf or current rises from zero to a maximum, falls to zero, increases to a maximum in the reverse direction and back to zero again, the complete set of values passed through is called a *cycle* (see Fig. 8-1).   The number of complete cycles passed through in 1 second is called the *frequency.* Frequency is expressed in *cycles per second,* or often *cycles,* the words

"per second" being understood. The common power frequency in the United States is 60 cycles per second (cps). This means that the current and emf in such a circuit rise to a maximum and return to zero in each direction 60 times each second. Other frequencies in use are 50 and 25 cycles, but 60 cycles is much more prevalent.

**8-4. Electrical Degrees: A Measure of Time**   In any generator, a conductor must be moved past a north and a south pole to have one complete cycle generated in it. Therefore, the space through which a conductor must be moved to generate one cycle depends on the number of poles on the generator. In a two-pole generator, a conductor must make one complete revolution, or pass through 360° in space. In a four-pole generator, a conductor need be moved through only ½ revolution, or 180°, to generate one cycle. It is evident then that if the number of space degrees passed through by a conductor were used in plotting the emf wave generated, the number of degrees per cycle would vary with the number of poles on the generator.

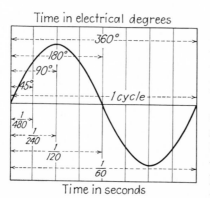

Since the time required to generate one cycle is constant for a given frequency, regardless of the number of poles on the generator, emf waves are plotted with time as the horizontal axis. Time in seconds may be used, but it is more convenient to divide the time required to generate one cycle into 360 divisions called *electrical degrees*. The

Fig. 8-2. Relation between time in seconds and time in electrical degrees for a frequency of 60 cps.

relation of time in seconds and time in electrical degrees for a frequency of 60 cps is shown in Fig. 8-2. The complete cycle is generated in $\frac{1}{60}$ sec or in the time required to move an armature conductor past one pair of poles. For this frequency, 360 electrical degrees is equivalent to $\frac{1}{60}$ sec. One-half cycle is generated in $\frac{1}{120}$ sec or 180 electrical degrees, ¼ cycle in $\frac{1}{240}$ sec or 90°, and ⅛ cycle in $\frac{1}{480}$ sec or 45°. It must be kept in mind that electrical degrees used in this sense represent *time*. This concept will be found useful in specifying phase relationships.

**8-5. Effective Values of Alternating Current and EMF**   As the value of an alternating current is continually fluctuating between a maximum in one direction and a maximum in the other direction, some effective value of an alternating current must be established. A natural question arises at this point. How can an alternating current deliver any power when it is continually changing its direction of flow? The answer to this is that the amount of power used by a d-c circuit is $P = I^2R$ regardless of the direction of the current flow through the resistance. This is easily verified experimentally by connecting a resistance to a battery through a reversing switch and measuring the power used with the current first in one direction and then in the other. It will be found that the power is the same in either case. Alternating current is merely a current that reverses its direction of flow periodically. It follows then that power is used during both halves of the cycle when an alternating current flows through a resistance.

The rate at which heat is produced in a resistance forms a convenient basis for establishing an effective value of alternating current. *An alternating current is said to have an effective value of one ampere when it will produce heat in a given resistance at the same rate as does one ampere of direct current.*

The symbol for effective alternating current is $I$. The rate at which heat is produced in a d-c circuit is equal to $I^2R$. Likewise, the rate at which heat is being produced by an alternating current at any instant is $i^2R$. Therefore, the heating effect of an alternating current over a period of time depends on the average of the squares of the instantaneous values of current over that period of time. For this reason, the effective value of a sine-wave current is often called the *root-mean-square*, or *rms*, value. It is the square root of the mean or average square of the instantaneous values. By squaring a number of instantaneous values, averaging these squared values, and extracting the square root of this average, the effective value of any sine-wave current may be found. By this method or by mathematical means, it may be shown that the *effective value* ($I$) *of any sine-wave current is always* 0.707 *times the maximum value* ($I_m$).

Since alternating currents are caused to flow by alternating emfs, the ratio between effective and maximum values of emfs is the same as for currents. The effective, or rms, value ($E$) of a sine-wave emf is 0.707 times the maximum value ($E_m$).

*When an alternating current or voltage is specified, it is always the effective value that is meant unless there is a definite statement to the contrary.* In practical work, effective values are of more importance than instantaneous or maximum values and the common types of measuring instruments are calibrated to read effective values of current and voltage.

**8-6. Average Value of Alternating EMFs and Currents**   The average value of an alternating emf or current is the average of the instantaneous values over $\frac{1}{2}$ cycle.   By actually averaging a number of instantaneous values for half a cycle or by mathematical means, it can be shown that the average value is 0.637 times the maximum value.

Average values of voltage and current are of little practical value, the effective values being much more important.

**8-7. Phase Relations**   Alternating currents are caused to flow by alternating voltages of the same frequency.   When the current and voltage pass through their zero values and increase to their maximum values in the same direction at the same time, the current is said to be

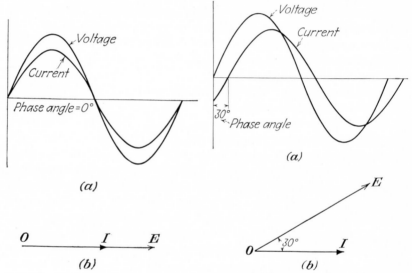

Fig. 8-3. The current and voltage are in phase.      Fig. 8-4. The current lags the voltage by 30°.

*in phase* with the voltage.   However, in some types of circuits (to be discussed in later articles) the current and voltage zero and maximum values do *not* occur at the same time.   When this happens, the current is said to be *out of phase* with the voltage.

There are three possible phase relations between a current and a voltage in a circuit:

1. The current and voltage may be in phase as shown in Fig. 8-3a.

2. The voltage may pass through its zero value and increase to a maximum at some time earlier than the current as in Fig. 8-4a.   In this case the current is said to *lag* the voltage.

3. The voltage may pass through its zero value and maximum value at some time later than the current as in Fig. 8-5a. In this case the current is said to *lead* the voltage.

The amount of time that a current leads or lags the voltage varies in different circuits from the *inphase* condition to a lead or lag of ¼ cycle, or 90°. Since time may be measured in electrical degrees (Art. 8-4), this difference in time, or *phase difference*, of a current and voltage is commonly expressed in electrical degrees and is called the *phase angle*. The usual symbol for the phase angle is the Greek letter theta ($\theta$).

Just as the current and voltage of a circuit may have a phase difference, two or more voltages or currents in the same circuit may be out of phase. This difference in phase must be taken into account when such voltages or currents are added or subtracted. Methods of combining currents and voltages that are out of phase will be discussed in Arts. 8-9 and 8-10.

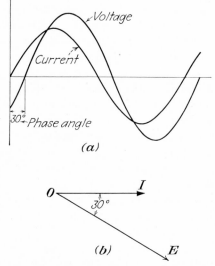

Fig. 8-5. The current leads the voltage by 30°.

**8-8. Vector Diagrams** It has been shown in the previous articles how alternating currents and voltages and their phase relations may be represented by means of sine waves. This method of representation is quite cumbersome, and a simplified method is commonly used in which currents and voltages are represented by straight lines having definite direction and length. Such lines are called *vectors*, and diagrams in which vectors represent currents, voltages, and their phase relations are called *vector diagrams*. Vector diagrams may be drawn to represent either maximum or effective values of voltage and current. Because effective values are of much more importance, however, vector diagrams are nearly always drawn to represent effective values.

When drawing vector diagrams, certain conventions should be adopted to ensure consistent and accurate results. Some of the more common conventions or usual practices in regard to vector diagrams are listed below.

1. It is common practice to consider the counterclockwise direction

as being the positive direction of rotation of vectors. That is, vectors rotated in a counterclockwise direction from a given vector are said to lead the given vector, while vectors rotated in a clockwise direction are said to lag the given vector.

2. For series circuits in which the current is common to all parts of the circuit, the current vector is usually drawn on a horizontal line and used as a reference line for other vectors in the same diagram.

3. Since, in a parallel circuit, a common voltage is applied to all branches of the circuit, the voltage vector is drawn on the horizontal reference line and other vectors are referred to the common voltage vector.

4. It is not necessary to use the same scale for current and voltage vectors; in fact it is often desirable to draw the current vector to a larger scale than the voltage vector when the values of current being represented are small. However, if several current vectors are to be used in the same diagram, they should all be drawn to the same scale. Likewise, all voltage vectors in the same diagram should be drawn to the same scale.

5. To distinguish between current and voltage vectors, the current vectors may be drawn with closed arrowheads and the voltage vectors with open arrowheads.

To illustrate the methods used in drawing vector diagrams, the sine-wave currents and voltages of Figs. 8-3a, 8-4a, and 8-5a are represented by vector diagrams in Figs. 8-3b, 8-4b, and 8-5b, respectively.

Figure 8-3 represents a case in which the current and voltages are in phase, that is, the phase angle is 0°. The vector diagram showing this relation is drawn in Fig. 8-3b. The vector representing the effective current is drawn to some convenient scale on a horizontal line, starting at the point O. Likewise, the vector representing the effective voltage is drawn starting at the same point O and extending in the same direction as the current vector. The fact that the two vectors lie along the same line indicates that the current and voltage being represented are in phase.

In Fig. 8-4 the current is shown lagging the voltage by 30°. The current vector is drawn as before on the horizontal reference line. However, to represent the fact that the current lags the voltage by 30°, the voltage vector is drawn 30° ahead of (or in the counterclockwise direction from) the current vector as in Fig. 8-4b.

Figure 8-5 represents a circuit in which the current *leads* the voltage by 30°. The current vector is drawn on the horizontal reference line as before but with voltage vector 30° behind (or in the clockwise direction from the current vector) as in Fig. 8-5b.

Thus, vector diagrams when drawn to scale provide a simple means of representing both the *phase relations* and the *magnitudes* of the currents and voltages involved in a given circuit.

## 8-9. Addition of Vectors

A vector has both direction and magnitude. Therefore, the addition of quantities that are represented as vectors, such as alternating currents and voltages, must take into account both the direction and magnitude of these quantities.

The resultant or sum of two vectors may be found by constructing a triangle, the two vectors forming two sides of the triangle and their resultant, or sum, forming the third side. To construct such a triangle, the first vector is drawn to scale starting at some point $O$. For convenience this vector is usually drawn as a horizontal line to the right of the origin $O$. The second vector is then drawn to scale from the arrow end of the first vector. If the second vector is defined as leading the first vector by $\theta$ degrees, the second vector is drawn $\theta$ degrees in a counterclockwise direction from the first vector. If it lags the first vector, it is drawn at the designated angle in a clockwise direction from the horizontal. The resultant is then the line drawn from the origin to the arrow end of the second vector.

Following are several examples that illustrate the addition of two vectors. Several special conditions are illustrated that are often encountered. However, it should be noted that the procedure in constructing each of the diagrams is the same. The two original vectors are placed without changing their direction so as to form two sides of a triangle. The third side of the triangle is then the vector sum or the *resultant* of the two original vectors.

*Addition of Inphase Vectors.* The vector sum of two inphase vectors is their direct or arithmetic sum.

**Example 1** Find the vector sum of a current of 3 amp and a current of 4 amp, the two currents being in phase.

$$\text{Resultant current} = 3 + 4 = 7 \text{ amp}$$

*Addition of Vectors Out of Phase by* 180°. The vector sum of two vectors 180° out of phase is their numerical difference, the direction of the resultant being the same as the larger vector.

**Example 2** A voltage $E_1$ of 125 volts leads a voltage $E_2$ of 100 volts by 180°. Find their vector sum.

$$\text{Resultant voltage} = 125 - 100 = 25 \text{ volts}$$

The direction of the resultant is the same as the direction of $E_1$.

*Addition of Vectors Out of Phase by* 90°    The vector sum $C$ of two vectors $A$ and $B$ that are out of phase 90° is

$$C = \sqrt{A^2 + B^2}$$

**Example 3**   A current $I_2$ of 8 amp leads a current $I_1$ of 6 amp by 90° as shown in Fig. 8-6a.   Find their vector sum.

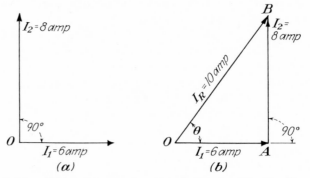

Fig. 8-6. The addition of two vectors out of phase by 90°.   See Example 3.

*Graphical Solution:* Lay off $I_1$ to scale along the horizontal to the right of the origin as in Fig. 8-6b.   Starting at the arrow end of $I_1$, lay off to scale $I_2$, 90° ahead of or in a counterclockwise direction from $I_1$.   The resultant is the length of the line $OB$.   The resultant leads $I_1$ by the angle $\theta$.

*Mathematical Solution:* Since the triangle $OAB$ is a right triangle,

$$I_R = \sqrt{(I_1)^2 + (I_2)^2} = \sqrt{6^2 + 8^2} = 10 \text{ amp}$$

and
$$\tan \theta = \frac{8}{6} = 1.33*$$

From the tables $\theta = 53°8'$.

*Addition of Vectors Out of Phase by Any Angle*

**Example 4**   Add two voltages of 100 volts each that are out of phase by 30°.

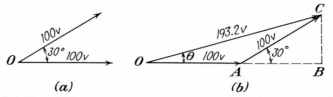

Fig. 8-7. The addition of two vectors out of phase by 30°.   See Example 4.

*Graphical Solution:* The two vectors drawn from the same origin are shown in Fig. 8-7a.   Lay off to scale one vector on the horizontal to the right of the

* Commonly used trigonometric functions and a table of values are given in Appendixes 5 and 6.

origin as in Fig. 8-7b.  Starting at the arrow end of the first vector, scale off the second vector 30° in a counterclockwise direction from the horizontal. Draw a line from the origin $O$ to the end of the second vector.  The length of this line is the vector sum, to scale, of the two vectors.  Measure angle $\theta$.

*Mathematical Solution:* In Fig. 8-7b, drop a perpendicular from $C$ to the horizontal.  The resultant $OC$ is then the hypotenuse of the right triangle $OBC$.

$$\text{Side } CB = 100 \sin 30° = 100 \times 0.5 = 50$$
$$\text{Line } AB = 100 \cos 30° = 100 \times 0.866 = 86.6$$
$$\text{Side } OB = OA + AB = 100 + 86.6 = 186.6$$
$$\text{Resultant } OC = \sqrt{(OB)^2 + (CB)^2}$$
$$= \sqrt{(186.6)^2 + (50)^2} = 193.2 \text{ volts}$$
$$\tan \theta = \frac{50}{186.6} = 0.268$$
$$\theta = 15°$$

**Example 5**  A voltage of 120 volts leads a voltage of 240 volts by 120° (Fig. 8-8a).  What is their vector sum?

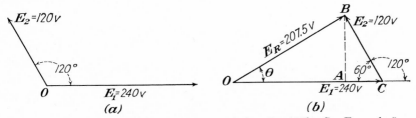

FIG. 8-8. The addition of two vectors out of phase by 120°.  See Example 5.

*Graphical Solution:* The graphical construction is shown in Fig. 8-8b.  The resultant is line $OB$ at the angle $\theta$ from the horizontal.

*Mathematical Solution:* In Fig. 8-8b, draw the perpendicular line $BA$.  The resultant $OB$ is then the hypotenuse of right triangle $OAB$.

$$\text{Side } AB = 120 \sin 60° = 120 \times 0.866 = 103.9$$
$$\text{Line } AC = 120 \cos 60° = 120 \times 0.5 = 60$$
$$\text{Side } OA = OC - AC = 240 - 60 = 180$$
$$\text{Resultant } OB = \sqrt{(OA)^2 + (AB)^2}$$
$$= \sqrt{(180)^2 + (103.9)^2} = 207.5 \text{ volts}$$
$$\tan \theta = \frac{103.9}{180} = 0.577$$
$$\theta = 30°$$

If three vectors are to be added, the resultant of two of the vectors may be found by the method outlined above, and their resultant may then be added to the third vector.  This method may be extended to any number of vectors.

## 8-10. Subtraction of Vectors

A vector $B$ may be subtracted from a vector $A$ by reversing the vector $B$ (rotating it by 180°) and adding it to the vector $A$. This can best be explained by an example.

**Example 6** Subtract a current of 10 amp from a current of 17.3 amp when the 17.3-amp current leads the 10-amp current by 30° (Fig. 8-9a).

*Graphical Solution:* Draw $I_1$, $I_2$, and $-I_2$ as shown in Fig. 8-9b. The resultant current is the line $OB$, which leads $I_2$ by the angle $\theta$.

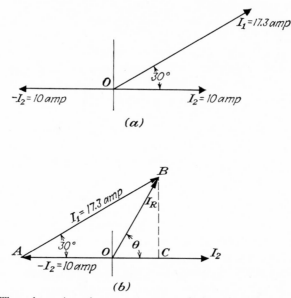

FIG. 8-9. The subtraction of two vectors out of phase by 30°. See Example 6.

*Mathematical Solution:* In Fig. 8-9b, drop a perpendicular from $B$ to the horizontal. The resultant $OB$ is then the hypotenuse of the right triangle $OBC$.

$$\text{Side } BC = 17.3 \sin 30° = 17.3 \times 0.5 = 8.66$$
$$\text{Side } AC = 17.3 \cos 30° = 17.3 \times 0.866 = 15$$
$$\text{Side } OC = 15 - 10 = 5$$
$$\text{Resultant } OB = \sqrt{(8.66)^2 + (5)^2} = 10 \text{ amp}$$
$$\tan \theta = \frac{8.66}{5} = 1.73$$
$$\theta = 60°$$

For those who may wish to use the complex quantity notation in the study of a-c circuits in this book and for those who wish to extend their study beyond the scope of this book, a brief discussion of the complex quantity notation used to represent vectors is presented in Appendix 7.

**8-11. Properties of an Electric Circuit**   The value of a direct current flowing in a circuit for a given constant value of impressed voltage is determined wholly by the *resistance* of the circuit.   The value of an alternating current flowing in a circuit depends not only on the resistance of the circuit, but on the *inductance* and *capacitance* of the circuit as well.   Resistance offers the same kind of opposition to the flow of an alternating current as it does to direct current, and for most practical purposes, the a-c resistance and d-c resistance of a circuit are considered to be the same.   Inductance and capacitance affect only a *change* in current or voltage.   Since alternating currents and voltages are continually changing in magnitude and direction, both inductance and capacitance affect the flow of an alternating current. The nature of the circuit properties and the effects of each in a-c circuits are discussed in the following articles.

**8-12. Resistance in an A-C Circuit**   When a d-c potential is applied to a resistance, the value of the current that flows, according to Ohm's law, is proportional to the voltage: the greater the voltage, the greater the current.   The same is true when an alternating voltage is applied to a resistance.   As the voltage is increased, the current is increased; as the voltage is decreased, the current is decreased.   The maximum value of current and voltage occur at the same time, and their zero values occur at the same time.   Thus, the current and the voltage are in phase and the *phase angle is zero in a purely resistive circuit.*

When a circuit contains resistance only, the effective current flowing in that circuit is equal to the effective applied voltage divided by the resistance of the circuit, or

$$I = \frac{E}{R} \tag{1}$$

**Example 7**   What is the effective current flowing through a resistance of 30 ohms when a 120-volt 60-cycle voltage is applied (Fig. 8-10a)?

$$I = \frac{E}{R} = \frac{120}{30} = 4 \text{ amp}$$

The vector diagram is shown in Fig. 8-10b.

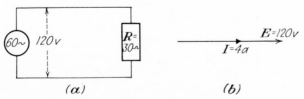

(a)                                                   (b)

FIG. 8-10. Circuit and vector diagram for Example 7.

**8-13. Inductance**  Inductance is a circuit property just as is resistance.  Any circuit that is capable of producing flux has inductance, as was pointed out in Chap. 5.  Any change in the value of current flowing in such a circuit also causes a change in the flux linking the circuit, thereby causing an emf to be induced.  Since the emf is induced in the circuit owing to a change of current in the circuit itself and since any induced emf opposes the change that produces it, it is called the *counter emf of self-induction*.  Thus, an opposition to any *change* in the current flowing is present in a circuit containing inductance.

The unit of inductance is the *henry*, and the symbol is $L$.  A circuit has an inductance of 1 henry if, when the current is changing at the rate of 1 amp per sec, the average counter emf induced is 1 volt.

An inductive circuit is usually in the form of a coil, very often wound around a magnetic core.  Motor, generator, and transformer windings are examples of circuits that have inductance.  However, a long, straight wire also has a certain amount of inductance, and calculations of transmission-line performance must take into account the inductance of the line.

**8-14. Inductive Reactance**  In an inductive d-c circuit, the inductance affects the current flow only when the current is changing in value.  Upon closing a d-c circuit, the inductance opposes the increase in current; upon opening the circuit, it opposes the decrease in current.  However, the flow of a steady direct current is opposed only by the resistance of the circuit.

In an inductive a-c circuit, the current is changing continuously and therefore is continuously inducing an emf of self-induction.  Because this induced emf opposes the continuous change in the current flowing, its effect is measured in ohms.  This opposition of the inductance to the flow of an alternating current is called *inductive reactance* and is represented by the symbol $X_L$.  The current flowing through a circuit that contains only inductive reactance is

$$I = \frac{E}{X_L} \qquad (2)$$

where $I$ = effective current, amp

$X_L$ = inductive reactance, ohms

$E$ = effective voltage across the reactance, volts

The value of inductive reactance in any circuit depends on the inductance of the circuit and on the rate at which the current through the circuit is changing.  The rate of change of current depends on the frequency of the applied voltage. Inductive reactance in ohms may be calculated from the formula

$$X_L = 2\pi f L \tag{3}$$

where $\pi = 3.14$

$f$ = frequency, cps

$L$ = inductance, henrys

The amount of any induced emf in a circuit depends on how fast the flux that links the circuit is changing. In the case of self-induction, a counter emf is induced in a circuit because of a change of current and flux in the circuit itself. This counter emf, according to Lenz's law, opposes any change in current, and its value at any time depends on the rate at which the current and flux are changing at the time. In an inductive circuit in which the resistance is negligible in

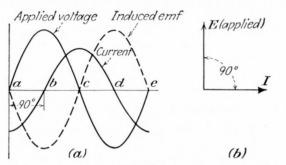

FIG. 8-11. (a) Variation of current, self-induced emf, and applied voltage in an inductive circuit. (b) Vector diagram showing the relation between the applied voltage and the current.

comparison to the inductive reactance, the voltage applied to the circuit must at all times be equal and opposite to the emf of self-induction.

Figure 8-11 shows the variation of the induced counter emf with the variation of a sine-wave current. At points $a$, $c$, and $e$ the current is not changing in value, and the self-induced emf is zero. Between the points $a$ and $c$ the current is increasing in value from its negative maximum to its positive maximum. Therefore, during this time, the induced emf is negative in value opposing the increase in current. Between the points $c$ and $e$, the current is decreasing from positive maximum to negative maximum so that the induced emf is positive and is attempting to oppose the decrease in current. The current changes at its greatest rate at the points $b$ and $d$, causing the induced emf to reach its maximum values at these points. The value of the self-induced emf then varies as a sine curve and lags the current by 90°

as shown in Fig. 8-11. Since the applied voltage must be equal and opposite to the self-induced emf at all times, it is evident from Fig. 8-11 *that the current lags the applied voltage by* 90° *in a purely inductive circuit.* If, as is usually the case, resistance is present in the circuit, the angle of lag will be less than 90°, depending on the relative values of resistance and inductive reactance in the circuit.

**Example 8**    A 0.2-henry choke coil with negligible resistance is connected to a 120-volt 60-cycle supply (Fig. 8-12*a*).    Find (*a*) the inductive reactance

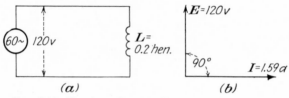

Fig. 8-12. Circuit and vector diagram for Example 8.

of the coil, and (*b*) the current flowing; (*c*) draw the vector diagram showing the phase relations between the current and the applied voltage.

(*a*) $X_L = 2\pi fL = 2 \times 3.14 \times 60 \times 0.2 = 75.4$ ohms

(*b*) $I = \dfrac{E}{X_L} = \dfrac{120}{75.4} = 1.59$ amp

(*c*) The vector diagram showing the current lagging the voltage by 90° is drawn in Fig. 8-12*b*.

**8-15. Capacitors**    Any two conductors that are separated by an insulating material form a simple *capacitor* or *condenser*.    The conductors are called the *plates* of the capacitor, and the insulating material is called the *dielectric*.    A common type of capacitor used in power and communication circuits is the parallel-plate capacitor. Such capacitors are constructed by interleaving sheets of tin foil or aluminum foil with sheets of waxed or paraffined paper.    Alternate plates are connected to each of two terminals so that each terminal and group of plates to which it is attached is insulated electrically from the group of plates connected to the other terminal.    Thus, each group of plates forms a large conductor surface that is separated from another large conductor surface by the dielectric.

Capacitors are used extensively in telephone and radio circuits. Power companies are using them in increasing numbers on distribution systems to correct for some of the effects of inductive loads.    Capacitors play an important part in the operation of various other kinds of electric apparatus, such as automobile ignition systems, single-phase motors, and control relays.

Figure 8-13 shows a capacitor $AB$ connected in series with two galvanometers (current-detecting instruments, see Art. 17-1) $C$ and $D$, with the switch $S$ arranged either to connect the capacitor to the battery or to short-circuit the terminals of the capacitor. Immediately after the switch is closed to the left, connecting the capacitor to the battery, galvanometer $C$ indicates a momentary current flow toward plate $A$ and galvanometer $D$ indicates a current flow away from plate $B$. A movement of electric charge or electrons takes place in the circuit until the potential difference between plates $A$ and $B$ becomes the same as the battery potential difference. This causes plate $A$ to become positively charged and plate $B$ to become negatively charged. Hence, a capacitor in this condition is said to be *charged*. If the switch is opened, the capacitor retains its charge indefinitely (if there is no leakage between the plates), since plate $B$ is left with an excess of electrons and plate $A$ has a deficiency of electrons.

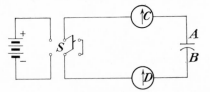

FIG. 8-13. The capacitor $AB$ is charged when the switch $S$ is closed to the left and discharged when the switch is closed to the right.

If the switch $S$ is closed to the right while the capacitor is still charged, the galvanometers indicate a flow of current out of plate $A$ and into plate $B$. This flow of current is momentary, being only long enough to neutralize the charged atoms on each plate. The capacitor is then said to be *discharged*.

The amount of charge that a capacitor receives for each volt of applied potential is called the *capacitance* of the capacitor. The unit of capacitance is the *farad*, and the symbol is $C$. A capacitor has a capacitance of 1 *farad* when an applied potential of 1 *volt* causes the capacitor to take a charge of 1 *coulomb*. The farad is much too large a unit for practical use, and therefore *microfarad* ($\mu$f) is more commonly used. One farad is equal to one million microfarads.

The capacitance of a capacitor is directly proportional to the area of the plates and inversely proportional to their separation. It has been found by experiment that the material used for the dielectric also affects the capacitance. For example, when glass is substituted for air as a dielectric, the capacitance increases approximately eight times. Likewise capacitors using mica, paraffin, transformer oil, paper, and various other insulating materials for dielectrics have a higher capacitance than do similar air capacitors. These materials are said to have a higher *dielectric constant* than air.

One ampere is defined as the rate of flow of an electric charge of 1 coulomb per sec. If the voltage applied to a 1-farad capacitor is increased at the rate of 1 volt every second, the increase in charge on the capacitor will be 1 coulomb every second. Since 1 coulomb of electricity or electric charge is moved every second, the average current flowing into the capacitor must be 1 amp. Likewise, if the potential being applied to a 1-farad capacitor is being decreased by 1 volt every second, the average current flowing out of the capacitor will be 1 amp. Thus a current flows in a circuit containing a capacitor while the applied voltage of that circuit is changing, even though there is a complete break in the circuit. *The amount of current flowing depends on the capacitance of the circuit and the rate at which the applied voltage is changing.* If either the capacitance of a circuit or the rate at which the applied voltage is changing (the frequency) is increased, the amount of current flowing is also increased.

**8-16. Capacitors in Series** It may be shown mathematically that the combined capacitance $C$ of several capacitors $C_1$, $C_2$, $C_3$, . . . in series may be found by the relationship

$$\frac{1}{C} = \frac{1}{C_1} + \frac{1}{C_2} + \frac{1}{C_3} + \cdots \tag{4}$$

The reciprocal of the combined capacitance of several capacitors in series is equal to the sum of the reciprocals of the capacitances of the separate capacitors.

**8-17. Capacitors in Parallel** When capacitors are connected in parallel, the effect is the same as increasing the number of plates and the capacitance of the circuit is increased. In a parallel circuit the combined capacitance of several capacitors $C_1$, $C_2$, $C_3$, . . . is

$$C = C_1 + C_2 + C_3 + \cdots \tag{5}$$

When capacitors are connected in parallel, their total capacitance equals the sum of the capacitances of the separate capacitors.

**8-18. Action of a Capacitor in an A-C Circuit** In a d-c circuit containing a capacitor, there is only a momentary flow of current immediately after the voltage is applied. As soon as the voltage across the capacitor reaches its steady-state value, the current flow ceases.

However, when a capacitor is connected to an a-c supply in series with an a-c ammeter, the ammeter indicates a flow of current as long as the supply is connected. The circuit appears to be complete and not one that has a complete break in it. The reason for this is that the current alternately flows into and out of the capacitor as the capacitor is charged, discharged, charged in the opposite direction, and discharged again.

The variation of an alternating voltage applied to a capacitor, the charge on the capacitor, and the current flowing are represented in Fig. 8-14. Since the current flowing in a circuit containing capacitance

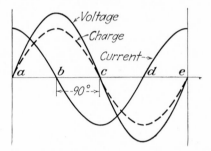

FIG. 8-14. Variation of voltage, charge, and current in a capacitor.

depends on the rate at which the voltage changes, the current flow is greatest at points $a$, $c$, and $e$; for at these points the voltage is changing at its maximum rate. Between the points $a$ and $b$, while the voltage and charge on the capacitor are both increasing, the current flow is into the capacitor but decreasing in value. At point $b$ the capacitor is fully charged, and the current is zero. From $b$ to $c$, the voltage and charge both decrease or the capacitor discharges, its current flowing in a direction opposite to the voltage. From $c$ to $d$, the capacitor begins to charge in the opposite direction and the voltage and current are again in the same direction. The capacitor is fully charged at $d$, where the current flow is again zero. From $d$ to $e$ the capacitor discharges, the flow of current being opposite to the voltage. The cycle then repeats. An inspection of Fig. 8-14 shows the current to be *leading* the applied voltage by 90°. This is true in any purely capacitive circuit and is in contrast to a purely inductive circuit in which the current *lags* the voltage by 90°. Therefore, the effect of capacitance in a circuit is exactly opposite to the effect of inductance.

**8-19. Capacitive Reactance** *Capacitive reactance* is the opposition offered by a capacitor or by any capacitive circuit to the flow of current. It was shown in Art. 8-15 that the current flowing in a capacitive circuit is directly proportional to the capacitance and to the rate at which the applied voltage is changing. The rate at which the voltage changes is determined by the frequency of the supply. Therefore, if either the frequency or the capacitance of a given circuit are increased, the current flow increases. This is equivalent to saying that if either the frequency or capacitance is increased the opposition to the current flow is *decreased*. Therefore capacitive reactance, which is the opposition to current flow, is *inversely* proportional to frequency and capacitance. Capacitive reactance, $X_C$, is measured in ohms, as is resistance and inductive reactance, and may be calculated by the formula

$$X_C = \frac{1}{2\pi fC} \tag{6}$$

where $f$ = frequency, cps
$\pi$ = 3.14
$C$ = capacitance, farads

If, as is usually the case, the capacitance is expressed in microfarads $C_{\mu f}$, then

$$X_C = \frac{1,000,000}{2\pi fC_{\mu f}} \tag{7}$$

The current flowing in a circuit containing only capacitive reactance is

$$I = \frac{E}{X_C} \tag{8}$$

where $I$ = effective current, amp
$E$ = effective voltage across the capacitive reactance, volts
$X_C$ = capacitive reactance, ohms

**Example 9**  An 8-$\mu$f capacitor is connected to a 240-volt 60-cycle circuit (Fig. 8-15). (*a*) Find the capacitive reactance, (*b*) find the current flowing, and (*c*) draw the vector diagram.

(*a*)  $X_C = \dfrac{1,000,000}{2\pi fC_{\mu f}} = \dfrac{1,000,000}{2 \times 3.14 \times 60 \times 8} = 331.7$ ohms

(*b*)  $I = \dfrac{E}{X_C} = \dfrac{240}{331.7} = 0.723$ amp

(*c*) The vector diagram showing the current leading the voltage by 90° is drawn in Fig. 8-15*b*.

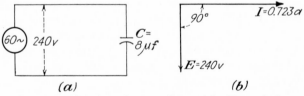

(*a*)                                                      (*b*)

Fɪɢ. 8-15. Circuit and vector diagram for Example 9.

**8-20. Reactance** Inductive reactance causes the current to *lag* behind the applied voltage, while capacitive reactance causes the current to *lead* the voltage. Therefore, when inductive reactance and capacitive reactance are connected in series, their effects neutralize each other and their combined effect is then their difference. The combined effect of inductive reactance and capacitive reactance is called *reactance* and is found by subtracting the capacitive reactance from the inductive reactance or as an equation

$$X = X_L - X_C \tag{9}$$

where $X$ = reactance, ohms
$\quad X_L$ = inductive reactance, ohms
$\quad X_C$ = capacitive reactance, ohms

**8-21. Impedance** *Impedance* is the total opposition offered by a circuit to the flow of current. It is the combined effect of the *resistance* and the *reactance* of a circuit. The symbol for impedance is $Z$, and it is measured in ohms. The impedance of an a-c circuit is equal to the effective applied voltage divided by the effective current that flows, or

$$Z = \frac{E}{I} \tag{10}$$

also $\qquad E = IZ \qquad$ and $\qquad I = \frac{E}{Z}$

In a circuit containing resistance only, the $IR$ drop is in phase with the current. In a circuit containing inductive reactance only, the $IX_L$ drop leads the current by 90°, which is, of course, equivalent to saying that the current lags the $IX_L$ drop by 90°. Likewise, in a capacitive circuit, the $IX_C$ drop lags the current by 90°. In a circuit containing both resistance and reactance, the total voltage drop, or the $IZ$ drop, is equal to the sum of $IR$ and $IX$ drops. Since the $IR$ and $IX$ drops are out of phase by 90°, this phase difference must be taken into account when they are added. As was shown in Art. 8-9, the sum of two vector quantities such as $IR$ and $IX$ that are out of phase by 90° is $\sqrt{(IR)^2 + (IX)^2}$. Thus,

$$IZ = \sqrt{(IR)^2 + (IX)^2}$$

and canceling $I$ from each term results in

$$Z = \sqrt{R^2 + X^2} \tag{11}$$

Because of their different effects, then, resistance and reactance cannot be added arithmetically but must be combined according to the relationship given in Eq. (11).

Since reactance has been defined as $X_L - X_C$, the complete expression for the impedance of a series circuit is

$$Z = \sqrt{R^2 + (X_L - X_C)^2} \qquad (12)$$

When a circuit contains a negligible amount of $X_C$ compared with its $R$ and $X_L$, the above expression reduces to

$$Z = \sqrt{R^2 + (X_L - 0)^2} = \sqrt{R^2 + X_L{}^2}$$

Likewise, when a circuit contains a negligible amount of $X_L$, the impedance becomes

$$Z = \sqrt{R^2 + (0 - X_C)^2} = \sqrt{R^2 + (-X_C)^2}$$

The minus sign has no effect on the magnitude of $Z$, since a minus number squared is equal to a positive number.

**Example 10**   A resistance of 30 ohms is connected in series with an inductive reactance of 60 ohms and a capacitive reactance of 20 ohms.   What is the impedance of the circuit?

$$Z = \sqrt{R^2 + (X_L - X_C)^2} = \sqrt{(30)^2 + (60 - 20)^2}$$
$$= \sqrt{900 + 1,600} = \sqrt{2,500} = 50 \text{ ohms}$$

## 8-22. Graphical Representation of Resistance, Reactance, and Impedance   The relations expressed by the formula

$$Z = \sqrt{R^2 + X^2}$$

may be represented by a right triangle, where $Z$ is the hypotenuse and $R$ and $X$ form the other two sides of the triangle, since the hypotenuse

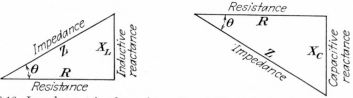

FIG. 8-16. Impedance triangle: resistance and inductive reactance in series.   FIG. 8-17. Impedance triangle: resistance and capacitive reactance in series.

of a right triangle is equal to the square root of the sum of the squares of the other two sides (see Appendix 5).   The value of the resistance is drawn to a convenient scale on the horizontal to form the base line. In a circuit containing only resistance and inductive reactance, the value of the reactance is laid off on a vertical line above the resistance line as in Fig. 8-16.   If the circuit contains capacitive reactance, the reactance line is laid off below the horizontal line (Fig. 8-17).   If the circuit contains both $X_L$ and $X_C$, the reactance is laid off on the vertical above or below the horizontal, depending on whether $X_L$ or $X_C$ is the larger.   Such a triangle is called an *impedance triangle*, and when it is carefully drawn to scale it affords an excellent check on the mathe-

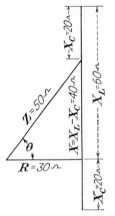

FIG. 8-18. Construction of the impedance triangle for Example 10.

matical calculations of impedance.   Figure 8-18 shows the impedance triangle for Example 10.

## REVIEW QUESTIONS

**1.** Give four advantages of alternating current over direct current.

**2.** List some applications in which direct current is preferred to alternating current.

**3.** Describe briefly the generation of an alternating emf.   In general, what two factors will determine the amount of emf generated in a conductor?

**4.** What is meant by an instantaneous value of emf?   What is the symbol? What is the unit?

**5.** What is meant by a maximum value of emf?   What is the symbol?   What is the unit?

**6.** When a conductor is revolved in a uniform magnetic field and the instantaneous values of emf are plotted against degrees of rotation, what is the resulting curve called?

**7.** Define an alternating current.

**8.** What is the symbol for (*a*) an instantaneous value of current; (*b*) for a maximum value?

**9.** What is a cycle?   What is frequency?   What is the unit of frequency?

**10.** How many electrical degrees correspond (*a*) to one cycle; (*b*) to one-half cycle; (*c*) to two cycles?   In a 60-cycle generator, what fraction of a second does it take to generate one cycle?

**11.** How many cycles are generated in a coil that makes one revolution in a 24-pole generator?

**12.** Define an effective a-c ampere.

**13.** What is the ratio of the effective to the maximum values of a sine-wave current?

**14.** What is the effective value of current sometimes called?

**15.** What is the symbol for effective current?

**16.** Do common a-c ammeters and voltmeters read instantaneous, maximum, or effective values?

**17.** What is the ratio of the average to the maximum value of an emf or current?

**18.** What is meant when it is said that a current and a voltage are in phase?

**19.** What are three possible phase relations between a current and a voltage?

**20.** What is the phase angle of a circuit?

**21.** What is a vector?   What is a vector diagram?

**22.** Two vectors are drawn starting at a common point.   Vector 1 extends to the right from the point along the horizontal, and vector 2 is drawn upward from the point at right angles to vector 1.   Does vector 1 lead or lag vector 2 by 90°?

**23.** Draw a vector diagram of a current of 10 amp lagging a voltage of 125 volts by 45°.

**24.** What are the three circuit properties?

**25.** What is the phase relation of the current and voltage in a circuit containing resistance only?

**26.** Why does inductance affect the flow of an alternating current and not the flow of a steady direct current?

**27.** What is the unit of inductance?   What is the symbol?

**28.** What is inductive reactance?   What is the unit?   What is the symbol?

**29.** What is the phase relation (*a*) between the applied voltage and the emf of self-induction; (*b*) between the applied voltage and the current in a circuit containing inductance only?

**30.** Describe a parallel-plate capacitor.

**31.** What is capacitance?   What is the unit?   What is the symbol?

**32.** Upon what three things does the capacitance of a capacitor depend?

**33.** Why does a circuit containing a capacitor appear to be complete when an alternating emf is applied?

**34.** What is the phase relation between the applied voltage and the current flowing in a circuit containing capacitance only?

**35.** What is the unit of capacitive reactance?   What is the symbol?

**36.** What is the effect on the capacitive reactance if the capacitance of a circuit is doubled, the frequency remaining constant?

**37.** To what is the reactance of a circuit equal?

**38.** Impedance is the combined effect of what two things in a circuit?

**39.** Show how an inductive reactance of 16 ohms and a resistance of 12 ohms may be combined graphically to form an impedance of 20 ohms.

**40.** Draw to scale an impedance triangle of a circuit in which the resistance is 3 ohms, the inductive reactance is 5 ohms, and the capacitive reactance is 2 ohms.

## PROBLEMS

**1.** An alternating current has a maximum value of 50 amp.   Find the effective and average values of the current.

**2.** Find the maximum value of an alternating current whose effective value is 100 amp.

**3.** Find the maximum value of an alternating voltage whose effective value is 220 volts.

**4.** Standard a-c ammeters and voltmeters read effective values of current and voltage. If the maximum value of current in a circuit is 7 amp, find the reading of an ammeter that is placed in the circuit.

**5.** A voltmeter reads 440 volts. Find the maximum value of the voltage wave. What is the effective value of the wave?

**6.** A current of 20 amp lags a current of 40 amp by 90°. Find the vector sum of the two currents.

**7.** What is the vector sum of two currents of 10 amp each that are out of phase by 60°?

**8.** Two voltages of 120 volts each are in phase. What is their vector sum?

**9.** Two voltages of 120 volts each are out of phase by 120°. What is their vector sum?

**10.** Three voltages of 240 volts are displaced symmetrically in time phase by 120°. What is their vector sum?

**11.** Subtract a current of 10 amp from a current of 14.14 amp when the 14.14-amp current leads the 10-amp current by 45°.

**12.** A coil has an inductance of 0.2 henry. Find its inductive reactance on a line frequency of 60, 120, and 600 cps.

**13.** A coil has an inductive reactance of 40 ohms at a frequency of 60 cps. Find the inductance of the coil.

**14.** A coil has an inductance of 0.05 henry. The inductive reactance is 100 ohms. Find the line frequency.

**15.** A certain coil has an inductance of 0.30 henry. What is its reactance at 60 and at 25 cycles?

**16.** The coil in the preceding problem is connected across 115 volts. What current will flow when the frequency is (a) 60 cycles; (b) 25 cycles? Neglect the resistance of the coil.

**17.** A capacitor has a capacitance of 40 μf. What is its capacitive reactance at 60 and at 120 cycles?

**18.** Determine the capacity of a capacitor if its capacitive reactance to a frequency of 60 cps is 80 ohms.

**19.** What is the capacitive reactance of a 0.5-μf capacitor at 60 cycles and at 600 kilocycles (600,000 cycles)?

**20.** What current will flow when a 10-μf capacitor is connected to a 240-volt 60-cycle supply?

**21.** A series a-c circuit has a capacitive reactance of 40 ohms and a resistance of 20 ohms. Compute the impedance.

**22.** A series circuit has negligible resistance. Its $X_C$ is 100 ohms, and its $X_L$ is 40 ohms. Compute the impedance.

**23.** Find the impedance of a series circuit if it has 30 ohms resistance and 20 ohms capacitive reactance.

**24.** What is the impedance of a coil that has a resistance of 8 ohms and an inductive reactance of 20 ohms?

**25.** Find the impedance of a circuit that consists of the coil of Prob. 24 in series with a capacitor that has a capacitive reactance of 32 ohms.

**26.** A coil has a resistance of 3 ohms and an $X_L$ of 30 ohms. Find the impedance of the circuit if a capacitor having an $X_C$ of 30 ohms is connected in series with the coil.

**27.** A coil having a resistance of 2 ohms and an inductance of 0.25 henry is connected to a 12-volt storage battery. What current will flow through the coil?

# CHAPTER 9

## SINGLE-PHASE CIRCUITS

**9-1. Power and Power Factor**  Power in a d-c circuit is equal to the product of the current and voltage.  The power in an a-c circuit at any instant is equal to the product of the values of current and voltage at that instant.  When an alternating current and voltage are in phase, the average power over a complete cycle is equal to the product of the effective current and voltage.  However, when reactance is present in the circuit, the current and voltage are out of phase so that at times during each cycle the current is negative while the voltage is positive.  This results in a value of power in the circuit which is less than the product of $I$ and $E$.

The product of the effective values of current and voltage in an a-c circuit is expressed in *volt-amperes* (va) or in *kilovolt-amperes* (kva), 1 kva being equal to 1,000 va.  The useful or *actual power* is measured in watts and is the value obtained when the volt-amperes of the circuit are multiplied by a factor called the *power factor*.  Thus, power in a single-phase a-c circuit is

$$P \text{ (in watts)} = EI \times \text{power factor} \tag{1}$$

$$P \text{ (in kilowatts)} = \frac{EI}{1,000} \times \text{power factor} \tag{2}$$

By transposing Eq. (1)

$$\text{Power factor} = \frac{P}{EI} \tag{3}$$

Thus, power factor may be defined as the ratio of the actual power in watts to the volt-amperes of an a-c circuit.

The value of the power factor depends on how much the current and voltage are out of phase.  When the current and voltage are in phase, power is equal to $I \times E$, or in other words the power factor is unity.  When current and voltage are out of phase by 90°, as in a purely capacitive or inductive circuit, the power factor is zero, resulting in a zero value of actual power.  In circuits containing both

164

resistance and reactance, the value of the power factor is some value between 1 and zero, its value depending on the relative values of resistance and reactance in the circuit.

Power factor may be expressed either as a decimal or as a percentage. For example, a power factor of 0.8 may be expressed as 80 per cent and a power factor of 1.0 as 100 per cent. Some typical average power factors are incandescent lights, 95 to 100 per cent; large induction motors carrying rated load, 85 to 90 per cent; fractional-horse-power induction motors, 60 to 75 per cent, all with the current lagging the voltage.

The current flowing in an a-c circuit may be considered as being made up of two components: a component in phase with the voltage and a component out of phase with the voltage by 90° as shown in Fig. 9-1. The inphase component is called the *active* component since this value when multiplied by the voltage gives the useful or actual power of the circuit. The out-of-phase component is called the *reactive* component, or the wattless component, since it contributes nothing to the actual power of the circuit. The product of the reactive component of the current and the voltage is called reactive power or reactive volt-amperes and is measured in *vars*, a word coined from the first letters of the words "volt-amperes reactive."

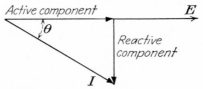

FIG. 9-1. The two components of current in an a-c circuit.

Figure 9-1 shows that the greater the phase angle $\theta$, the greater is the value of the reactive component and the smaller the value of the active component of a given value of total current.

In Fig. 9-1, the cosine of the phase angle $\theta$ is the ratio of the active current to the total current, or

$$\cos \theta = \frac{\text{active } I}{I}$$

or
$$\text{active } I = I \cos \theta$$

Then, since the actual power is the voltage multiplied by the active component of current,

$$P = E \times \text{active } I$$

or
$$P = EI \cos \theta \qquad (4)$$

Since power has already been shown to be $EI$ multiplied by a power factor, it follows that *the power factor of an a-c circuit is equal to the cosine of the phase angle.*

The values of the cosines of angles from 0° to 90° are given in Appendix 6. Note that the values range from 1.000 for an angle of 0° to 0.000 for an angle of 90°.

The relation between the power in watts, the volt-amperes, and the reactive volt-amperes, or vars, may be represented by a triangle as shown in Fig. 9-2, the angle $\theta$ being the phase angle of the circuit being

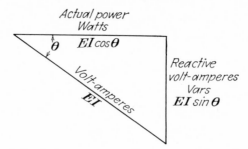

FIG. 9-2. The relation between power, volt-amperes, and reactive volt-amperes.

represented. The base of the triangle represents the actual power, the altitude the reactive volt-amperes, and the hypotenuse the volt-amperes. Since the volt-amperes are equal to $EI$, the actual power is $EI \cos \theta$, and the reactive volt-amperes are $EI \sin \theta$. Also the following relation is true:

$$\text{Volt-amperes} = \sqrt{(\text{power})^2 + (\text{reactive va})^2}$$

From the definition of the effective a-c ampere (Chap. 8), power is also equal to the effective current squared, multiplied by the resistance of the circuit, or

$$P = I^2 R \tag{5}$$

This is true in any single-phase a-c circuit regardless of the phase relation between the current and the voltage.

**9-2. Current and Voltage Relations in Series Circuits**  Current and voltage relations in a-c circuits containing resistance only, inductance only, and capacitance only were considered in the preceding chapter. In practice most circuits are combinations of two, or often all three, of these basic types of circuits. For example, transformer, generator, and motor windings all contain resistance and inductance. Even though the resistance and inductance are distributed throughout the windings, it is convenient when studying such circuits to consider the circuit as being made up of a pure resistance in series with a pure inductance.

Two rules similar to those of d-c series circuits apply to the current and voltage relations of an a-c series circuit:

1. In an a-c series circuit, the current has the same value in all parts of the circuit.

2. The voltage applied to an a-c series circuit is equal to the *vector* sum of the voltages across the several parts of the circuit.

## 9-3. Resistance and Inductance in Series

Figure 9-3$a$ represents a circuit with resistance and inductance in series. The vector diagram is drawn in Fig. 9-3$b$. The current vector is used as a reference, since

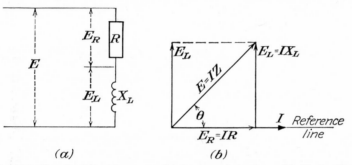

FIG. 9-3. (a) Circuit with resistance and inductance in series. (b) Vector diagram.

the current is the same in all parts of a series circuit. Since the voltage across a resistance is in phase with the current through the resistance, the vector $E_R = IR$ is drawn along the current vector. However, the voltage across an inductance leads the current through the circuit by 90°. Therefore, $E_L = IX_L$ is drawn 90° ahead of the current vector $I$. The applied voltage $E$ is equal to the vector sum of $E_R$ and $E_L$. The vector addition may be performed by moving the vector $E_L$ to the arrow end of $E_R$ and completing the triangle, the hypotenuse of the triangle representing $E$ or $IZ$. The angle $\theta$, or the angle between the applied voltage $E$ and the current $I$, is the phase angle of the circuit.

Power in the circuit of Fig. 9-3$a$ may be calculated from the formula

$$P = EI \times \text{power factor}$$

Since the power factor is the cosine of the phase angle, the power factor from Fig. 9-3$b$ is

$$\text{Power factor} = \cos \theta = \frac{E_R}{E} = \frac{IR}{IZ} = \frac{R}{Z} \tag{6}$$

Hence, the power factor of a series circuit is equal to the ratio of the resistance to the impedance of the circuit.

The following example will illustrate the method of calculating the current, power factor, and power of a simple $RL$ (resistance-inductance) series circuit.

**Example 1**   The circuit represented in Fig. 9-4 has a resistance of 6 ohms in series with an inductance of 0.0212 henry. The circuit is connected to a 120-volt 60-cycle supply. Find (a) the circuit impedance, (b) the current flowing, (c) the voltage across the resistance, (d) the voltage across the inductance, (e) the power factor, and (f) the power.

(a) $X_L = 2\pi f L$
$$= 2 \times 3.14 \times 60 \times 0.0212 = 8 \text{ ohms}$$
$$Z = \sqrt{R^2 + X^2} = \sqrt{6^2 + 8^2} = 10 \text{ ohms}$$

(b) $I = \dfrac{E}{Z} = \dfrac{120}{10} = 12 \text{ amp}$

(c) $E_R = IR = 12 \times 6 = 72 \text{ volts}$
(d) $E_L = IX_L = 12 \times 8 = 96 \text{ volts}$
$$E = \sqrt{E_R{}^2 + E_L{}^2} = \sqrt{72^2 + 96^2} = 120 \text{ volts (check)}$$

Note that $E$ is not equal to the arithmetic sum of $E_R$ and $E_L$ (72 + 96 = 168).

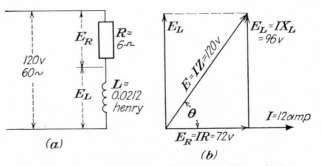

Fig. 9-4. Circuit and vector diagram for Example 1.

The vector diagram is drawn in Fig. 9-4b.

(e) Power factor $= \cos \theta = \dfrac{R}{Z} = \dfrac{6}{10} = 0.6$ or 60 per cent

(f) $P = EI \cos \theta = 120 \times 12 \times 0.6 = 864 \text{ watts}$
also      $P = I^2R = (12)^2 6 = 864 \text{ watts (check)}$

## 9-4. Resistance and Capacitance in Series

A capacitance and resistance in series are shown in Fig. 9-5. The current, being common to both branches, is used as a reference in the vector diagram. The vector representing the voltage across the resistance $E_R$ is drawn in phase with the current. However, the current through a capacitance leads the voltage across the capacitance by 90°. Thus, the vector $E_C$ is drawn 90° behind the current. Again the applied voltage $E$ is equal to the vector sum of the voltages across each part of the circuit. The vector addition by the triangle method is shown in Fig. 9-5*b*.

The power factor is equal to the cosine of the phase angle, or $R/Z$. The power taken by the circuit is equal to $EI \cos \theta$, or $I^2R$.  Example 2 illustrates the method of calculating $RC$ (resistance-capacitance) series circuits.

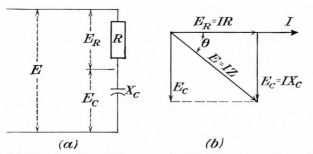

(*a*)                                (*b*)

FIG. 9-5. (*a*) Circuit with resistance and capacitance in series. (*b*) Vector diagram.

**Example 2**   A resistance of 80 ohms in series with a 50-μf capacitor is connected to a 120-volt 60-cycle source.   Find (*a*) the circuit impedance, (*b*) the current flowing, (*c*) the voltage across the resistance, (*d*) the voltage across the

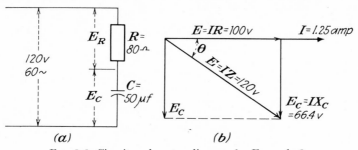

(*a*)                                (*b*)

FIG. 9-6. Circuit and vector diagram for Example 2.

capacitor, (*e*) the power factor, and (*f*) the power.   The circuit diagram and vector diagram are shown in Fig. 9-6*a* and *b*.

(*a*) $X = \dfrac{1}{2\pi f C} = \dfrac{1,000,000}{2\pi f C_{\mu f}}$

$$= \dfrac{1,000,000}{2 \times 3.14 \times 60 \times 50} = 53.1 \text{ ohms}$$

$$Z = \sqrt{R^2 + X^2} = \sqrt{80^2 + 53.1^2} = 96 \text{ ohms}$$

(*b*) $I = \dfrac{E}{Z} = \dfrac{120}{96} = 1.25 \text{ amp}$

(*c*) $E_R = IR = 1.25 \times 80 = 100 \text{ volts}$

(d) $E_C = IX_C = 1.25 \times 53.1 = 66.4$ volts

$E = \sqrt{E_R{}^2 + E_C{}^2} = \sqrt{100^2 + 66.4^2} = 120$ volts (check)

(e) Power factor $= \cos \theta = \dfrac{R}{Z} = \dfrac{80}{96} = 0.833$

(f) $P = EI \cos \theta = 120 \times 1.25 \times 0.833 = 125$ watts

$P = I^2R = (1.25)^2 \times 80 = 125$ watts (check)

## 9-5. Resistance, Inductance, and Capacitance in Series

This type of circuit may be solved by the same methods as those used in Arts. 9-3 and 9-4. The current vector is used as a reference in series circuits in general because it is common to all elements of the circuit. The voltage drop across the resistance of the circuit ($E_R = IR$) is in phase with the current, and its vector is drawn along the current vector. The vectors representing the voltage drop across the inductance ($E_L = IX_L$) and the voltage drop across the capacitance ($E_C = IX_C$) are drawn 90° ahead of and 90° behind the current vector, respectively. The vector sum of the voltages $E_R$, $E_L$, and $E_C$ is equal to the impressed voltage $E$. The power factor and power are also found by the same methods used in the simpler series circuits. An example will illustrate.

**Example 3** Figure 9-7a shows a circuit diagram of a circuit containing a resistance of 20 ohms, an inductance of 0.10 henry, and a 100-μf capacitor all connected in series. The applied voltage is 240 volts at 60 cycles. It is

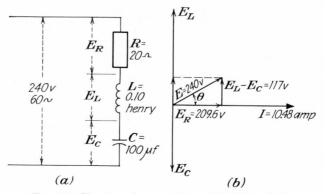

(a)               (b)

Fig. 9-7. Circuit and vector diagram for Example 3.

desired to find (a) the circuit impedance, (b) the current flow, (c) the voltage across each part, (d) the power factor, (e) the volt-amperes, and (f) the power.

(a) $X_L = 2\pi fL = 2 \times 3.14 \times 60 \times 0.10 = 37.7$ ohms

$X_C = \dfrac{1{,}000{,}000}{2\pi fC_{\mu f}} = \dfrac{1{,}000{,}000}{2 \times 3.14 \times 60 \times 100} = 26.5$ ohms

$X = X_L - X_C = 37.7 - 26.5 = 11.2$ ohms

$Z = \sqrt{R^2 + X^2} = \sqrt{20^2 + 11.2^2} = 22.9$ ohms

(b) $I = \dfrac{E}{Z} = \dfrac{240}{22.9} = 10.48$ amp

(c) $E_R = IR = 10.48 \times 20 = 209.6$ volts

$E_L = IX_L = 10.48 \times 37.7 = 395$ volts

$E_C = IX_C = 10.48 \times 26.5 = 278$ volts

The vector diagram is drawn in Fig. 9-7$b$ showing the position of the three voltages relative to the current. As a check on the work, the three voltages may be added vectorially by first adding $E_L$ and $E_C$ and then adding the result to $E_R$. Since $E_L$ and $E_C$ are exactly opposed, their resultant is $E_L - E_C$ as shown. This resultant is added to $E_R$ by the triangle method as shown.

Mathematically

$$E = \sqrt{E_R{}^2 + (E_L - E_C)^2}$$
$$= \sqrt{(209.6)^2 + (395 - 278)^2} = 240 \text{ volts (check)}$$

(d) Power factor $= \cos \theta = \dfrac{R}{Z} = \dfrac{20}{22.9} = 0.873$

The current lags the voltage since $X_L$ is greater than $X_C$.

(e) Volt-amperes $= EI = 240 \times 10.48 = 2{,}515$ va

(f) $P = EI \cos \theta = 2{,}515 \times 0.873 = 2{,}195$ watts

or $\quad P = I^2R = (10.48)^2 \times 20 = 2{,}195$ watts (check)

## 9-6. Impedances in Series

When several electric devices are connected in series, the total impedance of the circuit is the vector sum of the impedances of the separate parts. This total impedance may be found by adding arithmetically all the resistances, all the inductive reactances, and all the capacitive reactances and combining these totals, using the relationship

$$Z = \sqrt{R^2 + (X_L - X_C)^2}$$

**Example 4** Find the total impedance of two coils and a capacitor in series. Coil 1 has a resistance of 15 ohms and an inductive reactance of 35 ohms. Coil 2 has a resistance of 20 ohms and an inductive reactance of 45 ohms. The capacitor has a capacitive reactance of 60 ohms and has negligible resistance.

The total resistance of the circuit is the sum of the resistances of each part, or

$$R = 15 + 20 = 35 \text{ ohms}$$

The total inductive reactance is

$$X_L = 35 + 45 = 80 \text{ ohms}$$

The net reactance of the circuit is

$$X_L - X_C = 80 - 60 = 20 \text{ ohms (inductive)}$$

The combined impedance is

$$Z = \sqrt{R^2 + X^2} = \sqrt{35^2 + 20^2} = 40.3 \text{ ohms}$$

**9-7. Series Resonance**    A series circuit in which the inductive and capacitive reactances are equal is said to be *resonant*. In such a circuit, the net reactance is zero and the impedance is equal to the resistance.

As an example, consider a circuit consisting of a 10-ohm resistance, a 30-ohm inductive reactance and a 30-ohm capacitive reactance all connected in series to a 120-volt 60-cycle supply. Since $X_L = X_C$, the reactance of the circuit is zero and the impedance is equal to the resistance, i.e., 10 ohms. The power factor of the circuit is unity since power factor is equal to $R/Z$. The current in the circuit is $E/Z$ or 12 amp. The voltage drop $E$ across the resistance is $IR$ or 120 volts. Likewise, the voltage drop $E$ across each reactance is $IX$ or 360 volts. However, the voltage across the inductive reactance is 180° out of phase with the voltage across the capacitive reactance and while the effective value of each of these voltages may be relatively large, their vector sum is zero.

If the frequency of the supply voltage for the circuit just described were lower than 60 cycles, the $X_L$ of the circuit would be less than 30 ohms, the $X_C$ would be greater than 30 ohms, and the total impedance would be greater than 10 ohms. Likewise, the impedance of the circuit would be greater than 10 ohms at frequencies greater than 60 cycles. In other words, a given series circuit is resonant at only one frequency and, at the resonant frequency, the impedance is at a minimum. Since at resonance $X_L = X_C$ then

$$2\pi fL = \frac{1}{2\pi fC}$$

Solving this equation for $f$ results in the following value of frequency at resonance:

$$f = \frac{1}{2\pi \sqrt{LC}}$$

Resonance is usually to be avoided in power circuits because of the possibility of excessive voltages existing across parts of the circuit. However, in communications circuits, advantage is taken of the phenomenon in the tuning of circuits to obtain selectivity or the ability to respond strongly to a given frequency and discriminate against others.

**9-8. Parallel Circuits**    Practically all lighting and power circuits are constant-voltage circuits with the loads connected in parallel. As in parallel d-c circuits, the voltage is the same across each branch of a parallel a-c circuit.   The total line current supplied to the circuit is equal to the *vector* sum of the branch currents.   The total current supplied to a parallel circuit may be found by finding the current taken by each branch and adding these currents, taking into account their phase relations, or by finding an equivalent impedance and dividing the applied voltage by the equivalent impedance.

The aid offered by a vector diagram in the solution of parallel-circuit problems will be found to be indispensable.   Some examples will illustrate the principles involved in parallel-circuit calculations.

**Example 5** (Resistance and inductance in parallel)   A 0.06-henry inductance coil with negligible resistance is connected in parallel with a 30-ohm resistance

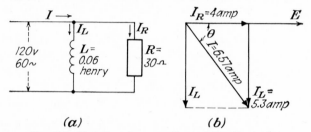

(a)                             (b)

FIG. 9-8. Circuit and vector diagram for Example 5.

as in Fig. 9-8.   When a voltage of 120 volts at 60 cycles is applied, find (a) the current, (b) the power factor, and (c) the power taken by the circuit.

(a)  $X_L = 2\pi f L = 2 \times 3.14 \times 60 \times 0.06 = 22.62$ ohms

$$I_L = \frac{E}{X_L} = \frac{120}{22.62} = 5.3 \text{ amp}$$

$$I_R = \frac{E}{R} = \frac{120}{30} = 4 \text{ amp}$$

The vector diagram is drawn in Fig. 9-8b.   In a parallel circuit the voltage vector is used as a reference, since the voltage is the same for all branches of the circuit.   Hence, the voltage vector is laid off along the horizontal line. The current $I_R$ is in phase with the voltage, and the current $I_L$ lags the voltage by 90° as shown in the vector diagram.   The total current $I$ is the vector sum of $I_R$ and $I_L$, the vector addition being made as shown.

Mathematically

$$I = \sqrt{I_R^2 + I_L^2} = \sqrt{4^2 + 5.3^2} = 6.57 \text{ amp}$$

(b) The total current $I$ lags behind the applied voltage by the angle $\theta$. The power factor of the circuit is

$$\text{Power factor} = \cos \theta = \frac{I_R}{I} = \frac{4}{6.57} = 0.609$$

(c)  $P = EI \cos \theta = 120 \times 6.57 \times 0.609 = 480$ watts

**Example 6** (Resistance, inductance, and capacitance in parallel)   A resistance of 80 ohms, an inductance of 0.15 henry, and a capacitance of 25 μf are connected in parallel, and a voltage of 240 volts at 60 cycles is applied.   Find (*a*) the current, (*b*) the power factor, (*c*) the power, and (*d*) the equivalent or combined impedance of the combination.

The circuit and vector diagrams are shown in Fig. 9-9.   Note that the

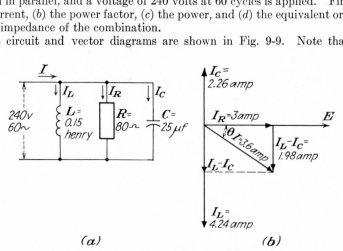

(*a*)                              (*b*)

FIG. 9-9. Circuit and vector diagram for Example 6.

voltage vector is used as a reference and that the current taken by the inductance lags the voltage by 90° and that taken by the capacitance leads the voltage by 90°.

(*a*)  $I_R = \dfrac{E}{R} = \dfrac{240}{80} = 3$ amp

$X_L = 2\pi f L = 2 \times 3.14 \times 60 \times 0.15 = 56.55$ ohms

$I_L = \dfrac{E}{X_L} = \dfrac{240}{56.55} = 4.24$ amp

$X_C = \dfrac{1{,}000{,}000}{2\pi f C_{\mu f}} = \dfrac{1{,}000{,}000}{2 \times 3.14 \times 60 \times 25} = 106.1$ ohms

$I_C = \dfrac{E}{X_C} = \dfrac{240}{106.1} = 2.26$ amp

The total current is the vector sum of the branch currents.   Combining $I_L$ and $I_C$, which are in opposition,

$$I_L - I_C = 4.24 - 2.26 = 1.98 \text{ amp}$$

and the total current is

$$I = \sqrt{I_R{}^2 + (I_L - I_C)^2} = \sqrt{3^2 + 1.98^2} = 3.6 \text{ amp}$$

(*b*)  Power factor $= \cos \theta = \dfrac{I_R}{I} = \dfrac{3}{3.6} = 0.833$

As $I_L$ is larger than $I_C$, the total current lags the voltage by the angle $\theta$.

(*c*)  $P = EI \cos \theta = 240 \times 3.6 \times 0.833 = 720$ watts

also   $P = (I_R)^2 R = 3^2 \times 80 = 720$ watts (check)

(*d*)  $Z = \dfrac{E}{I} = \dfrac{240}{3.6} = 66.7$ ohms

**Example 7** A resistance of 30 ohms is connected in parallel with a coil that has a resistance of 12 ohms and an inductive reactance of 16 ohms. Find (a) the line current and (b) the power taken by the circuit when it is connected to a 240-volt supply as in Fig. 9-10.

(a) $Z_2 = \sqrt{R^2 + X^2} = \sqrt{12^2 + 16^2} = 20$ ohms

$I_2 = \dfrac{E}{Z_2} = \dfrac{240}{20} = 12$ amp

$I_1 = \dfrac{E}{Z_1} = \dfrac{240}{30} = 8$ amp

The vector diagram is drawn in Fig. 9-10b. The current $I_1$ is in phase with

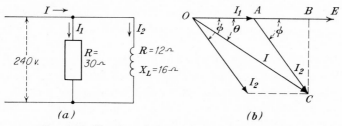

(a)                    (b)

FIG. 9-10. Circuit and vector diagram for Example 7.

the voltage, while $I_2$ lags the voltage by an angle $\phi$ whose cosine is $R_2/Z_2$, or

$$\cos \phi = \frac{R_2}{Z_2} = \frac{12}{20} = 0.6$$

$$\phi = 53°8' \qquad \text{(from tables)}$$

The vector addition of $I_1$ and $I_2$ is performed by completing the triangle $OBC$ as shown in Fig. 9-10b.

$$OA = 8$$
$$AC = 12$$
$$AB = 12 \cos 53°8' = 12 \times 0.6 = 7.2$$
$$OB = OA + AB = 8 + 7.2 = 15.2$$
$$BC = 12 \sin 53°8' = 12 \times 0.8 = 9.6$$
$$I = OC = \sqrt{(OB)^2 + (BC)^2}$$
$$= \sqrt{15.2^2 + 9.6^2} = 18 \text{ amp}$$

(b) $\cos \theta = \dfrac{OB}{OC} = \dfrac{15.2}{18} = 0.8444$

also
$$P = EI \cos \theta = 240 \times 18 \times 0.8444 = 3,648 \text{ watts}$$
$$P_1 = I_1^2 R_1 = (8)^2 \times 30 = 1,920 \text{ watts}$$
$$P_2 = I_2^2 R_2 = (12)^2 \times 12 = 1,728 \text{ watts}$$
$$P = P_1 + P_2 = 1,920 + 1,728 = 3,648 \text{ watts (check)}$$

## 9-9. Power-factor Correction

More current is required to supply a given kilowatt load at a low power factor than at a power factor of unity. Since both voltage drop and line losses in any power line supplying a load are proportional to the line current, it follows that the lower the power factor, the higher are the line drop and losses to transmit a given kilowatt load. Because of the large number of induction motors and other inductive devices used on modern power systems, the power factors of many such systems are quite low resulting in substantial voltage drops and line losses.

Many utilities correct for low power factors by the use of power-factor-corrective capacitors connected to their systems at various points. Since the current drawn by a capacitor leads the applied voltage by 90° (neglecting the small amount of resistance in the capacitor), the current drawn by such a device effectively cancels the effect of the inductive reactive component of the load devices on the same circuit.

To illustrate the effect of a power-factor-corrective capacitor, consider the circuit of Example 7. The total current drawn by the circuit is 18 amp and the current lags the applied voltage by an angle whose cosine is 0.8444. From the vector diagram in Fig. 9-10$b$, this current has an active component $OB$ of 15.2 amp in phase with the voltage and a reactive component $BC$ of 9.6 amp lagging the voltage by 90°. If a capacitor with a current rating of 9.6 amp is connected in parallel with the resistor and coil, the resulting circuit power factor is unity. This is because the current drawn by the capacitor leads the voltage by 90° and is therefore 180° out of phase with the reactive component of the load current. Since there is no net reactive component in the circuit, the total line current is thus reduced from 18 to 15.2 amp. Even though the total line current has been reduced, the resistor and coil are still supplied the same currents as before and the kilowatt load on the circuit is unchanged.

Further information on power-factor correction, including the use of synchronous motors for this purpose, is included in Art. 14-7.

## REVIEW QUESTIONS

**1.** In an a-c circuit, how may the power at any instant be calculated? Is the instantaneous power a constant value over an entire cycle?

**2.** Draw a sine-wave voltage in phase with a sine-wave current. Is the instantaneous power zero at any time during a complete cycle? When is the instantaneous power at a maximum?

**3.** Under what condition is the power in an a-c circuit equal to $EI$?

**4.** In general, what unit is used to express the product of volts and amperes in an a-c circuit?

**5.** Define power factor. How is it used in finding the power of an a-c circuit? What are its maximum and minimum values?

**6.** What is meant when it is said that an alternating current has an active and a reactive component?

**7.** In a circuit in which the current and voltage are in phase, what is the value of the reactive component of the current? What is the value of the reactive volt-amperes, or vars, of the circuit?

**8.** What is the phase angle in degrees of a circuit in which the vars are equal to the watts? What is the phase angle of a circuit in which the volt-amperes are equal to the watts?

**9.** When the resistance and current of an a-c circuit are known, how may power be calculated regardless of power factor?

**10.** Give the current and voltage rules for an a-c series circuit.

**11.** When a series circuit contains inductance and resistance, does the current lead or lag the applied voltage? What is the phase relation between the voltage across the inductance and the current through the inductance?

**12.** How may the power factor of a series a-c circuit be calculated from the circuit constants?

**13.** What is the phase relation between current and voltage in an $RC$ series circuit?

**14.** Describe the procedure for finding the current, power factor, and power of a resistance-inductance-capacitance series circuit when the circuit constants, the frequency, and the voltage are given. Under what conditions in this circuit will the current lead the voltage?

**15.** When several impedances are connected in series, how is the combined impedance found?

**16.** Give the current and voltage rules for a parallel a-c circuit.

**17.** Is the line current necessarily the arithmetic sum of the branch currents in a parallel a-c circuit? When is this the case?

**18.** If the applied voltage and the branch currents of a parallel circuit are known, explain how the equivalent impedance of the circuit might be found.

**19.** Explain how the power factor of an inductive circuit may be improved.

## PROBLEMS

**1.** When a voltage of 440 volts is applied to a certain load, the current that flows is 20 amp. What are (a) the volt-amperes of the circuit; (b) the kilovolt-amperes?

**2.** The power taken by a motor is 800 watts when the current is 9 amp. If the line voltage is 120 volts, at what power factor is the motor operating?

**3.** A certain load draws 85 kw and 105 kva from an a-c supply. At what power factor is it operating?

**4.** What full-load power can a 5-kva single-phase a-c generator supply at a power factor of 90 per cent? What is the full-load line current if the terminal voltage is 120 volts?

**5.** A single-phase motor operates at a power factor of 70 per cent lagging. The line voltage is 220 volts, and the line current is 20 amp. Find the volt-amperes and the actual power in watts taken by the motor.

**6.** A single-phase circuit has a unity power factor. The applied voltage is 110 volts. The line current is 30 amp. Find the actual power in watts.

**7.** The power consumed in a single-phase circuit is 4 kw. The line current is 40 amp and the voltage is 110 volts. Find the volt-amperes and the power factor of the circuit.

**8.** A single-phase motor is operating at a power factor of 0.8 lagging on a 220-volt line. The motor consumes 8 kw. Find the motor line current.

**9.** A motor draws 1,000 watts and 1,500 va from a single-phase line. What is the value of the reactive volt-amperes, or vars, drawn by the motor? What is the power factor?

**10.** Find the kilovolt-amperes of a circuit when the actual power is 1,200 watts and the reactive volt-amperes are 600 vars. What is the power factor?

**11.** An inductive reactance of 12 ohms is connected in series with a resistance of 16 ohms. A 115-volt 60-cycle voltage is applied. Find (a) the impedance, (b) the current flowing, (c) the power factor, (d) the volt-amperes, and (e) the power.

**12.** Find the voltage applied to a coil that has a reactance of 8 ohms and a resistance of 3 ohms, when a current of 11 amp is flowing through the coil. What is the power used by the coil?

**13.** A resistance of 40 ohms and a capacitance of 50 μf are connected in series across a 120-volt 60-cycle line. Find (a) the impedance, (b) the current, (c) the power factor, (d) the volt-amperes, and (e) the power.

**14.** A circuit consisting of a capacitor and a resistance in series takes 60 watts at a power factor of 28 per cent (leading) from a 110-volt 60-cycle line. Find (a) the current, (b) the impedance, (c) the resistance, and (d) the capacitance of the circuit.

**15.** A 100-μf capacitor is connected to a 120-volt 60-cycle line. Find the current that will flow. If a resistance of 10 ohms is connected in series with the capacitor, what will be the new value of current?

**16.** A series circuit consists of a resistance of 10 ohms, an 80-μf capacitor, and an inductance of 0.1 henry. What current will flow when the circuit is connected to a 240-volt 60-cycle supply?

**17.** A capacitor, a resistor, and a coil with negligible resistance are connected in series. The voltage drop across the capacitor is 50 volts, across the resistor 80 volts, and across the coil 20 volts. Find the voltage drop across the entire circuit.

**18.** A resistance of 40 ohms and a capacitive reactance of 60 ohms are connected in series across a 110-volt circuit. Find (a) the current, (b) the power factor, and (c) the power.

**19.** When a resistance of 4 ohms and an inductance of unknown value are connected in series across 110-volt 60-cycle supply lines, the current is 20 amp. Find the value of the inductance.

**20.** The following meter readings were taken in an inductive single-phase circuit; wattmeter, 2,400 watts; voltmeter, 240 volts; ammeter, 15 amp; frequency meter, 60 cycles. Find (a) the volt-amperes, (b) the power factor, (c) the impedance, (d) the resistance, (e) the inductive reactance, (f) the inductance, and (g) the value of a series capacitor that will make the power factor 100 per cent.

**21.** A 120-volt a-c motor delivers 5 hp at an efficiency of 85 per cent. The motor operates at a power factor of 80 per cent lagging. Find (a) the power input and (b) the current drawn by the motor.

**22.** Find the total current required by a circuit having a resistance of 20 ohms, an inductive reactance of 10 ohms, and a capacitive reactance of 15 ohms, all connected in parallel to a 120-volt line.

**23.** A resistance of 16 ohms is connected in parallel with a coil that has a resistance of 4 ohms and a reactance of 12 ohms. The supply voltage is 120 volts. Find (a) the total current, (b) the power factor, and (c) the power taken by the circuit.

**24.** A resistance of 20 ohms is connected in parallel with an inductive reactance of 10 ohms to a 100-volt 60-cycle line. Find (a) the current through the resistance, (b) the current through the reactance, and (c) the reactance of a capacitor which, when connected in parallel with the circuit, will improve the power factor of the circuit to 100 per cent.

**25.** A coil with a resistance of 5 ohms and an inductive reactance of 12 ohms is connected in parallel with a capacitor which has a capacitive reactance of 10 ohms and negligible resistance. When the parallel combination of coil and capacitor is connected to a 120-volt 60-cycle supply, find (a) the current in each branch, (b) the total line current, (c) the total power in watts, and (d) the circuit power factor.

**26.** A coil having an inductive reactance of 8 ohms and a resistance of 0.5 ohm is connected in series with a 5.5-ohm resistor. The coil and the 5.5-ohm series resistor are connected in parallel with a 20-ohm resistor to a 120-volt 60-cycle supply. Determine (a) the current flowing through the coil, (b) the current flowing through the 20-ohm resistor, (c) the total line current, (d) the power taken by the circuit, and (e) the power factor of the circuit.

**27.** The input to a motor is 5.5 kva at 80 per cent power factor. What must be the reactive volt-ampere rating of a capacitor connected across the motor terminals to correct the power factor to 100 per cent?

**28.** A 2-hp 60-cycle motor has a full-load input of 2,200 watts and 12 amp at 230 volts. (a) Find the reactive volt-ampere rating of a capacitor to be connected across the terminals of the motor to correct the full-load power factor to 100 per cent. (b) What is the size of the capacitor in microfarads? (c) What is the total current drawn by the motor and the capacitor?

**29.** A 5-kvar (5,000-var) capacitor added in parallel to a given 440-volt load corrects the circuit power factor to unity and the resulting line current is 5 amp. (a) What was the line current drawn by the load before the addition of the capacitor? (b) What was the power factor of the original 440-volt load?

# CHAPTER 10

# THREE-PHASE CIRCUITS

A three-phase circuit is merely a combination of three single-phase circuits. Because of this fact, current, voltage, and power relations of balanced three-phase circuits may be studied by the application of single-phase rules to the component parts of the three-phase circuit. Viewed in this light, it will be found that the analysis of three-phase circuits is little more difficult than that of single-phase circuits.

**10-1. Reasons for Use of Three-phase Circuits** In a single-phase circuit, the power is of a pulsating nature. At unity power factor the power in a single-phase circuit is zero twice each cycle. When the power factor is less than unity, the power is negative during parts of each cycle. Although the power supplied to each of the three phases of a three-phase circuit is pulsating, it may be proved that the total three-phase power supplied a balanced three-phase circuit is constant. Because of this, the operating characteristics of three-phase apparatus, in general, are superior to those of similar single-phase apparatus.

Three-phase machinery and its control equipment are smaller, lighter in weight, and more efficient than single-phase equipment of the same rated capacity. In addition to the above-mentioned advantages offered by a three-phase system, the distribution of three-phase power requires only three-fourths as much line copper as does the single-phase distribution of the same amount of power.

**10-2. Generation of Three-phase Voltages** A three-phase electric circuit is energized by three alternating emfs of the same frequency and differing in time phase by 120 electrical degrees. Three such sine-wave emfs are shown in Fig. 10-1. These emfs are generated in three separate sets of armature coils in an a-c generator or, as it is sometimes called, alternator. These three sets of coils are mounted 120 electrical degrees apart on the generator armature. The coil ends may all be brought out of the generator to form three separate single-phase cir-

cuits. However, the coils are ordinarily interconnected either inter-
nally or externally to form a three-wire or four-wire three-phase system.

There are two ways of connecting the coils of three-phase generators,
and in general, there are two ways of connecting devices of any sort to
a three-phase circuit. These are the *wye connection* and the *delta
connection*. Most generators are wye-connected, but loads may be
either wye-connected or delta-connected.

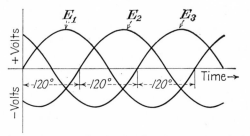

FIG. 10-1. Three sine-wave emfs differing in phase by 120 electrical degrees such as
are used for energizing a three-phase circuit.

## 10-3. Voltage Relations in a Wye-connected Generator Figure

10-2*a* represents the three coils or phase windings of a generator.
These windings are so spaced on the armature surface that the emfs
generated in them are 120° apart in time phase. Each coil is lettered *S*
and *F* (start and finish). In Fig. 10-2*a*, all the coil ends marked *S* are
connected to a common point *N*, called the neutral, and the three coil
ends marked *F* are brought out to the line terminals *A*, *B*, and *C* to
form a three-wire three-phase supply. This type of connection is
called the *wye connection*. Often the neutral connection is brought
out to the terminal board, as shown by the dotted line in Fig. 10-2*a*,
to form a four-wire three-phase system.

The voltages generated in each phase of an a-c generator are called
the *phase voltages* (symbol $E_P$). If the neutral connection is brought
out of the generator, the voltage from any one of the line terminals
*A*, *B*, or *C* to the neutral connection *N* is a phase voltage. The voltage
between any two of the three line terminals *A*, *B*, or *C* is called a line-
to-line voltage or, simply, a *line voltage* (symbol $E_L$).

The order in which the three voltages of a three-phase system
succeed one another is called the *phase sequence* or the phase rotation
of the voltages. This is determined by the direction of rotation of the
generator but may be reversed outside the generator by interchanging
any two of the three line wires (not a line wire and a neutral wire).

It is helpful when drawing circuit diagrams of a wye connection to
arrange the three phases in the shape of a *Y* as shown in Fig. 10-2*b*.

Note that the circuit of Fig. 10-2*b* is exactly the same as that of Fig. 10-2*a*, with the *S* end of each coil connected to the neutral point and the *F* end brought out to the terminal in each case. After a circuit diagram has been drawn with all intersections lettered, a vector diagram

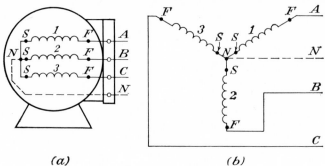

*(a)*                                              *(b)*

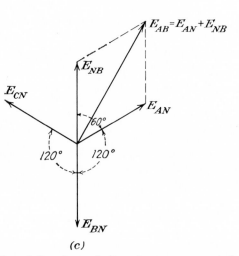

*(c)*

FIG. 10-2. (*a*) Connection of the phase windings in a wye-connected generator. (*b*) Conventional diagram of a wye connection. (*c*) Vector diagram showing the relation between phase and line voltages.

may be drawn as in Fig. 10-2*c*. The vector diagram shows the three phase voltages $E_{AN}$, $E_{BN}$, and $E_{CN}$ which are 120° apart.

It should be noted in Fig. 10-2 that each vector is lettered with two subscripts. The two letters indicate the two points between which the voltage exists, and the order of the letters indicates the relative polarity of the voltage during its positive half-cycle. For example, the symbol $E_{AN}$ indicates a voltage $E$ between the points $A$ and $N$, with the point $A$ being positive with respect to point $N$ during its positive half-cycle.

In the vector diagram shown, it has been assumed that the generator terminals were positive with respect to the neutral during the positive half-cycle. Since the voltage reverses every half-cycle, either polarity may be assumed if this polarity is assumed consistently for all three phases. It should be noted that if the polarity of point $A$ with respect to $N$ ($E_{AN}$) is assumed for the positive half-cycle, then $E_{NA}$ when used in the same vector diagram should be drawn opposite to, or 180° out of phase with, $E_{AN}$.

The voltage between any two line terminals of a wye-connected generator is the difference between the potentials of these two terminals with respect to the neutral. For example, the line voltage $E_{AB}$ is equal to the voltage $A$ with respect to neutral ($E_{AN}$) minus the voltage $B$ with respect to neutral ($E_{BN}$). To subtract $E_{BN}$ from $E_{AN}$, it is necessary to reverse $E_{BN}$ and add this vector to $E_{AN}$. The two vectors $E_{AN}$ and $E_{NB}$ are equal in length and are 60° apart, as shown in Fig. 10-2c. It may be shown graphically or proved by geometry that $E_{AB}$ is equal to $\sqrt{3}$, or 1.73, multiplied by the value of either $E_{AN}$ or $E_{NB}$. The graphical construction is shown in the vector diagram. Therefore, in a balanced wye connection

$$E_L = \sqrt{3}\, E_P = 1.73 E_P \tag{1}$$

**10-4. Current Relations in a Wye-connected Generator** The current flowing out to the line wires from the generator terminals $A$, $B$, and $C$ (Fig. 10-2) must flow from the neutral point $N$, out through the generator coils. Thus, the current in each line wire ($I_L$) must equal the current in the phase ($I_P$) to which it is connected. In a wye connection

$$I_L = I_P \tag{2}$$

**10-5. Voltage Relations in a Delta-connected Generator** A *delta-connected* generator is shown in Fig. 10-3a. This connection is formed by connecting the $S$ terminal of one phase to the $F$ terminal of the adjacent phase. The line connections are then made at the common points between phases as shown. The conventional circuit diagram in which the three coils are arranged in the shape of the Greek letter delta ($\Delta$) is shown in Fig. 10-3b. An inspection of the diagram shows that the voltage generated in each phase is also the voltage between two line wires. For example, the voltage generated in phase 1 is also the voltage between lines $A$ and $B$. Therefore in a delta connection

$$E_L = E_P \tag{3}$$

**10-6. Current Relations in a Delta-connected Generator**   The phase
currents in the delta connection of Fig. 10-3b are $I_1$, $I_2$, and $I_3$.   The
vector diagram representing these currents is shown in Fig. 10-3c.
To find the current in any of the three line wires it is necessary to add
vectorially the currents flowing in the two phases to which that line is

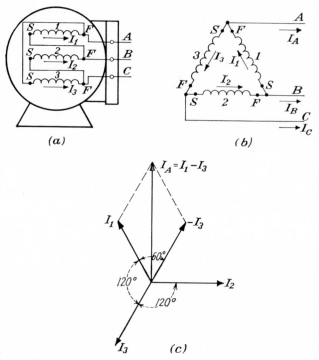

(a)                                              (b)

(c)

Fɪɢ. 10-3. (a) Connection of the phase windings in a delta-connected generator.
(b) Conventional diagram of a delta connection.   (c) Vector diagram showing the
relation between phase and line currents.

connected.   For example, the current flowing out toward the load
through line $A$ must be

$$I_A = I_1 + (-I_3)$$

Since $I_1$ and $-I_3$ are two equal vectors 60° apart, their vector sum
is $\sqrt{3}$, or 1.73, times the value of either $I_1$ or $-I_3$ (Fig. 10-3c).   Therefore, in the delta connection

$$I_L = \sqrt{3}\,I_P = 1.73 I_P \tag{4}$$

**10-7. Three-phase Power**   From the formula for power in a single-
phase circuit, the power developed in each phase ($P_P$) of either a delta
or wye connection is

$$P_P = E_P I_P \cos \theta$$

where $\theta$ is the angle between the phase current and the phase voltage. The power developed in all three phases of a balanced three-phase connection is then

$$P = 3P_P = 3E_P I_P \cos \theta \qquad (5)$$

But in a wye connection

$$I_P = I_L \qquad \text{and} \qquad E_P = \frac{E_L}{\sqrt{3}}$$

Thus, the three-phase power in a wye-connected system in terms of line voltage and current is

$$P = 3 \frac{E_L}{\sqrt{3}} I_L \cos \theta$$
$$= \sqrt{3} E_L I_L \cos \theta$$
$$= 1.73 E_L I_L \cos \theta$$

In a delta connection

$$E_P = E_L \qquad \text{and} \qquad I_P = \frac{I_L}{\sqrt{3}}$$

Again the three-phase power in terms of line current and voltage is

$$P = 3 E_L \frac{I_L}{\sqrt{3}} \cos \theta$$
$$= \sqrt{3} E_L I_L \cos \theta$$
$$= 1.73 E_L I_L \cos \theta$$

Thus, the expression for three-phase power in a balanced system, either wye- or delta-connected, is equal to

$$P = 1.73 E_L I_L \cos \theta \qquad (6)$$

If $E_P I_P \cos \theta$ is the power per phase in watts, then $E_P I_P$ represents the volt-amperes per phase. It follows, then, that the three-phase volt-amperes are equal to $3E_P I_P$, or $1.73E_L I_L$. The total three-phase kilovolt-amperes in either a wye or delta system may be found by

$$\text{kva} = \frac{1.73 E_L I_L}{1,000} \qquad (7)$$

The power factor of a balanced three-phase connection is equal to

$$\text{Power factor} = \frac{P}{1.73 E_L I_L} \qquad (8)$$

or is equal to the cosine of the angle between the *phase* current and *phase* voltage.

**Example 1** A three-phase wye-connected generator has a terminal voltage of 450 volts and delivers a full-load current of 300 amp per terminal at a lagging power factor of 75 per cent. Find (a) the voltage per phase, (b) the full-load current per phase, (c) the kilovolt-ampere rating, and (d) the full-load power in kilowatts.

(a) $E_P = \dfrac{E_L}{1.73} = \dfrac{450}{1.73} = 260$ volts

(b) As the generator is wye-connected, the phase current is equal to the line current.

$$I_P = I_L = 300 \text{ amp}$$

(c) $\text{kva} = \dfrac{1.73 E_L I_L}{1,000} = \dfrac{1.73 \times 450 \times 300}{1,000} = 233.6 \text{ kva}$

(d) $P(\text{kw}) = \dfrac{1.73 E_L I_L \times \text{power factor}}{1,000}$

$= \text{kva} \times \text{power factor} = 233.6 \times 0.75$

$= 175.5 \text{ kw}$

**Example 2** Each phase of a three-phase delta-connected generator supplies a full-load current of 100 amp at a voltage of 240 volts and at a power factor of 0.6, lagging. Find (a) the line voltage, (b) the line current, (c) the three-phase kilovolt-amperes, and (d) the three-phase power in kilowatts.

(a) The line voltage is equal to the phase voltage in a delta system.

$$E_L = E_P = 240 \text{ volts}$$

(b) $I_L = 1.73 I_P = 1.73 \times 100 = 173 \text{ amp}$

(c) $\text{kva} = \dfrac{1.73 E_L I_L}{1,000} = \dfrac{1.73 \times 240 \times 173}{1,000} = 72 \text{ kva}$

(d) $P = \text{kva} \times \text{power factor} = 72 \times 0.6 = 43.2 \text{ kw}$

## 10-8. Wye- and Delta-connected Loads

Not only may generators be connected in either wye or delta, but various types of loads such as motor windings, lamps, or transformers may also be wye- or delta-connected. The same current, voltage, and power relations that are used for three-phase generators are used for three-phase load connections. The following examples will illustrate these relations for load connections.

**Example 3** Three resistances of 15 ohms each (power factor = 100 per cent) are wye-connected to a 240-volt three-phase line. Find (a) the current through each resistance, (b) the line current, and (c) the power taken by the three resistances.

(a) The circuit diagram is shown in Fig. 10-4. The phase voltage or the voltage applied to each resistance is

$$E_P = \dfrac{E_L}{1.73} = \dfrac{240}{1.73} = 138.7 \text{ volts}$$

(b) The current in each resistance is (no reactance present)

$$I_P = \frac{E_P}{Z_P} = \frac{E_P}{R_P} = \frac{138.7}{15} = 9.25 \text{ amp}$$

As the line and phase currents are equal

$$I_L = I_P = 9.25 \text{ amp}$$

(c) The power taken by one resistance is

$$P_P = E_P I_P \cos \theta = 138.7 \times 9.25 \times 1 = 1{,}280 \text{ watts}$$

The three-phase power is

$$P = 3P_P = 3 \times 1{,}280 = 3{,}840 \text{ watts}$$

or     $P = 1.73 E_L I_L \cos \theta$
$$= 1.73 \times 240 \times 9.25 \times 1 = 3{,}840 \text{ watts (check)}$$

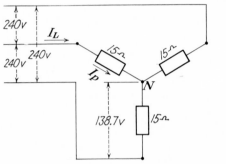

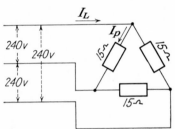

FIG. 10-4. Circuit diagram for Example 3.     FIG. 10-5. Circuit diagram for Example 4.

**Example 4**   Repeat the preceding problem if the three resistances are reconnected in delta.

(a) The circuit diagram is shown in Fig. 10-5.   Now the voltage applied to each phase is equal to the line voltage or 240 volts.

$$I_P = \frac{E_P}{Z_P} = \frac{E_P}{R_P} = \frac{240}{15} = 16 \text{ amp}$$

(b) The line current is

$$I_L = 1.73 I_P = 1.73 \times 16 = 27.7 \text{ amp}$$

(c) The three-phase power is

$$P = 1.73 E_L I_L \cos \theta$$
$$= 1.73 \times 240 \times 27.7 \times 1 = 11{,}520 \text{ watts}$$

or     $P = 3 E_P I_P \cos \theta$
$$= 3 \times 240 \times 16 \times 1 = 11{,}520 \text{ watts (check)}$$

**Example 5**   A 15-hp 220-volt three-phase induction motor has a full-load current of 38 amp per terminal.   (a) What is the full-load kilovolt-ampere input?   (b) If the full-load power factor is 85 per cent, what is the kilowatt input?

(a) $\text{kva} = \dfrac{1.73 E_L I_L}{1,000}$

$= \dfrac{1.73 \times 220 \times 38}{1,000} = 14.46 \text{ kva}$

(b) $P$ (in kw) = kva $\times$ power factor
$= 14.46 \times 0.85 = 12.29 \text{ kw}$

## Summary of Three-phase Relationships

Wye Connection
Load or Source

Delta Connection
Load or Source

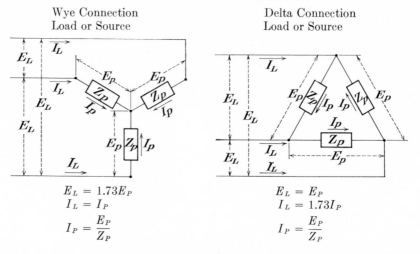

$E_L = 1.73 E_P$
$I_L = I_P$

$I_P = \dfrac{E_P}{Z_P}$

$E_L = E_P$
$I_L = 1.73 I_P$

$I_P = \dfrac{E_P}{Z_P}$

### For Either Connection

Volt-amperes per phase $= E_P I_P$

Kilovolt-amperes per phase $= \dfrac{E_P I_P}{1,000}$

Three-phase volt-amperes $= 3 E_P I_P$
$= 1.73 E_L I_L$

Three-phase kilovolt-amperes $= \dfrac{3 E_P I_P}{1,000}$

$= \dfrac{1.73 E_L I_L}{1,000}$

Power factor $=$ cosine of angle between $E_P$ and $I_P = \dfrac{R_P}{Z_P}$

$= \dfrac{P}{1.73 E_L I_L}$

Power per phase $= E_P I_P \cos \theta$ (in watts)

$= \dfrac{E_P I_P \cos \theta}{1,000}$ (in kw)

Three-phase power $= 3 E_P I_P \cos \theta$ (in watts)
$= 1.73 E_L I_L \cos \theta$ (in watts)

## REVIEW QUESTIONS

**1.** What is a three-phase circuit?

**2.** What are some advantages of three-phase systems over single-phase systems?

**3.** In the three-phase generator, the three emfs are generated how many electrical degrees out of phase?

**4.** What are two commonly used connections in a three-phase circuit?

**5.** Explain briefly how generator phase windings are connected in wye.

**6.** How is a wye-connected generator connected to supply (a) a three-wire three-phase system; (b) a four-wire three-phase system?

**7.** In a wye connection, what is the line-to-neutral voltage called? What is meant by a line voltage?

**8.** What is meant by phase sequence? How may it be reversed?

**9.** If $E_{AB}$ represents a line voltage in a vector diagram, what would be the symbol for the voltage that is equal and opposite to $E_{AB}$ in the same diagram?

**10.** Give the relationship between phase and line voltages in a wye connection. How are the phase and line currents related?

**11.** Show how the phase windings of an a-c generator may be connected in delta.

**12.** What is the relation between phase and line voltages in a delta connection? between phase and line currents?

**13.** Give two three-phase power formulas. Since power in a single-phase circuit is equal to $I^2R$, how could this relationship be used in finding three-phase power?

**14.** Give the formula for finding three-phase volt-amperes.

**15.** If the three-phase watts and volt-amperes of a circuit are known, how could the three-phase vars be found?

## PROBLEMS

Note: Balanced three-phase connections are assumed in all the following problems.

**1.** The phase voltage of a wye-connected generator is 120 volts. What is the line voltage?

**2.** If the terminal voltage of a wye-connected generator is 13,200 volts, what is the voltage generated in each of the phases?

**3.** What is the *maximum* value of the line voltage of a wye connection if the effective value of the phase voltage is 127 volts?

**4.** For a given load, the phase current of a wye-connected generator is 50 amp. What is the current flowing in the line wires?

**5.** Each phase of a wye-connected generator delivers a current of 30 amp at a phase voltage of 254 volts and a power factor of 80 per cent, lagging. What is the generator terminal voltage? What is the power developed in each phase? What is the three-phase power developed?

**6.** At full load, each of the three phases of a wye-connected generator delivers 150 amp at 1,329 volts at a power factor of 75 per cent, the current lagging. Find (a) the terminal voltage rating, (b) the kilovolt-ampere rating, and (c) the kilowatt rating.

**7.** It is desired that a 10,000-kva three-phase 60-cycle generator have a rated terminal voltage of 13,800 volts when it is wye-connected. What must be the voltage rating of each phase? Find the kilovolt-ampere rating per phase and the rated current per terminal.

**8.** The line current of a delta connection is 40 amp. What is the phase current?

**9.** The phase current in a delta connection is 50 amp. Find the line current.

**10.** The voltage per phase of a delta-connected generator is 450 volts. What is the terminal or line voltage?

**11.** If the generator of Prob. 6 is reconnected for delta operation, what is the new voltage rating? What is the new kilovolt-ampere rating?

**12.** A three-phase motor takes a current of 20 amp per terminal. The line voltage is 440 volts, and the power factor is 80 per cent, lagging. What is the power used by the motor?

**13.** In a three-phase delta-connected load, the phase current is 20 amp and the phase voltage is 220 volts. The power factor is 90 per cent, lagging. Find the total three-phase power in kilowatts.

**14.** A three-phase load consumes 60 kw when connected to a 440-volt line. The line current is 100 amp. Find the kilovolt-amperes and the power factor of the load.

**15.** A wye-connected load draws 20 kw from a 440-volt line. The line current is 30 amp. Find the phase voltage and the power factor.

**16.** A three-phase generator delivers 150 amp at 6,600 volts. What is the kilovolt-ampere output? If the power output is 1,500 kw, what is the power factor?

**17.** Find the current rating of a three-phase 440-volt 60-cycle 50-hp induction motor, if it operates at an 85 per cent lagging power factor. The full-load input is 38.8 kw.

**18.** If a generator delivers 26,000 kw at a power factor of 80 per cent, lagging, what is its kilovolt-ampere output?

**19.** A wye-connected load of three 10-ohm resistors (power factor = 100 per cent) is connected to a 220-volt three-phase supply. Find (a) the voltage applied to each resistor, (b) the line current, and (c) the total power used.

**20.** Three loads, each having a resistance of 16 ohms and an inductive reactance of 12 ohms, are wye-connected to a 220-volt three-phase supply. Find (a) the impedance per phase, (b) the current per phase, (c) the three-phase kilovolt-amperes, (d) the power factor, and (e) the three-phase power in kilowatts.

**21.** Work Prob. 19 if the resistors are delta-connected.

**22.** Work Prob. 20 if the loads are delta-connected.

**23.** A delta-connected load draws 28.8 kw from a three-phase supply. The line current is 69.2 amp and the power factor is 80 per cent, lagging. Find the resistance and the reactance of each phase.

# CHAPTER 11

## TRANSFORMERS AND REGULATORS

**11-1. Introduction** Transformers provide a simple means of changing an alternating voltage from one value to another. If a transformer receives energy at a low voltage and delivers it at a higher voltage, it is called a *step-up* transformer. When a transformer is supplied energy at a given voltage and delivers it at some lower voltage, it is called a *step-down* transformer. Any transformer may be operated as either a step-up or step-down transformer; however, the voltage for which the transformer is designed must be applied in either case.

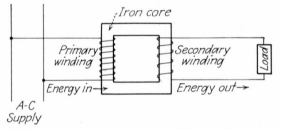

Fig. 11-1. Elementary diagram of a transformer.

To transmit a given amount of energy, less current is required at a high voltage than at a low voltage. This means that energy may be transmitted with less $I^2R$ or line loss when high transmission voltages are used. In order to secure high transmission voltages, such as 220,000 or 345,000 volts, step-up transformers are used at the generating station, since it is not feasible to generate voltages this high. Then at the points where energy is to be used, step-down transformers are used to reduce the high transmission voltage to safe and usable values. Thus, transformers make possible the economical transmission of electric energy over long distances.

A simple transformer consists of two coils wound on a closed iron core as represented in Fig. 11-1. Energy is supplied to one winding, called the *primary winding,* and is delivered to the load from the other winding, called the *secondary winding*. When the transformer is used as a step-up transformer, the low-voltage winding is the primary. In a step-down transformer, the high-voltage winding is the primary.

Standard markings have been adopted for transformer terminals. The terminals of the high-voltage winding are marked $H_1$, $H_2$ . . . ; the terminals of the low-voltage winding are marked $X_1$, $X_2$ . . . . It is convenient, therefore, to call the high-voltage winding the $H$ winding and the low-voltage winding the $X$ winding and to designate the number of turns of each winding as $T_H$ and $T_X$.

Since a transformer has no moving parts, it requires little attention and the maintenance expense is low. Transformer efficiencies are high, running as high as 98 or 99 per cent at full load in the larger sizes.

**11-2. Theory of Operation: No Load**    When an alternating voltage is applied to the high-voltage ($H$) winding of the step-down transformer of Fig. 11-2, with the load switch open, a small current called the exciting current flows.    As in any highly inductive circuit, the current

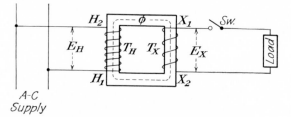

FIG. 11-2. A step-down transformer.

is limited by the counter emf of self-induction which is induced in the winding. Transformer windings are designed with a sufficient number of turns to make the counter emf practically equal to the applied voltage at no load. This limits the no-load or exciting current to a very low value.

The exciting current causes an alternating flux to be set up in the core. This alternating flux cuts across the turns of both the $H$ and $X$ windings as it increases and decreases in alternate directions, thereby inducing an emf in both windings. As noted previously, the emf induced in the $H$ winding opposes the applied voltage $E_H$. Since the turns of both windings are cut by the same flux, the emf induced in each turn of both windings is the same. If $E_{Hi}$ is the emf induced in the $H$ winding and $E_X$ is the emf induced in the $X$ winding, then the voltage per turn in the two windings is $E_{Hi}/T_H$ and $E_X/T_X$, respectively, and $E_{Hi}/T_H = E_X/T_X$.

If the resistance of the $H$ winding is small, as is usually the case, $E_{Hi}$

will be very nearly equal to $E_H$. Neglecting this small difference, then $E_H/T_H = E_X/T_X$. Cross multiplying and dividing by $E_X T_X$ results in

$$\frac{E_H}{E_X} = \frac{T_H}{T_X} \qquad (1)$$

This equation shows that the voltages across the windings of a transformer are directly proportional to the turns in each winding.

**Example 1** A transformer with 200 turns on the $H$ winding is to be wound to step the voltage down from 240 to 120 volts. Find the number of turns $T_X$ on the $X$ winding.

$$\frac{E_H}{E_X} = \frac{T_H}{T_X}$$

$$\frac{240}{120} = \frac{200}{T_X}$$

$$240 T_X = 24{,}000$$

$$T_X = 100$$

**11-3. Operation under Load** When the secondary circuit of the transformer in Fig. 11-2 is closed, a current $I_X$, equal to $E_X$ divided by the load impedance, will flow. By Lenz's law, any current caused to flow by an induced emf flows in such direction as to oppose the action that causes the emf to be induced. In the case of a transformer, this means that $I_X$ will always flow in a direction such that its magnetizing action will oppose the magnetizing action of the $H$ winding. The current $I_X$, then, tends to reduce the flux in the transformer core. However, if the flux is reduced, the counter emf $E_{Hi}$ is reduced, thereby permitting more primary current $I_H$ to flow which restores the flux to its original value.

If more load is added, causing $I_X$ to increase further, its increased demagnetizing action lowers the flux again, which permits still more primary current to flow. Thus the magnetizing action of the primary winding adjusts itself with each change in secondary current. The action is somewhat similar to the condition in a d-c motor in which the amount of current drawn by the armature is dependent upon the amount of counter emf generated. An increase in motor load causes the counter emf to drop, which in turn permits more armature current to flow. Likewise in the transformer, an addition of load to the secondary causes a decrease in primary counter emf that permits more primary current to flow.

From the above discussion the following relations are evident:

Primary ampere-turns = secondary ampere-turns

or
$$I_H T_H = I_X T_X \qquad (2)$$

If both sides of Eq. (2) are divided by $I_H T_X$, then

$$\frac{I_X}{I_H} = \frac{T_H}{T_X} \tag{3}$$

that is, the ratio of the currents in a transformer is inversely proportional to the ratio of the turns.

From Eqs. (1) and (3), $E_H/E_X = I_X/I_H$, and by cross multiplication

$$E_H I_H = E_X I_X \tag{4}$$

Equation (4) shows that the volt-ampere input of a transformer is equal to the volt-ampere output.

It should be noted in connection with Eqs. (1) to (4) that they are approximate equations only. They are true only for an ideal transformer, that is, a transformer with no losses. However, they are sufficiently accurate for most practical purposes.

**Example 2** A transformer supplies a load with 30 amp at 240 volts. If the primary voltage is 2,400 volts, find (a) the secondary volt-amperes, (b) the primary volt-amperes, and (c) the primary current.

(a) $E_X I_X = 30 \times 240 = 7,200$ va

(b) $E_H I_H = E_X I_X = 7,200$ va

(c) $E_H I_H = 7,200$ va

    $2,400 I_H = 7,200$ va

$$I_H = \frac{7,200}{2,400} = 3 \text{ amp}$$

**11-4. Ratings** Transformer capacity is rated in *kilovolt-amperes*. An output rating for a transformer is based on the maximum current that the transformer can carry without exceeding a certain temperature rise. Since power in an a-c circuit depends on the power factor of the load as well as the current flowing, an output rating in kilowatts would have to be at some specified power factor. For this reason, transformers, and a-c machines in general, are rated in kilovolt-amperes which are independent of power factor.

**Example 3** What is the rated kilowatt output of a 5-kva 2,400/120-volt transformer at (a) 100 per cent, (b) 80 per cent, and (c) 30 per cent power factor? (d) What is the rated current output?

(a) $P = $ kva $\times$ power factor $= 5 \times 1.0 = 5$ kw

(b) $P = 5 \times 0.8 = 4$ kw

(c) $P = 5 \times 0.3 = 1.5$ kw

(d) $I = \dfrac{\text{va}}{E} = \dfrac{5,000}{120} = 41.7$ amp

Full rated current of 41.7 amp is supplied by the transformer at the three different power factors even though the kilowatt output is different in each case.

Data other than kilovolt-ampere rating and manufacturer's type and serial numbers commonly found on transformer nameplates include the voltage ratings of both high- and low-voltage windings; the rated frequency; the impedance drop expressed as a percentage of rated voltage; and a connection diagram.

**11-5. Transformer Construction** There are several types of transformer-core construction in use. In the *core-type* transformer repre-

Fig. 11-3. Core and coil assembly of a single-phase core-type transformer. (*Courtesy of Westinghouse Electric Corporation.*)

sented diagrammatically in Figs. 11-1 and 11-2, the winding surrounds the laminated iron core. For the sake of simplicity the primary winding is represented as being on one leg of the core and the secondary on the other. Commercial transformers are not constructed in this manner because a large amount of the flux produced by the primary winding does not cut the secondary winding, or it is said that the transformer has a large *leakage flux*. To keep the leakage flux to a minimum, the windings are divided with half of each winding being placed on each leg of the core. The low-voltage winding is placed next to the core with the high-voltage winding placed around the low-voltage winding. The completed core and coil assembly of a 333-kva 4,800 to 240/480-volt core-type transformer is shown in Fig. 11-3. The entire assembly shown is placed in a steel tank to which oil is added so that the core and coils operate entirely under oil.

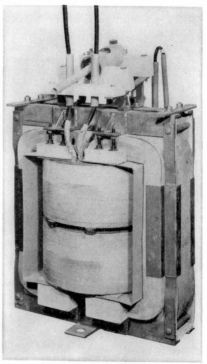

In the *shell-type* core construction the iron surrounds the winding. This type is shown diagrammatically in Fig. 11-4.

In another type of transformer construction, the core is made from a continuous strip of silicon steel that is wound in a tight spi-

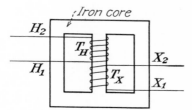

FIG. 11-4. Shell-type transformer-core construction.

FIG. 11-5. Core and coil assembly of a 250-kva wound-core-type transformer. (*Courtesy of General Electric Company.*)

ral around the insulated windings. Advantages claimed for the *wound-core-type* transformer, as it is called, are a lowered manufacturing cost and a lowered value of core loss. The assembled core and coils of a 250-kva wound-core transformer rated 7,200 to 2,400 volts is shown in Fig. 11-5.

**11-6. Transformer Losses and Efficiency** It has been stated that the efficiency of a transformer is high. This is especially true for the larger transformers operating at 50 to 100 per cent of full load. However, some losses are present in all transformers. These losses may be classified as *copper* or $I^2R$ losses and *core* losses.

Copper losses are proportional to the load being supplied by the transformer and for this reason are sometimes called the load losses. These losses may be calculated for any given load if the resistances of both windings are known.    If $R_H$ and $R_X$ are the high-voltage-winding and low-voltage-winding resistances, then the copper loss is

$$\text{Copper loss} = I_H{}^2 R_H + I_X{}^2 R_X \tag{5}$$

As in generators and motors, the core or iron loss is due to the effects of hysteresis and eddy currents.    Low-loss silicon steel is used to decrease hysteresis loss, and the cores are laminated to reduce eddy-current losses.    Core losses are substantially constant for all loads. They may be measured by a wattmeter when rated sine-wave voltage and frequency are applied to one winding with the other winding open-circuited.

If the losses are known or can be measured, the efficiency may be calculated for any given load from the formula

$$\text{Per cent efficiency} = \frac{\text{output}}{\text{input}} \times 100$$

$$= \frac{E_X I_X \cos \theta_X}{E_X I_X \cos \theta_X + I_X{}^2 R_X + I_H{}^2 R_H + \text{core loss}} \times 100 \tag{6}$$

where $E_X$ = output voltage
$\quad\quad I_X$ = output current
$\quad \cos \theta_X$ = load power factor

**11-7. Transformer Cooling**    When a transformer is operating under load, heat is generated in both the windings and the core owing to the losses mentioned in the preceding article.    Means must be provided to conduct this heat from the transformer.

Probably the most commonly used type of transformer is the *self-cooled liquid-immersed transformer*.    In this type, the core and windings are placed in a metal tank and the tank is filled with an insulating liquid.    The liquid may be an insulating oil or a noninflammable liquid. The liquid serves two purposes: it provides some of the insulation between windings, and it conducts heat from the windings to the surface of the tank where it is given off to the surrounding air.    In the larger sizes, the enclosing tank is provided with cooling tubes or fins as shown in Fig. 11-6, so that the cooling liquid has contact with a larger radiating surface.    The liquid circulates through the tank by natural convection.

*Air-cooled transformers* are often used where the use of oil-cooled transformers is prohibited because of the fire hazard.    The windings are designed so that the natural circulation of the air conducts the heat from the windings and core.   These transformers are protected by metal enclosures that are perforated to allow a maximum circulation of the air through the windings.

Other means of cooling are by forced-air circulation, forced-oil circulation, oil-immersion with water cooling, and various combinations of these methods.

**11-8. Instrument Transformers**   It is generally not a safe practice to connect instruments, meters, or control apparatus directly to high-voltage circuits.   Instrument transformers are universally used to reduce high voltages and currents to safe and usable values for the operation of such apparatus.

Instrument transformers perform two functions: (1) They act as *ratio devices*, making possible the use of standardized low-voltage and low-current meters and instruments.   (2) They act as *insulating devices*, to protect the apparatus and the operating personnel from high voltages.   There are two kinds of instrument transformers: *potential transformers* and *current transformers*.

Fig. 11-6. Self-cooled oil-immersed 100-kva transformer, 7,200/12,470 to 120/240 volts. (*Courtesy of General Electric Company.*)

**11-9. Potential Transformers**   Potential transformers supply a voltage to meters, instruments, or control devices which has a definite ratio to the line voltage.   The potential transformer operates on the same principle as a power transformer.   When the primary winding is connected across the line, a current flows which sets up a flux in the core.   The flux linking the secondary winding induces an emf that is proportional to the ratio of primary to secondary turns.   Potential transformers are commonly designed to have a rated voltage of 115 or 120 volts at the secondary terminals when rated voltage is applied to the primary winding.   Since the amount of load supplied by potential transformers is small, volt-ampere ratings are small, common ratings being 50 and 200 volt-amperes. A 460- to 115-volt 50-va potential transformer with fuses attached is shown in Fig. 11-7.

**11-10. Current Transformers** The purpose of a current transformer is to provide a means of reducing line current to values that may be used to operate standard low-current measuring and control devices, with these devices being completely insulated from the main circuits. As the current transformer is used in conjunction with current-measuring devices, its primary winding is designed to be connected in

series with the line. It is therefore necessary that the impedance of the primary winding be made as low as possible. This is done by using a few turns of low-resistance wire capable of carrying rated line current.

Since a current transformer is used ordinarily to decrease current, the secondary contains more turns than the primary, the ratio of primary to secondary current being inversely proportional to the ratio of primary to secondary turns. Current transformers are usually designed so that when rated current flows in the primary, 5 amp

FIG. 11-7. Indoor-type fused potential transformer. (*Courtesy of General Electric Company.*)

will flow in the secondary. A current transformer, having a ratio of 75 to 5 amp, is shown in Fig. 11-8.

Since the impedance of the primary winding of a current transformer is low, the current through the primary depends primarily on the load connected to the primary circuit rather than on the secondary load of the transformer itself. When the secondary circuit is closed, the secondary current establishes an mmf that opposes the primary mmf, thereby limiting the flux density in the core. When the secondary circuit is opened while the primary is energized, the secondary demagnetizing mmf is no longer present. This means that the flux density may become very high, causing a dangerously high voltage to be induced in the open secondary winding. To prevent injury to the apparatus and operating personnel, it is necessary that the secondary terminals of a current transformer be short-circuited before removing or inserting an instrument in the secondary circuit while the primary winding is energized. Modern current transformers are provided

FIG. 11-8. Indoor-type 5,000-volt current transformer. (*Courtesy of General Electric Company.*)

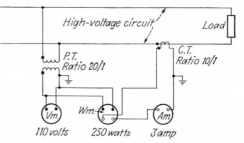

FIG. 11-9. Instrument-transformer connections.

with a device for short-circuiting the secondary winding when changes must be made in the secondary circuit. However, anyone working with a secondary circuit of a current transformer should always make certain that the short-circuiting device is closed before the secondary wiring is disturbed.

Figure 11-9 illustrates the method of connecting instrument transformers into a high-voltage circuit. Note that the secondary circuits are grounded.    This is a general safety practice when the transformers are connected in circuits that have a potential above ground of 300 volts or more.

**Example 4**  Find the current, voltage, and power supplied to the load by the high-voltage circuit of Fig. 11-9, as indicated by the instrument readings.

$$\text{Current} = 3 \times 10 = 30 \text{ amp}$$
$$\text{Voltage} = 110 \times 20 = 2{,}200 \text{ volts}$$
$$\text{Power} = 250 \times 10 \times 20 = 50 \text{ kw}$$

**11-11. Autotransformers**  A transformer in which the primary and secondary windings are connected *electrically* as well as *magnetically* is called an autotransformer.   Figure 11-10 shows a connection diagram of an autotransformer.   If this transformer is to be used as a

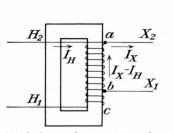

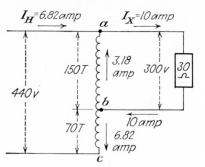

FIG. 11-10. A step-down autotransformer.    FIG. 11-11. A step-down autotransformer winding supplying load.

step-down transformer, the entire winding *ac* forms the primary winding and the section *ab* forms the secondary winding.   In other words, the section *ab* is common to both primary and secondary.   As in the standard two-winding transformer, the ratio of voltage transformation is equal to the ratio of primary to secondary turns if the losses and exciting currents are neglected and

$$\frac{E_H}{E_X} = \frac{T_H}{T_X} = \frac{I_X}{I_H}$$

Figure 11-11 represents an autotransformer winding with a total of 220 turns, with the sections *ab* and *bc* having 150 and 70 turns, respectively.   If a voltage of 440 volts is applied to the winding *ac*, the voltage across each turn will be 2 volts.   The voltage from *a* to *b* will then be 150 × 2, or 300, volts.

When a noninductive load of 30 ohms is connected to winding *ab*, a current, $I_X$, of 300/30 or 10 amp flows and the power output of the transformer is $300 \times 10$ or 3,000 watts.  Neglecting the transformer losses, the power input must be 3,000 watts and the primary current 3,000/440 or 6.82 amp.

An application of Kirchhoff's current law to point $a$ shows that when $I_X$ is 10 amp and $I_H$ is 6.82 amp then the current from $b$ to $a$ must be 3.18 amp.  Similarly, the current from $b$ to $c$ must be 6.82 amp.

Thus the section of the winding that is common to both primary and secondary circuits carries only the difference of primary and secondary currents.  For this reason, an autotransformer requires less copper and is more efficient than a two-winding transformer of a similar rating.

For some applications that require a multivoltage supply, an autotransformer in which the winding is tapped at several points is used.  The connections from the various taps are brought out of the tank to terminals or to a suitable switching device so that any one of several voltages may be selected.

Autotransformers are used when voltage transformations of near unity are required.  Such an application of an autotransformer is in "boosting" a distribution voltage by a small percentage to compensate for line drop.  Another common application is in the starting of a-c motors, in which case the voltage applied to the motor is reduced during the starting period.

Autotransformers are not safe, however, for supplying a low voltage from a high-voltage source; for, if the winding that is common to both primary and secondary should accidentally become open, the full primary voltage will appear across the secondary terminals.

**11-12. Polarity**  It sometimes becomes necessary to operate two transformers in parallel.  In order to connect two transformers for successful parallel operation, the instantaneous polarities of the transformers must be known.  Two transformers with their primaries connected to the same supply are shown in Fig. 11-12.  As viewed from the top, both primary windings are wound in a counterclockwise direction around the core.  The secondary winding of transformer No. 1 is wound counterclockwise, while that of No. 2 is wound clockwise.  At an instant when line $A$ is positive, the direction of current flow will be from line $A$ to line $B$ through both primary windings.  When a primary current flows, emfs are induced in the secondary windings which are opposite to the applied primary voltages.  Since the secondaries are wound in opposite directions, the upper terminal of No. 1 is negative while the upper terminal of No. 2 is positive at the instant being considered.  If the secondary windings are to be connected in parallel, both positive terminals must be connected to one line, such as $C$, and both negative terminals connected to the other line, such as $D$.   The instantaneous emfs induced in the two secondary windings will then be in phase.   *If terminals of unlike polarity should be connected to the same line, the two secondary windings would be short-circuited on each other with a resulting excessive current flow.*

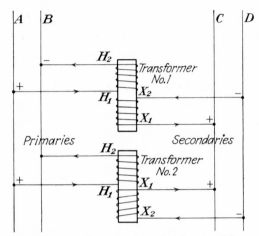

FIG. 11-12. Two transformers connected for parallel operation.

Standard polarity markings have been adopted so that by referring to them transformers may be correctly connected in parallel.   The transformers in Fig. 11-13 are so marked that if the $H_1$'s are connected to one primary line and the $H_2$'s to the other primary line then the $X_1$'s should be connected to the same secondary line and the $X_2$'s to

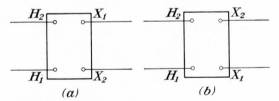

(a)                (b)

FIG. 11-13. Standard polarity markings of transformers: (*a*) additive polarity, (*b*) subtractive polarity.

the remaining secondary line. If the transformer terminals are arranged as shown in Fig. 11-13*a*, the transformer is said to have *additive polarity*, and if arranged as shown in Fig. 11-13*b*, the transformer is said to have *subtractive polarity*.   Note that for either polarity the $H_1$ terminal is on the right-hand side when the transformer is viewed from the high-voltage side of the tank.

If the polarity of a transformer is not known, it may be determined by the test connections shown in Fig. 11-14. If the terminals are not marked, the right-hand and left-hand high-voltage terminals, as viewed from the high-voltage side of the transformer, may be marked $H_1$ and $H_2$, respectively. For

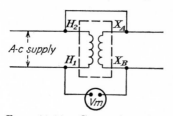

convenience, the low-voltage terminals may be marked $X_A$ and $X_B$ temporarily as shown. Adjacent terminals such as $H_2$ and $X_A$ are then connected, and a voltmeter is connected across the other two terminals $H_1$ and $X_B$. Any convenient alternating voltage is then applied to the high-voltage winding of the trans-

FIG. 11-14. Connection for checking the polarity of a transformer.

former. If the voltmeter reads less than the value of the applied voltage, the polarity is subtractive and the terminals $X_A$ and $X_B$ may be marked as the $X_2$ and $X_1$ terminals, respectively. If the voltmeter reads more than the applied voltage, the polarity is additive and the terminals $X_A$ and $X_B$ are marked $X_1$ and $X_2$, respectively.

## 11-13. No-load Tap Changing

For small adjustments of transformer ratio, to compensate for line drop, high-voltage windings of transformers are often equipped with tap-changing devices. The winding is tapped at several points, and connections from these points are made either to a tap-changing switch or to a terminal block inside

FIG. 11-15. Self-cooled oil-immersed distribution transformer with tank cover removed to show tap-changing switch. (*Courtesy of General Electric Company.*)

the transformer tank.  A distribution transformer equipped with a
tap-changing switch inside the tank is shown in Fig. 11-15.  By
operating the switch or by changing the connections on the terminal
block, changes are made in the number of active turns in the high-
voltage winding.  These changes must be made with the transformer
deenergized except in certain types of transformers in which special
provision is made for tap changing under load.

### 11-14. Single-phase Connections

Distribution transformers are usu-
ally made with the secondary or low-voltage winding in two sections
as shown in Fig. 11-16.  The two sections may be connected in series
as in Fig. 11-16a to supply either a two-wire 240-volt load or a three-
wire 120/240-volt load.  Or the two sections may be connected in
parallel as is shown in Fig. 11-16b to supply a two-wire 120-volt load.

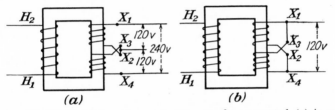

FIG. 11-16. The divided low-voltage winding may be connected (a) in series to
supply a three-wire 120/240-volt system or (b) in parallel to supply a two-wire
120-volt system.

Earlier transformers were made with four insulated secondary leads
brought out of the transformer tank, the series or parallel connection
being made outside the tank.  In modern transformers, the connections are made inside the tank, with only three secondary terminals
being brought out of the transformer.  The three secondary terminals
of the distribution transformer shown in Fig. 11-15 may be seen in the
foreground.

### 11-15. Three-phase Connections

Single-phase transformers can be
connected to form three-phase transformer banks for raising or lowering the voltages of three-phase systems.  Four common methods of
connecting three transformers for three-phase transformations are
the delta-delta, wye-wye, wye-delta, and delta-wye connections.
The first three of these are shown in Fig. 11-17; the delta-wye is not
shown since it is simply the reverse of the wye-delta connection.
     The delta-delta connection shown in Fig. 11-17a is often used for
moderate voltages.  An advantage of this connection is that if one
transformer becomes damaged or is removed from service the remain-

ing two can be operated in what is known as the open-delta or V connection. By being operated in this way, the bank still delivers three-phase currents and voltages in their correct phase relationships, but the capacity of the bank is reduced to 57.7 per cent of what it was with all three transformers in service.

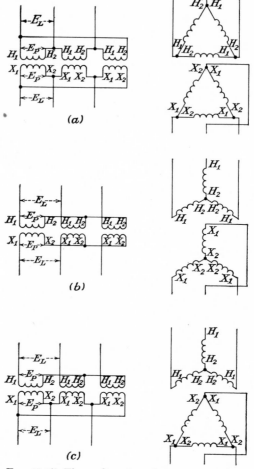

FIG. 11-17. Three-phase transformer connections.

In the wye-wye connection shown in Fig. 11-17b, only 57.7 per cent (or 1/1.73) of the line voltage is impressed upon each winding, but full line current flows in each transformer winding. Power circuits supplied from a wye-wye bank often create serious disturbances in communication circuits in their immediate vicinity. Because of this and other disadvantages, the wye-wye connection is seldom used.

The delta-wye connection is well adapted for stepping up voltages since the voltage is increased by the transformer ratio multiplied by the factor 1.73. Likewise the wye-delta connection (Fig. 11-17c) is used for stepping down voltages. The high-voltage windings of most transformers operating at above 100,000 volts are wye-connected.

It will be noticed that in order to match transformer polarities correctly, the terminals should be connected symmetrically. If in a wye connection an $H_1$ or $X_1$ terminal is connected to the neutral, then all the $H_1$ or $X_1$ terminals should be connected to the neutral, and the remaining $H_2$ or $X_2$ terminals brought out as the line connections.

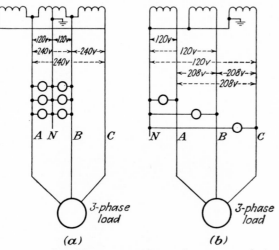

FIG. 11-18. (a) Four-wire delta-connected transformer secondaries. (b) Four-wire wye-connected transformer secondaries.

In a delta connection, $H_1$ should always be connected to $H_2$ and $X_1$ to $X_2$ and the line connections made at these junctions.

Power circuits for the operation of three-phase motors or other three-phase devices are often supplied from 240-volt delta-connected transformer secondaries. To provide 120 volts for lighting circuits, the mid-point of one of the transformers is brought out to form what is called a *four-wire delta system*. This connection is shown in Fig. 11-18a, a three-wire single-phase lighting circuit being formed by lines $A$, $N$, and $B$, and a three-wire three-phase power circuit being formed by lines $A$, $B$, and $C$. The center-tapped transformer should have a larger kilovolt-ampere rating than the other two transformers.

When a large number of single-phase loads are to be served from a three-phase transformer bank, the wye-connected low-voltage winding is desirable, since the single-phase loads can be balanced evenly on all three phases.   Figure 11-18*b* shows the method of connecting both three-phase and single-phase loads to four-wire wye-connected secondaries.   The single-phase loads are connected from the three line wires *A*, *B*, and *C* to the neutral or grounded wire, while the three-phase loads are connected to lines *A*, *B*, and *C*.   This connection, with phase and line voltages of 120 and 208 volts, is used in underground networks in metropolitan areas to supply both single- and three-phase loads.

**11-16. Three-phase Transformers**   Three-phase voltages may be transformed by means of three-phase transformers.   The core of a three-phase transformer is made with three legs, a primary and secondary winding of one phase being placed on each leg.   It is

Fig. 11-19. Three-phase distribution transformer core and coil assembly.   (*Courtesy of General Electric Company.*)

possible to build the core with only three legs since the fluxes established by the three windings are 120° apart in time phase.   Two core legs act as the return for the flux in the third leg.   For example, if flux is at a maximum value in one leg at some instant, the flux is half that value and in the opposite direction through the other two legs at the same instant.   A core and coil assembly of a three-phase transformer rated 37.5 kva, 2,400/4,160Y to 240/416Y volts, 60 cycles is shown in Fig. 11-19.

Because the three windings can be placed compactly on one core, the three-phase transformer occupies less space than do three single-phase transformers with the same total kilovolt-ampere rating. The three-phase transformer is slightly more efficient than the single-phase transformer and in the larger ratings has a lower first cost. A disadvantage of the three-phase transformer lies in the fact that when one phase becomes defective the entire three-phase unit must be removed from service. When one transformer in a bank of three single-phase transformers becomes defective, it may be removed from service and the other two transformers may often be reconnected to supply service on an emergency basis until repairs can be made.

Three-phase transformers may also be connected according to the four combinations mentioned for three single-phase transformers. These connections are made inside the tank, and for delta-delta connections only three high-voltage and three low-voltage leads need to be brought outside the tank. Four connections are brought out from wye-connected windings.

## FEEDER-VOLTAGE REGULATORS

Much of the load on an electrical system is at some distance from the generating station. Because of this distance, there is a drop in voltage between the generating station and the point of utilization. Furthermore, this voltage drop is not constant but is proportional to the amount of load on the circuit at any one time. As the load varies, the voltage drop varies also.

Many appliances and electrical equipments are designed to operate at a given voltage, and the efficiency of operation of this equipment is affected appreciably if the applied voltage deviates from the rated value. This is especially true with domestic loads such as incandescent lighting, electric ranges, and electric heaters. With 90 per cent of rated voltage applied to an incandescent lamp, for example, the illumination output is only about 70 per cent of rated value. Heating time of electric heaters and ranges is about 120 per cent of normal when 90 per cent of rated voltage is applied. While induction-motor operation is not affected as greatly by voltage variation as lamps and heaters, there are changes in efficiency, heating, and speed occasioned by variations in voltage.

Feeder-voltage regulators are used extensively as an aid to maintaining a reasonably constant voltage at the point of use on an electrical system. There are two major types of feeder-voltage regulators: the *induction type* and the *step type*. Both are in effect autotransformers with variable ratios.

**11-17. Voltage-regulator Principle**  The basic principle of the voltage regulator may be illustrated by the diagram shown in Fig. 11-20. The transformer shown has a voltage ratio of 2,400 to 240.  By means of the reversing switch, the transformer may be connected as an autotransformer, and, depending upon the switch position, the voltage induced in the low-voltage winding may be added to or subtracted from the voltage applied to the high-voltage winding.  Thus, when the generator voltage is 2,400 volts, as shown in Fig. 11-20, the output voltage of the transformer is either 2,640 or 2,160 volts.  When the generator voltage is 10 per cent low, the transformer may be used to raise the voltage 10 per cent.  When the generator voltage is 10 per cent high, the transformer may be used to lower the voltage by 10 per cent.

Feeder-voltage regulators are constructed with the two separate windings as shown in Fig. 11-20 and are provided with means for varying the amount of voltage induced in the low-voltage or series

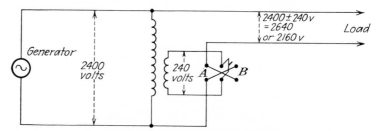

Fig. 11-20. Circuit for illustrating the principle of the feeder-voltage regulator.

winding in small increments.  These small increments of voltage may be added to or subtracted from the regulator input voltage, so that it is possible to maintain a nearly constant output voltage from the regulator.

As may be seen from Fig. 11-20, the autotransformer used as a voltage regulator actually transforms only 10 per cent of the circuit kilovolt-amperes, so the kilovolt-ampere rating of the regulator need be only 10 per cent of the circuit kilovolt-amperes.  If, for example, the circuit full-load current in Fig. 11-20 were 100 amp, the regulator kilovolt-ampere rating would be 240 × 100 or 24,000 va (24 kva), while the circuit rating would be 240 kva.  In general, the kilovolt-ampere rating of a single-phase regulator is the product of the rated load amperes and the per cent regulation expressed in kilovolts.  For a three-phase regulator this product is multiplied by 1.73.

**11-18. Induction Voltage Regulators**  The single-phase induction voltage regulator has two separate and distinct windings: primary

and secondary.   The primary winding is connected across the circuit
which is being regulated; the secondary is connected in series with the
circuit.

The basic principle of the single-phase induction regulator is illustrated in Fig. 11-21.   The primary coils are assembled on a rotor, or
movable core.   The secondary coils, as shown, are assembled on the
stator, or stationary core.   In the position shown, all the flux produced by the primary, or shunt, coils passes through the secondary,
or series, coils and the voltage induced in the secondary winding is
proportional to the turn ratio, as in a conventional transformer.   If
the turn ratio is 10 to 1, as is usually the case in induction regulators,

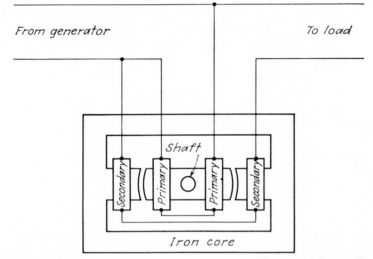

FIG. 11-21. Elementary induction voltage regulator.   (*Courtesy of General Electric
Company.*)

an emf equal to 10 per cent of the primary voltage is induced in the
secondary winding.   Depending on the relative polarities of the coils
shown, this voltage is then either added to or subtracted from the
primary voltage.

As the movable core and the primary coils are rotated from the
position shown in Fig. 11-21, not all the flux produced by the primary
coils passes through the secondary coils, and the emf induced in the
secondary coils is decreased.   When the rotor is moved to a position
at right angles to that shown in Fig. 11-21, no primary flux passes
through the secondary coils, and the induced voltage in these coils
is zero.   When the core is rotated still further, the amount of flux
linking the secondary winding is increased, and increasing amounts

Fig. 11-22. Assembled rotor of a single-phase induction voltage regulator.   (*Courtesy of General Electric Company.*)

of voltage are induced in the secondary winding.  However, the flux is in the opposite direction, and the voltage is reversed.  When the rotor has been turned 180° from the position shown in Fig. 11-21, full voltage is again induced in the secondary winding, but in the opposite direction.  Means are provided in the induction regulator, then, for raising or lowering circuit voltage throughout the range of the regulator in an infinite number of steps.

The actual design of the induction regulator is a modification of the simplified arrangement shown in Fig. 11-21.  Both the stationary and movable cores are circular, and the coils are placed in recessed slots similar to those of an induction motor.  In addition to the shunt and series windings mentioned, a short-circuited winding is placed on the rotor at right angles to the primary, or shunt, winding. The short-circuited winding equalizes the losses and reactance of the regulator in its various rotor positions.  An assembled rotor for a single-phase regulator is illustrated in Fig. 11-22, and the external appearance of a complete regulator is shown in Fig. 11-23.

Fig. 11-23. Completely assembled induction voltage regulator. (*Courtesy of General Electric Company.*)

The discussion so far has been concerned with single-phase induction regulators. Polyphase induction regulators are somewhat similar to single-phase regulators in constructional features, there being one series and one shunt winding for each phase placed on circular cores as in the single-phase regulator. However, the change in voltage in a polyphase regulator is produced by a phase displacement of the induced voltage and not by a change in voltage magnitude as in the single-phase regulator.

Induction regulators of the station type are available in several voltage ratings, the more common ratings being 2,500, 5,000, and 7,620 volts. For each voltage rating several kilovolt-ampere and current ratings are available. For example, the 2,500-volt single-phase induction regulator is available in ratings of 12.5 kva and 50 amp through 125 kva and 500 amp in steps of about 25 kva.

Induction regulators, like transformers, are available in air-cooled or noninflammable-liquid-cooled designs for indoor use. Oil-cooled regulators are ordinarily used outdoors.

**11-19. Step Voltage Regulators** Step-type voltage regulators are tapped autotransformers with a tap-changing-under-load switching mechanism to change tap settings and thereby change the ratio between the primary and secondary windings. Step regulators consist of three major parts: the transformer, the tap-changing mechanism, and the control mechanism. A typical three-phase station-type 32-step regulator is shown in Fig. 11-24.

The transformer section of a regulator is a conventional transformer with the primary (shunt) and secondary (series) windings wound on an iron core. The series winding is tapped at regular intervals, the number of taps depending upon the type of regulator. Pole-mounted regulators for regulating small loads may have taps arranged for 16 or 32 steps with a total range of regulation of 10 or 20 per cent. Station-type regulators used for regulating entire feeders or substations usually have 32 steps with a 20 per cent range in regulation. Voltage is adjusted in steps of $\frac{5}{8}$ of 1 per cent in these regulators.

A schematic diagram of connections of a single-phase 32-step regulator is shown in Fig. 11-25. The taps of the series winding are connected to wide stationary contacts arranged physically in a circle on an insulating panel in the tap-changing mechanism. Two contacts mounted a fixed distance apart on the movable arm are used to make contact with the stationary contacts. The two moving contacts are so spaced that for each operating position they are either both on the same stationary contact, or one of them is on each of two adjacent stationary contacts.

The operation of the tap-changing mechanism of a 32-step 20 per cent regulator may be explained by referring to Fig. 11-25. The two movable contacts $A$ and $B$ as shown in the diagram are in contact with stationary contact number 1, the maximum LOWER position. The load current divides equally through the two halves of the reactor, which is connected to the two movable contacts. The movable arm of the switch assembly is operated by a motor that drives a spring-loaded quick-operating mechanism for changing taps. The switch

FIG. 11-24. A three-phase 32-step voltage regulator. *(Courtesy of General Electric Company.)*

arm and movable contacts are latched in place until the driving springs are fully loaded, at which time the latch releases and the switch arm moves with a quick snap to the next position where it is latched in place again.

A change of the switch arm from tap 1 to tap 2 to raise voltage is made in two operations. First, the movable contact arm snaps to a point where contact $B$ is on contact 2 but $A$ is still on contact 1. In this position, the reactor acts as an autotransformer, and the resulting voltage is halfway between the voltages of taps 1 and 2. It should be noted that the load current is not interrupted during the changing of the switch position, since the movable contact $A$ is in contact with stationary contact 1 during the instant that the movable contact $B$ is moving from 1 to 2. During this instant, all the load current is carried by one-half of the reactor. The next movement of the tap changer moves both $A$ and $B$ to contact 2, and the resulting voltage

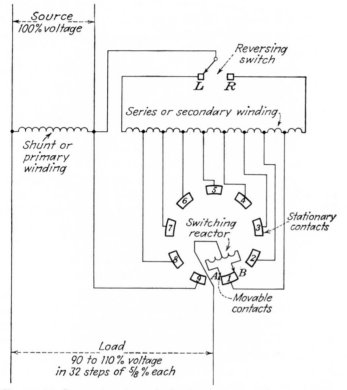

FIG. 11-25. Connections for a single-phase 32-step voltage regulator.

is that of tap 2. As the tap-changing switch arm is moved on around toward contact 9, the voltage is raised in ⅝ per cent steps until the number 9 contact is reached. When the two movable contacts are on stationary contact 9, the regulator is in the NEUTRAL position, and the series winding is completely out of the circuit, so that voltage is neither raised nor lowered by the regulator. As the mechanism is moved through the neutral position to the RAISE positions, the reversing switch is operated automatically, reversing the polarity of the series winding. Thus the first RAISE position is contact 1, and the voltage is raised in ⅝ per cent steps as the contact arm moves around to contact 8, which is the maximum RAISE position. Thus the full range of plus and minus 10 per cent voltage regulation in thirty-two ⅝ per cent steps with one neutral position is obtained with only eight taps in the series winding.

Step regulators are manufactured in both single- and three-phase units. The transformer section of the three-phase unit is assembled on a three-phase core, and the tap-changer switch is of a three-pole design, so that taps on all three phases are changed simultaneously. Step regulators are available in much higher voltage ratings than are induction regulators, with 34,500- and 69,000-volt ratings being quite commonly used. Kilovolt-ampere ratings range from approximately 100 to 750 kva, depending upon the voltage classification.

### 11-20. Voltage-regulator Control and Accessory Equipment

Voltage regulators ordinarily are equipped with controls and accessories that operate the regulator automatically to maintain a predetermined output voltage. Regulators are operated by electric motors which, in the induction regulator, position the rotor and, in the step-type regulator, operate the tap changer. Modern regulators have self-contained auxiliary transformers that supply the necessary potential and current indication for the control system and the necessary power for the operating motors.

The device that initiates any change in regulator position is the *voltage-control relay* or contact-making voltmeter. This relay is arranged so that its moving member is held in a balanced position at a predetermined value of voltage. The operating coil of this relay is connected to the auxiliary transformer of the regulator. If the voltage of the circuit being regulated drops below the balance voltage of the relay, a contact of the relay closes the operating-motor circuit, causing the regulator to raise the voltage until the relay is again balanced. In a similar manner the relay causes the regulator to decrease voltage if the line voltage rises above normal.

So that the regulator does not operate excessively to attempt to correct minor momentary voltage disturbances on the system, some type of time-delay or holding action is usually used with the regulator control equipment. Such a device is the so-called *voltage integrator* used on one type of step voltage regulator. This device integrates the system voltage variation by summing the lengths of time that the voltage is abnormal, and if the voltage is either high or low for a predetermined length of time, the integrator causes the regulator to operate. This results in the maintenance of correct average voltage even with widely fluctuating voltages. The amount of time delay introduced by the integrator is adjustable between the approximate limits of 5 and 45 seconds.

Regulators of the station type are equipped with *line-drop compensators*. The compensator consists of an adjustable resistance and a reactance inserted in series with the voltage-control relay. Current is supplied to the line-drop compensator from a current transformer in the load circuit of the regulator. This current produces a voltage drop in the control circuit that is proportional to the load current (and therefore proportional to the line-impedance drop). In this way the voltage regulator automatically increases the voltage as the load increases to compensate for the increasing drop in the line. Regulators equipped with line-drop compensators may be adjusted to maintain a constant voltage at a remote point on a feeder rather than at the point at which the regulator is installed.

Other control equipment and accessories used with voltage regulators include bypass lightning arresters for the series winding, a control switch to change the regulator from manual to automatic operation, a manual raise-and-lower switch, a voltmeter or test terminals for connecting a portable voltmeter, an auxiliary relay for the operating motor, limit switches to prevent overtravel of the regulator, a position indicator, and protective and switching equipment for the auxiliary operating power.

**11-21. Tap-changing-under-load Transformers** Tap-changing-under-load transformers, or *load-ratio-control transformers*, as they are sometimes called, are essentially combined transformers and voltage regulators. One winding of the transformer is tapped at various points, and these taps are connected to a tap-changing switch as in the step-type voltage regulator. These transformers are nearly always constructed as three-phase units.

One application of the tap-changing-under-load transformer is in a step-down station used to supply a load from a transmission line. In this application a constant voltage may be maintained for the load even though the transmission-line voltage varies considerably. One other common application of this transformer is in tie lines between two generating stations. A tap-changing-under-load transformer in such a tie line permits each station to maintain correct voltage at its own bus for supplying local loads, yet maintains the tie-line voltage at the correct value for interchange of power between the two stations. On many such interconnections it has been found that there has been a heavy interchange of reactive or wattless current over the tie line when the tie line is operated without tap-changing-under-load equipment.   In effect, the variable-ratio transformer provides these interconnections with reactive volt-ampere control.

## REVIEW QUESTIONS

**1.** What is the function of a transformer?

**2.** How does the efficiency of a transformer compare with rotating electric machinery studied thus far?

**3.** What is meant by (a) a primary winding; (b) a secondary winding?

**4.** How are transformer terminals marked?

**5.** What relationship exists between the voltages and the number of turns on the two windings of a transformer?

**6.** What relationship exists between the ratio of the voltages and the ratio of the currents in the high- and low-voltage windings?

**7.** Explain how a transformer regulates the amount of primary current required to supply a given secondary current.

**8.** What information is commonly found on a transformer nameplate?

**9.** What are two types of core construction used in transformers?

**10.** What is meant by leakage flux?   How is it kept to a minimum?

**11.** What transformer losses vary with the amount of load on the transformer? Which losses are practically constant?

**12.** Why is oil placed in transformers?

**13.** Why are air-cooled transformers desirable in some locations?

**14.** Instrument transformers perform what two functions?

**15.** Are potential transformers connected in parallel or series with the load? How are current transformers connected?

**16.** What precaution must be observed when working with current transformers?

**17.** What is an autotransformer?   What are some of the advantages and disadvantages of the autotransformer?

**18.** Why must the transformer polarities be known when transformers are being connected for parallel operation?

**19.** What is meant by (a) additive polarity; (b) subtractive polarity?

**20.** What is a tap-changing switch?   When might a transformer equipped with taps be desirable?

**21.** Why are single-phase distribution transformers made with the low-voltage winding in two sections?

**22.** What are four types of three-phase transformer connections?

**23.** What voltages are commonly provided by four-wire delta secondaries for light and power loads? by four-wire wye secondaries?

**24.** What are some advantages of using three-phase transformers in place of three single-phase transformers?   What are some disadvantages?

**25.** Why is it necessary to maintain substantially constant voltage on an electrical system?

**26.** Describe how a transformer may be used to raise or lower voltage in a circuit.

**27.** How is the kilovolt-ampere rating determined for (a) a single-phase voltage regulator; (b) a three-phase voltage regulator?

**28.** Explain how a variable voltage is induced in the secondary winding of an induction voltage regulator.

**29.** What are some common voltage ratings of induction feeder-voltage regulators?

**30.** Describe briefly the basic principle of operation of the step voltage regulator.

**31.** What is the purpose of the switching reactor in a step voltage regulator?

**32.** Describe briefly the operation of the voltage-control relay used with a voltage regulator.

**33.** What are some of the usual voltage-regulator accessories?

## PROBLEMS

**1.** The high-voltage winding of a transformer has a voltage rating of 480 volts and has 400 turns. How many turns are there on the low-voltage winding if its voltage rating is 120 volts?

**2.** A 1,000-kva 24,000/2,400-volt transformer operates at 40 volts per turn. Find the number of turns on each winding and the current rating of each winding.

**3.** A 5-ohm resistance is connected across the 120-volt secondary winding of a step-down transformer. If the primary current is 6 amp, what is the primary voltage?

**4.** The low-voltage winding of a step-down welding transformer has one turn and the high-voltage winding 600 turns. When the transformer delivers 100 amp what is the current in the high-voltage winding?

**5.** Find the current ratings of each winding of a 100-kva 2,400/120-volt 60-cycle transformer.

**6.** A transformer is rated at 500 kva, 60 cycles, and 2,400/480 volts. There are 200 turns on the 2,400-volt winding. When the transformer supplies rated load, find (a) the ampere turns of each winding and (b) the current in each winding.

**7.** Find the size of wire in circular mils needed in each winding of a 10-kva 2,400/240-volt 60-cycle transformer if the number of circular mils per ampere to be used in each winding is 1,000. What is the closest AWG size in each case?

**8.** Following are data from a test of a 3-kva 240/120-volt 60-cycle transformer:

> Resistance of 115-volt winding.......... 0.055 ohm
> Resistance of 230-volt winding.......... 0.184 ohm
> Core loss............................ 28 watts

Find the efficiency of the transformer when it delivers rated kilovolt-amperes at unity power factor.

**9.** A voltmeter, ammeter, and wattmeter are connected with suitable instrument transformers into a single-phase circuit and the following data taken:

> Current transformer ratio.......... 5 to 1
> Potential transformer ratio......... 20 to 1
> Voltmeter reading................ 110 volts
> Ammeter reading................ 4 amp
> Wattmeter reading............... 360 watts

Find the voltage, current, volt-amperes, power factor, and power of the primary circuit.

**10.** A step-down 600/480-volt autotransformer supplies a 10-kva load. Find the primary and secondary line currents and the current in the winding common to both primary and secondary circuits.

**11.** An autotransformer starter used to start an induction motor on a 440-volt line applies 65 per cent of line voltage to the motor during the starting period.   If the motor current is 140 amp at starting, what is the current drawn from the line?

**12.** A 5-kva 480/120-volt transformer is equipped with high-voltage taps so that it may be operated at 480, 456, or 432 volts depending on the tap setting. Find the current in the high-voltage winding for each tap setting, the transformer supplying rated kilovolt-ampere load at 120 volts in each case.

**13.** A distribution transformer has two 120-volt secondary windings that may be connected either in series or in parallel.   The current rating of each winding is 41.7 amp.   What is the kilovolt-ampere rating of the transformer with the coils connected (*a*) in series and (*b*) in parallel?

**14.** Three single-phase transformers having a 20-to-1 ratio are delta-connected to a 2,400-volt three-phase line as step-down transformers.   Find the voltage between the secondary terminals of each transformer.   Find the secondary voltage of each transformer if the transformers are wye-connected to the same line.

**15.** The secondaries of a three-phase transformer bank supplying a three-phase 240-volt motor are delta-connected.   When the motor current is 10 amp per terminal, find the current in each transformer winding.

**16.** A three-phase motor requires 80 kw at 80 per cent power factor when operated at 240 volts.   If the motor is supplied from a 4,160/240-volt wye-delta step-down transformer bank, find the line currents on both the high- and low-voltage sides of the transformers.

**17.** The primary windings of three single-phase transformers are wye-connected, and the secondary windings are delta-connected.   The voltage applied to each primary winding is 2,300 volts, and the secondary line voltage is 230 volts. Find the secondary line current when the primary line current is 20 amp.

**18.** What is the kilovolt-ampere rating of a single-phase voltage regulator that has a rated voltage of 2,400 volts, a current rating of 200 amp, and a total regulation range of 20 per cent (10 per cent raise and 10 per cent lower)?

**19.** A 12,000-volt three-phase step regulator has a rating of 208 kva and has a range of regulation of 10 per cent raise and 10 per cent lower.   What is the full-load current rating of this regulator?   How much kilovolt-ampere load can be carried by a circuit in which this regulator is installed without overloading the regulator?

# CHAPTER 12

# ALTERNATING-CURRENT GENERATORS

The terms *alternating-current generator, synchronous generator, synchronous alternator,* and *alternator* are commonly used interchangeably in engineering literature and will be so used in this chapter.   The term alternating-current generator is not strictly correct if it is being applied only to synchronous generators since induction generators are also alternating-current generators.   Because synchronous generators are so much more commonly used than induction generators, the term alternating-current generator as often used and as used here applies only to synchronous generators.

**12-1. Construction**   In d-c generators the armature windings are placed on the rotating part of the machine in order to provide a way of converting the alternating voltage generated in the windings to a direct voltage at the terminals through the use of a rotating commutator. The field poles are placed on the stationary part of the machine.   In all but small, low-voltage alternating-current generators, the field is placed on the rotating part, or *rotor*, and the armature winding on the stationary part, or *stator*, of the machine.

The revolving-field and stationary-armature construction simplifies the problems of insulation of an a-c generator.   Since voltages as high as 33,000 volts are sometimes generated, this high voltage need not be brought out through slip rings and sliding contacts but can be brought directly to the switchgear through insulated leads from the stationary armature.   This construction also has mechanical advantages in that armature windings are subjected to less vibration and centrifugal forces and can be braced better mechanically.   The rotating field is supplied with direct current, usually at 125 or 250 volts, through slip rings and brushes.

The armature or stator winding may be any one of many types, a widely used type being an open-circuited winding formed from separately insulated form-wound coils similar to the lap winding of the d-c generator. Such a winding partially assembled is shown in Fig. 12-1. Actually, such a winding is composed of three separate windings (on a three-phase generator), each displaced from the other two by 120 electrical degrees. The three windings may be either wye- or delta-connected. The wye connection is the more common since it lends itself well to the generation of high voltages directly, and a neutral

FIG. 12-1. A partly wound a-c generator stator showing how the insulated coils are placed in the core slots. (*Courtesy of Westinghouse Electric Corporation.*)

wire can be brought out with the three lines to form a three-phase four-wire system as was shown in Chap. 10.

A developed view of a simple three-phase winding is shown in Fig. 12-2. The winding shown in Fig. 12-2a is wye-connected; the method of connecting the terminals for a delta connection is shown in Fig. 12-2b. The winding pictured is called a *concentrated winding* since all the conductors of each phase are included in one slot under each pole. Commercial windings such as that shown in Fig. 12-1 are distributed windings, with the conductors of each phase group occupying

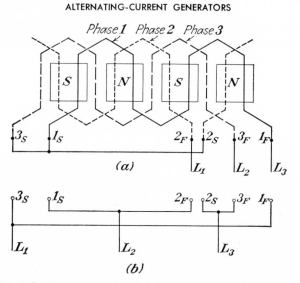

FIG. 12-2. (a) A developed view of a simple three-phase stator winding, wye-connected. (b) Method of reconnecting the terminals for a delta connection.

FIG. 12-3. Salient-pole rotor for a slow-speed a-c generator. (*Courtesy of Westinghouse Electric Corporation.*)

two or more slots under each pole.   The distributed winding provides a more uniform heat distribution and results in the generation of a better emf wave.

There are two distinct types of synchronous-generator field structures: the *salient-pole type* and the *cylindrical type*.

Slow-speed generators such as those driven by diesel engines or water turbines have rotors with projecting or salient field poles like

Fig. 12-4. A salient-pole a-c generator designed for diesel-engine drive.   (*Courtesy of Westinghouse Electric Corporation.*)

the rotor shown in Fig. 12-3.   The laminated pole pieces with their field coils are mounted on the rim of the steel spider, which is in turn keyed to the shaft.   A completed a-c generator designed for diesel-engine drive at a speed of 200 rpm is shown in Fig. 12-4.

High-speed or turbo-type generators have cylindrical rotors such as that shown in Fig. 12-5.   The rotor shown is wound for two poles and is designed to operate at 3,600 rpm.   The cylindrical construction is essential in high-speed machines because the salient-pole type is

FIG. 12-5. Rotor for 3,600-rpm a-c generator. (*Courtesy of General Electric Company.*)

FIG. 12-6. Modern turbogenerator installation showing turbine, a-c generator, and direct-connected exciter. The generator is rated at 15,625 kva and 13,800 volts. (*Courtesy of Stanley Engineering Company.*)

difficult to build to withstand the stresses at high speeds. Furthermore, salient-pole rotors have high windage losses at high speeds. Alternating-current generators with the cylindrical-rotor construction are driven by steam turbines. A turbine-driven generator with its direct-connected exciter is shown in Fig. 12-6.

Direct-current field excitation is supplied to both types of generators through two slip rings and brushes. A small d-c generator called an *exciter*, which is either direct-connected or belt-driven from the prime mover, supplies the d-c excitation. Separate motor-driven and electronic exciters are also used in some cases.

**12-2. Voltage Generation**   After an a-c generator is brought up to its proper speed by its prime mover, its field is excited from a d-c supply. As the poles move under the armature conductors on the stator, the field flux cutting across the conductors induces an emf in them. This is an alternating emf, since poles of alternate polarity successively pass by a given stator conductor. Since no commutator is used, the alternating emf generated appears at the stator winding terminals.

The amount of any generated emf depends on the rate at which lines of force are cut; or in the case of the a-c generator, the amount of emf depends on the field strength and the speed of the rotor. Since most generators are operated at a constant speed, the amount of emf generated becomes dependent on the field excitation. This means that the amount of emf generated can be controlled by adjusting the amount of field excitation supplied to the generator. The field excitation may be readily controlled by varying the amount of excitation voltage applied to the generator field.

The power factor at which the generator operates is determined by the characteristics of the load being supplied (unless the generator is operating in parallel with other generators as explained in Art. 12-6).

The frequency of the generated emf depends on the number of field poles and on the speed at which the generator is operated. In a given coil, one complete cycle of emf is generated when a pair of rotor poles (a north and a south pole) is moved past the coil. Thus the number of cycles generated in one revolution of the rotor will be equal to the number of pairs of poles on the rotor or $p/2$, where $p$ is the total number of poles. If $n$ is the rotor speed in revolutions per minute, then $n/60$ is equal to the revolutions per second. The frequency in cycles per second is therefore

$$f = \frac{p}{2} \times \frac{n}{60} = \frac{pn}{120}$$

By far the most common power frequency used in the United States is 60 cycles per second, 50 and 25 cycles per second (cps) being used to a much lesser extent.

## 12-3. Generator Regulation

As load is added to an a-c generator operating at a constant speed and with a constant field excitation, the terminal voltage will change. The amount of change will depend on the machine design and on the power factor of the load. The effects of different load power factors on the change in the terminal voltage with changes of load on an a-c generator are shown in Fig. 12-7.

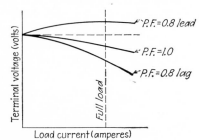
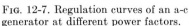

Fig. 12-7. Regulation curves of an a-c generator at different power factors.

Regulation of an a-c generator is defined as the percentage rise in terminal voltage as load is reduced from the rated full-load current to zero, the speed and excitation being constant, or

Per cent regulation (at a stated power factor)
$$= \frac{\text{no-load voltage} - \text{full-load voltage}}{\text{full-load voltage}} \times 100$$

Factors affecting generator regulation are as follows:
1. $IR$ drop in the armature winding
2. $IX_L$ drop in the armature winding
3. Armature reaction (magnetizing effect of the armature currents)

In a d-c generator, the generated emf $E_g$ is the sum of the terminal voltage $E_t$ and the $IR$ drop in the armature circuit. In an a-c generator, the voltage drop due to the inductive reactance of the winding must also be taken into account. Thus the generated emf of an a-c generator is equal to the terminal voltage plus both the $IR$ and $IX_L$ drops in the armature winding.

A simplified vector diagram of an a-c generator operating at unity power factor is shown in Fig. 12-8a. The generated emf $E_g$ is the vector sum of the terminal voltage $E_t$, the $IR$ drop which is in phase with the current $I$, and the $IX_L$ drop, which leads $I$ by 90°.

The vector diagram of Fig. 12-8b represents the generator with the same load current as in Fig. 12-8a but with the current lagging the terminal voltage by 36°50' (power factor = 0.8 lag). As before, the generated emf is the vector sum of $E_t$, the $IR$ drop, and the $IX_L$ drop in the armature winding. An inspection of Figs. 12-8a and 12-8b shows that for a given generated emf the terminal voltage is less in the case of the 0.8 lagging power factor. At lower lagging power factors, the $IR$ and $IX_L$ drops lower the terminal voltage still further.

Figure 12-8c represents a case in which a generator supplies a load with a leading power factor. When the $IR$ and $IX_L$ drops are added vectorially to the terminal voltage, it is found that the generated emf

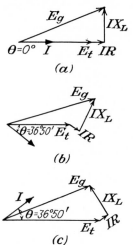

(a)

(b)

(c)

Fig. 12-8. Simplified vector diagrams of an a-c generator operating at (a) unity power factor, (b) 0.8 lagging power factor, and (c) 0.8 leading power factor.

is less than the terminal voltage. This is possible because of the phase relations of the $IR$ and $IX_L$ drops with respect to the terminal voltage.

The vector diagrams of Fig. 12-8a, b, and c show the effect of the $IR$ and $IX_L$ drops on the terminal voltage for a given $E_g$. However, $E_g$ is *not* constant in an a-c generator but varies with the amount of load and the power factor of the load due to the effect of armature reaction. At unity power factor, the effect of armature reaction is at a minimum, its effect being merely a distorting action on the main field flux. However, at lagging power factors, the magnetizing effect of the armature currents opposes the main field mmf, resulting in a weakened field flux and a lowered $E_g$. The lower the power factor in the lagging direction, the more the armature mmf demagnetizes the field.

At leading power factors, the armature mmf aids or strengthens the main field mmf, resulting in a higher generated emf with increases in load. This magnetizing effect increases as the power factor becomes more leading.

## 12-4. Voltage Regulators

Since the terminal voltage of an a-c generator varies considerably with changes in load, some means must be provided to maintain the constant voltage required for the operation of most electric equipment. A common way of doing this is to use an auxiliary device called a *voltage regulator* to control the amount of d-c field excitation supplied to the generator. When the generator terminal voltage drops because of changes in load, the voltage regulator automatically increases the field excitation, which restores normal rated voltage. Similarly, when the terminal voltage increases because of load changes, the regulator restores normal rated voltage by decreasing the field excitation.

Most voltage regulators control the field excitation of the generator indirectly by operating in the exciter field circuit. Much less current need be handled by the regulator in the exciter field circuit than in the generator field circuit.

One commonly used generator-voltage regulator, the direct-acting rheostatic type, is shown in elementary form in Fig. 12-9. Essentially the regulator consists of an automatically controlled variable resistance in the exciter field circuit.

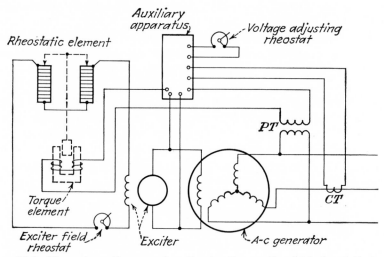

FIG. 12-9. Elementary diagram of a direct-acting exciter-field rheostatic-type generator-voltage regulator.

The rheostatic element, which is connected in series with the exciter field, consists of stacks of nonmetallic resistance blocks or wafers, stacked so that the resistance of the stack is varied as it is tilted forward or backward by the torque element. The resistance stack is constructed so that a total movement of only a small fraction of an inch is necessary to change the resistance from a maximum value to a minimum value.

As shown in the diagram, the torque element is connected to the potential transformer at the generator terminals through the auxiliary apparatus. When the a-c generator output voltage is constant, the torque element is stationary, holding the resistance elements stationary. However, should the output voltage of the generator drop, the amount of torque on the control element decreases, thereby causing the resistance elements to be tilted forward to decrease the resistance in the exciter field circuit. This allows the exciter field current and the exciter voltage to increase, which results in a higher generator field current.  As soon as the generator terminal voltage increases to its normal value, a balance is restored on the regulator resistance stack and the exciter field excitation is held constant at a new higher value.  The reverse procedure takes place when voltage rises at the generator terminals.

The auxiliary apparatus includes a rectifier to provide direct current for an unidirectional magnetic flux in the torque element and a stabilizer to damp out undue oscillations in the regulator and to prevent overshooting of the regulator on rapid changes in voltage.  The current transformer connections are made to a compensating rheostat in the auxiliary apparatus which is used in connection with a cross-current compensation scheme to regulate automatically the division of kilovar load between generators operating in parallel.

### 12-5. Paralleling Generators; Synchronizing

If the load on a single generator becomes so large that the rating of the generator is exceeded, it becomes necessary to add another generator in parallel to increase the power available from the generating station.

Before two synchronous generators may be paralleled, the following conditions must be fulfilled:

1. Their terminal voltages must be equal.
2. Their voltages must be in phase.
3. Their frequencies must be equal.

When two generators are operating so that these requirements are satisfied, they are said to be *in synchronism*.  The operation of getting the machines into synchronism is called *synchronizing*.

In the following discussion it will be assumed that one generator is in operation and that a second generator, called the *incoming generator*, is being synchronized with the running generator for the first time.

The incoming generator is brought up to speed and its voltage built up.  Voltmeter readings are taken on the bus and on the incoming generator to ensure equal terminal voltages.

In order to get the voltages in phase, the phase sequence of the two machines must be the same and their frequencies must be equal.  Three lamps provide a simple means of checking these relationships.

For the "lamps-dark" method of synchronizing, three lamps are connected across an open three-pole switch between the bus and the incoming machine, as shown in Fig. 12-10.  If the lamps increase and decrease in brilliance together, the phase sequences of the two machines are the same.  If the lamps rotate in brilliance, the phase sequences are not identical and any two of the three leads from the incoming machine may be interchanged to obtain the correct phase sequence.

The speed at which the lamps increase and decrease in brilliance indicates the *difference* in frequency between the two machines. A difference of 1 cps in their frequencies causes the lamps to come on and off once per second. With the lamps as an indication, the frequency of the incoming machine may next be adjusted to equal the

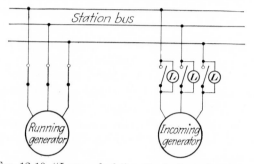

Fig. 12-10. "Lamps-dark" method of synchronizing.

bus frequency. When the lamps are dark, the voltages are in phase and the paralleling switch may be closed. Thus from the indications of the lamps and voltmeter, an operator is able to satisfy the three synchronizing requirements each time he parallels generators. The lamps indicate that the frequencies are equal and that the voltages are in phase; the voltmeter indicates that the voltages are equal.

After the phase sequences of two generators have once been determined and permanent connections have been made to the paralleling switch, it is not necessary to check phase sequence each time the generators are paralleled. If the phase sequence is known to be correct, synchronism may be indicated with a single-phase device. The *synchroscope* is such a single-phase device and is very commonly used since it provides a more accurate indication of synchronism than do lamps.

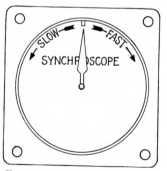

Fig. 12-11. Synchroscope dial.

The synchroscope is an instrument for indicating differences of phase and frequency between two voltages. It is essentially a split-phase motor in which torque is developed if the two voltages applied differ in frequency. Voltages from corresponding phases of the incoming and running generators are applied to the synchroscope. A pointer, which is attached to the rotor of the instrument, moves over the dial face in either a clockwise or counterclockwise direction, depending on whether the incoming generator is fast or slow. The dial markings of a synchroscope are shown in Fig. 12-11.

When the pointer stops, the frequencies of the two generators are equal. When the pointer stops in the vertical position, the frequencies are equal, the voltages are in phase, and the paralleling switch may be closed.

In practice it is sometimes difficult to adjust the speed of the incoming generator closely enough to stop the synchroscope pointer in the correct position. If this is the case, the speed of the incoming machine should be adjusted as closely as possible and the paralleling switch closed just before the pointer reaches the vertical position when traveling in the *fast direction*. This causes the incoming generator to take a small amount of load immediately after closure of the switch and results in stable operation.

**12-6. Parallel Operation**   After two synchronous generators have been paralleled, the load should be divided between them in proportion to their ratings. That is, the larger the machine, the larger the share of the load it should carry.

The proper division of load between generators is made by adjusting the governors of the prime movers on the generators. One prime-mover governor is opened while the other is closed slightly. In this way the system frequency is maintained at a constant value while the load is shifted from one machine to the other. Governor-control switches are mounted on the switchboard so that the operator is able to watch the switchboard instruments while making adjustments in load division.

The power factor of any a-c distribution system depends on the load. A generator operating singly, then, must operate at the power factor of the load it supplies. However, when two or more generators operate in parallel, the power factor at which each operates is determined by its field excitation.

In general, the proper amount of field excitation for generators operating in parallel is the amount of excitation each generator would require if it were carrying its load alone at the same voltage and frequency.

If the excitation of a generator operating in parallel with other generators is increased above this normal value of excitation, its power factor changes in the lagging direction and its current output increases with no appreciable change in kilowatt load. Likewise, if the generator is underexcited, its power factor becomes more leading and its current output increases with no change in kilowatt output. The increased current in either case is not supplied to the load but circulates between the generators connected to the system, thereby increasing their losses and decreasing their useful capacity. It is desirable in most cases, therefore, to operate each generator at the same power factor, keeping the circulating current to a minimum.

Thus a change in field excitation causes a change in *ampere* load but not in *kilowatt* load. *Kilowatt-load division between synchronous generators must be made by adjusting the governor controls.*

The voltage of the system with which several generators are paralleled may be raised or lowered by increasing or decreasing, simultaneously, the field excitation of all generators. Likewise, system frequency can be raised or lowered by increasing or decreasing the speed of the several prime movers.

**12-7. Hunting** Synchronous generators operating in parallel sometimes have a tendency to *hunt*. If the driving torque applied to a generator is pulsating, such as that produced by a diesel engine, the generator rotor may be pulled periodically ahead of or behind its normal position as it rotates. This oscillating action is called *hunting*.

Hunting causes generators to shift load from one to another. In some cases this oscillation of power becomes cumulative and violent enough to cause the generators to fall out of synchronism.

The tendency of diesel-driven generators to hunt is reduced by using a heavy flywheel to reduce torque variations. Damper windings, often called *amortisseur* windings, are placed on the surface of some generator rotors to decrease the tendency to hunt. The rotor shown in Fig. 12-3 is equipped with a damper winding consisting of short-circuited conductors embedded in the pole faces. When hunting occurs, there is a shifting of the armature flux across the pole faces, thereby inducing currents in the damper winding. Since any induced current opposes the action that produces it, the hunting action is opposed by the flow of the induced currents. Generators driven by steam turbines generally do not have a tendency to hunt since the torque applied does not pulsate.

**12-8. Ratings** Figure 12-12 shows data found on a typical a-c generator nameplate. Note that generator capacity is rated in kilovolt-amperes and kilowatts at a specified power factor. Other nameplate data include voltage, current, frequency, and speed ratings; number of phases, field amperes and volts; and maximum temperature rise.

| MANUFACTURER'S NAME |
|---|
| A-C GENERATOR   AIR COOLED   NO. 6750616   TYPE ATB 3600 RPM |
| 2  POLES   60  CYCLES   3-PHASE   WYE-CONNECTED  FOR 13,800 VOLTS |
| RATING  15,625  KVA  12,500  KW  0.80  PF  EXCITER 250 VOLTS |
| ARMATURE 654 AMP.   FIELD 183 AMP. |
| GUARANTEED TEMP. RISE NOT TO EXCEED: 60°C ON ARMATURE BY DETECTOR 80°C ON FIELD BY RESISTANCE |

Fig. 12-12. Nameplate data for the a-c generator shown in Fig. 12-6.

**12-9. Losses and Efficiency**   Losses of a synchronous generator are similar to those of a d-c generator and include mechanical and iron losses, armature copper loss, and field-excitation loss.

The efficiency of an a-c generator may be determined by a direct measurement of input and output or by calculation after the losses have been determined.   Because of the difficulty of providing suitable power supply and loading devices required for a direct measurement, the efficiencies of a-c generators, especially of larger ratings, are usually determined from their losses.

Alternating-current generator efficiency varies with the power factor at which the generator operates, since the kilowatt output decreases with a decrease in power factor while the field excitation (and field loss) must be changed to maintain rated voltage.

### REVIEW QUESTIONS

**1.** Why are a-c generators built with a stationary armature and revolving field?

**2.** Name two types of a-c generator construction.

**3.** How is the field of an a-c generator excited?

**4.** Upon what does the amount of emf generated in an a-c generator depend? In actual operation which of these is variable?

**5.** Write the formula for frequency of an a-c generator.   What is the common frequency in use in the United States?

**6.** What is meant by generator regulation?

**7.** What factors affect generator regulation?

**8.** How does the load power factor change the effect of armature reaction?

**9.** What is the purpose of a voltage regulator?

**10.** What requirements must be satisfied before a-c generators are paralleled?

**11.** What is meant when it is said that two a-c generators are being synchronized?

**12.** Show how three lamps may be connected to check phase relations between generators.

**13.** If when using the "lamps-dark" method of synchronizing, it is found that the lamps increase and decrease in brilliance once every 2 sec, what is the difference in frequency between the two machines?

**14.** How often must the phase sequence of two a-c generators be checked?

**15.** What two things are indicated by a synchroscope? Is this the only instrument needed to indicate synchronism?

**16.** How is the kilowatt load divided in the desired proportion between two a-c generators operating in parallel?

**17.** How is it possible to adjust the power factor of an a-c generator that is operating in parallel with other generators?

**18.** How does the operation of changing the load division between a-c generators differ from changing the load division between d-c generators in parallel?

**19.** What is hunting?

**20.** What information is found on an a-c generator nameplate?

**21.** Name three types of generator losses. Are a-c generator losses the same at all power factors?

## PROBLEMS

**1.** A diesel-driven synchronous generator is operated at 200 rpm and has a frequency rating of 60 cycles. How many poles does it have?

**2.** How many cycles are generated in one revolution of a 24-pole a-c generator? How many revolutions per second must it make to generate a frequency of 60 cps? How many rpm?

**3.** What must be the speed of a 2-pole 25-cycle synchronous generator?

**4.** A three-phase generator has a load of 100 kw per phase at a power factor of 80 per cent, lagging. (a) What is the three-phase kilowatt load; (b) the three-phase kilovolt-ampere load; (c) the current per terminal if the terminal voltage is 7,200 volts?

**5.** A wye-connected 2,400-volt 600-kva unity power factor generator is reconnected for delta operation. What is the new voltage, current, and kilovolt-ampere rating?

**6.** Find the regulation of an a-c generator that has a full-load voltage of 2,400 volts and no-load voltage of 3,240 volts at 80 per cent lagging power factor. Will the per cent regulation at unity power factor be larger than, smaller than, or the same as at 80 per cent lagging power factor?

**7.** What is the kilowatt rating of a three-phase 875-kva generator at (a) unity power factor; (b) 80 per cent power factor; (c) 50 per cent power factor? If the voltage rating is 2,400 volts, what is the current rating at each power factor?

**8.** A three-phase 480-volt 1,200-kva synchronous generator supplies rated load at a lagging power factor of 75 per cent. If the efficiency of the generator is 90 per cent, what horsepower is the prime mover delivering to the generator?

# CHAPTER 13

## POLYPHASE INDUCTION MOTORS

Because of its simple, rugged construction and good operating characteristics, the induction motor is the most commonly used type of a-c motor. It consists of two parts: the stator, or stationary part, and the rotor, or rotating part. The stator is connected to the a-c supply. The rotor is not connected electrically to the supply but has current induced in it by transformer action from the stator. Because of this, the stator is sometimes referred to as the primary and the rotor as the secondary of the motor.

Three-phase induction motors, which are discussed in this chapter, are classified according to two types: squirrel-cage and wound-rotor motors. Both motors operate on the same basic principle and have the same stator construction but differ in rotor construction. Single-phase induction motors are discussed in Chap. 15.

**13-1. Construction** The parts of a three-phase squirrel-cage motor are shown in Fig. 13-1. Note the extremely simple construction as compared, for example, with a d-c motor.

The stator core is built of slotted sheet-steel laminations that are supported in a stator frame of cast iron or fabricated steel plate. Windings, very similar to those of the revolving field a-c generator, are spaced in the stator slots 120 electrical degrees apart. The phase windings may be either wye- or delta-connected.

The rotor of a squirrel-cage motor is constructed of a laminated core with the conductors placed parallel, or approximately parallel, to the shaft and embedded in the surface of the core. The conductors are not insulated from the core, since the rotor currents naturally follow the path of least resistance, that is, the rotor conductors. At each end of the rotor, the rotor conductors are all short-circuited by continuous end rings. The rotor conductors and their end rings are similar to a revolving squirrel cage, thus explaining the name.

Figure 13-2 shows the construction of a typical squirrel-cage rotor

FIG. 13-1. A dismantled squirrel-cage induction motor. (*Courtesy of Robbins & Myers, Inc.*)

FIG. 13-2. Squirrel-cage rotor in which the copper windings are cast directly into the steel rotor core. (*Courtesy of Fairbanks, Morse & Co.*)

used in motors up to about 50 hp. In the rotor shown, the rotor bars and the end rings are cast of copper in one piece on the rotor core. Aluminum is also used for conductor material in some motors. In the larger motors, the rotor bars, instead of being cast, are wedged into the rotor slots and are then welded securely to the end rings.

Squirrel-cage rotor bars are not always placed parallel to the motor shaft but are skewed as shown in Figs. 13-1 and 13-2. This results in a more uniform torque and also reduces the magnetic humming noise when the motor is running.

FIG. 13-3. Wound-rotor induction motor. (*Courtesy of Fairbanks, Morse & Co.*)

FIG. 13-4. Rotor from a wound-rotor induction motor. (*Courtesy of Fairbanks, Morse & Co.*)

Wound-rotor or slip-ring motors differ from the squirrel-cage motor in rotor construction. As the name implies, the rotor is wound with an insulated winding similar to the stator winding. The rotor phase windings are wye-connected with the open end of each phase brought out to a slip ring mounted on the rotor shaft. Figure 13-3 shows the over-all appearance of a wound-rotor motor, and Fig. 13-4 shows the rotor construction. The rotor winding is not connected to a supply, the slip rings and brushes merely providing a means of connecting an external variable-control resistance into the rotor circuit.

Wound-rotor motors are less extensively used than squirrel-cage motors because of their higher first cost and greater maintenance costs.

**13-2. The Rotating Magnetic Field** An induction motor depends for its operation on a rotating magnetic field which is established in the air gap of the motor by the stator currents. As mentioned above, a three-phase stator winding is wound with the phase windings spaced 120 electrical degrees apart.

A simplified stator winding layout of a two-pole wye-connected motor is shown in Fig. 13-5a. When the winding is energized from a three-phase supply, the phase currents vary in time phase as shown in Fig. 13-5b, and a pulsating flux is built up by each of the three windings. However, owing to the spacing of the windings and the phase difference of the currents in the windings, the flux produced by each phase combines to form a resultant flux that moves around the stator surface at a constant speed. This resultant flux is called the *rotating magnetic field*.

The manner in which the rotating magnetic field is established by a three-phase stator winding may be illustrated by considering the direction of current flow through the three phases at several successive instants. These different times are marked off at 60° intervals on the current waves in Fig. 13-5b. It will be assumed that, when currents have positive values in Fig. 13-5b, current is flowing in the direction of the arrows in Fig. 13-5a. For example, at time 1 (Fig. 13-5b), currents in phases A and C are positive and the current in phase B is negative. Therefore, current is flowing toward the motor or with the arrows in lines A and C and away from the motor or against the arrow in line B.

Figure 13-5c shows the current directions in the stator conductors and the resulting field at each of the six different instants chosen in Fig. 13-5b. At time 1, the current is outward in the three coil sides on the upper half of the stator and is inward in the three coil sides on the lower half of the stator. The resulting field is established toward the right, creating a south pole on the stator surface at the right and a north pole at the left as shown. At time 2, the current is still in the same direction in phases A and B but has reversed in phase C. This establishes a field of the same strength as at time 1 but in a position 60° in a clockwise direction from time 1. At time 3, the current in phase $B$ has reversed, causing the resulting field to be moved another 60° in the clockwise direction. The remaining diagrams in Fig. 13-5c show the resultant field at times 4, 5, and 6.

It is evident from Fig. 13-5 that the field resulting from the currents

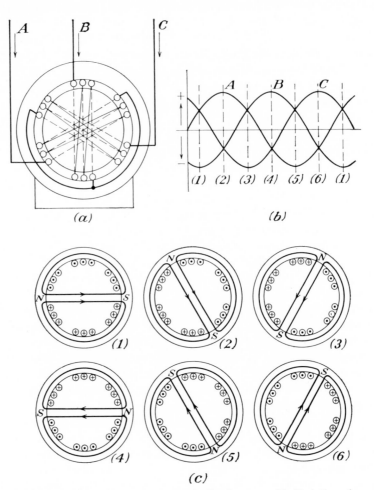

FIG. 13-5. (a) Simplified two-pole stator winding layout. (b) Variation of current in the phase windings. (c) Resulting flux distribution in the motor at the successive instants indicated by the numbers on the curves in (b).

flowing in the three stator windings shifts around the stator surface, moving through a definite distance in each of the time intervals considered. Use is made of the principle of this rotating magnetic field in both induction and synchronous motors.

**13-3. Speed of the Rotating Magnetic Field**   In the two-pole winding of Fig. 13-5, the field makes one complete revolution in one cycle of the current.   In a four-pole winding in which each phase has two separate groups of coils connected in series, it may be shown that the rotating field makes one revolution in two cycles of the current.   In a six-pole winding, the field makes one revolution in three cycles of the current.   In general, the field makes one revolution in $p/2$ cycles, or

$$\text{Cycles} = \frac{p}{2} \times \text{revolutions}$$

and    $$\text{Cycles per second} = \frac{p}{2} \times \text{revolutions per second}$$

Since revolutions per second equal revolutions per minute $n$ divided by 60 and the number of cycles per second is frequency $f$,

$$f = \frac{p}{2} \times \frac{n}{60} = \frac{np}{120}$$
$$n = \frac{120f}{p} \tag{1}$$

The speed at which the rotating magnetic field revolves is called the *synchronous speed* of the motor.   It will be noted that the same relation exists between the frequency, poles, and synchronous speed of a motor as exists between the frequency, poles, and speed of rotation of a synchronous generator.   For a constant supply frequency, the synchronous speed is constant in any given motor.

If any two of the three supply lines to the stator winding in Fig. 13-5a are reversed, thereby reversing the phase sequence of the stator currents, an analysis similar to that of Art. 13-2 will show the rotation of the magnetic field to be in the reverse direction, or counterclockwise. As will be shown in the following articles, the rotor turns in the same direction as the rotating flux.   Therefore, *the direction of rotation of a three-phase motor may be reversed by interchanging any two of the three motor supply lines.*

**13-4. Principle of Operation**   In a d-c motor, current is drawn from the supply and conducted into the armature conductors through the brushes and commutator.   When the armature conductors carry current in the magnetic field established by the field circuit, a force is exerted on the conductors which tends to move them at right angles to the field.

In an induction motor, there is no electrical connection to the rotor, the rotor currents being induced currents. However, the same condition exists as in the d-c motor, that is, the rotor conductors carry current in a magnetic field and thereby have a force exerted upon them tending to move them at right angles to the field.

When the stator winding is energized from a three-phase supply, a rotating magnetic field is established which rotates at synchronous speed. As the field sweeps across the rotor conductors, an emf is induced in these conductors just as an emf is induced in the secondary winding of a transformer by the flux of the primary currents. The rotor circuit being complete, either through end rings or an external resistance, the induced emf causes a current to flow in the rotor conductors. The rotor conductors carrying current in the stator field thus have a force exerted upon them.

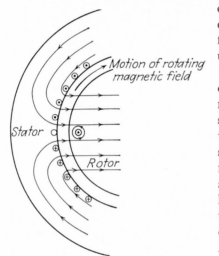

FIG. 13-6. Section of an induction motor rotor and stator showing the magnetic field in the air gap.

Figure 13-6 represents a section of an induction motor stator and rotor, with the magnetic field assumed to be rotating in a clockwise direction and with the rotor stationary, as at starting. For the flux direction and motion shown, an application of Fleming's right-hand rule shows the direction of the induced current in the rotor conductor to be toward the reader. At the instant being considered, with the current-carrying conductor in the magnetic field as shown, force is exerted upward upon the conductor since the magnetic field below the conductor is stronger than the field above. For simplicity, only one rotor conductor is shown. However, other adjacent rotor conductors in the stator field likewise carry current in the same direction as the conductor shown and also have an upward force exerted upon them. One-half cycle later, the stator field direction will have reversed, but the rotor current will have also reversed, so that the force on the rotor is still upward. Likewise rotor conductors under other stator field poles will have a force exerted upon them all tending to turn the rotor in the clockwise direction. If the developed torque is great enough to overcome the resisting torque of the load, the motor will accelerate in the clockwise direction or in the same direction as the rotation of the stator field.

**13-5. Speed and Slip** An induction motor cannot run at synchronous speed. If it were possible, by some means, for the rotor to attain synchronous speed, the rotor would then be standing still with respect to the rotating flux. Then no emf would be induced in the rotor, no rotor current would flow, and therefore there would be no torque developed. The rotor speed even at no load must be slightly less than synchronous speed in order that current may be induced in the rotor, thereby producing a torque. This difference between rotor speed and synchronous speed is called *slip*. Slip may be expressed in rpm but is more commonly expressed as per cent of synchronous speed.

$$\text{Per cent slip} = \frac{\text{synchronous speed} - \text{rotor speed}}{\text{synchronous speed}} \times 100$$

Or writing the above expression using symbols

$$\text{Per cent } S = \frac{N_s - N_r}{N_s} \times 100 \tag{2}$$

**Example 1** A four-pole 60-cycle squirrel-cage motor has a full-load speed of 1,740 rpm. What is the per cent slip at full load?

The synchronous speed from Eq. (1) is

$$N_s = \frac{120f}{p} = \frac{120 \times 60}{4} = 1,800 \text{ rpm}$$

$$\text{Slip in rpm} = 1,800 - 1,740 = 60 \text{ rpm}$$

$$\text{Per cent slip} = \frac{60}{1,800} \times 100 = 3.33 \text{ per cent}$$

**13-6. Rotor Frequency** If a two-pole 60-cycle induction motor (synchronous speed = 3,600 rpm) operates at 5 per cent slip, the slip in rpm is $3,600 \times 0.05$ or 180 rpm. This means that a pair of stator poles passes a given rotor conductor 180 times every minute, or three times every second. When a pair of poles moves across a conductor, one cycle of emf is induced in that conductor. Thus the above rotor conductor will have induced in it an emf with a frequency of 3 cps. If the slip is increased to 10 per cent or 360 rpm, the frequency of the rotor emf and current is increased to 6 cps. If the motor slip is increased to 100 per cent, the rotor frequency will be 60 cps.

It is obvious then that the rotor frequency depends on the slip—the greater the slip, the greater the rotor frequency. For any value of slip, the rotor frequency $f_r$ is equal to the stator frequency $f_s$ multiplied by the slip $S$ expressed as a decimal, or

$$f_r = Sf_s \tag{3}$$

Rotor frequency is significant because as it varies, the rotor reactance $(X_r = 2\pi f_r L_r)$ also varies, thus affecting both starting and running characteristics of the motor, as will be explained in following articles.

### 13-7. Torque and Speed of an Induction Motor

Torque is produced in an induction motor by the interaction of the stator and rotor fluxes. The flux produced by the stator currents revolves at synchronous speed. In order that rotor currents may be induced, making possible the production of a torque, the rotor must turn at a speed less than synchronous speed. At no load, the rotor lags behind the stator flux only a small amount, since the only torque required is that needed to overcome the motor losses. As mechanical load is added, the rotor speed decreases. A decrease in rotor speed allows the constant-speed rotating field to sweep across the rotor conductors at a faster rate, thereby inducing larger rotor currents. This results in a larger torque output at a reduced speed.

Since the rotor impedance is low, a small decrease in speed produces a large increase in rotor current. For this reason the speed regulation of a standard squirrel-cage motor is low, the full-load slip being 3 to 5 per cent. Although the motor speed does decrease slightly with increased load, the speed regulation is good enough that the induction motor is classed as a constant-speed motor.

With increasing loads, the increased rotor currents are in such a direction as to decrease the stator flux, thereby temporarily decreasing the counter emf in the stator windings. The decreased counter emf allows more stator current to flow, thereby increasing the power input to the motor. It will be noted that the action of the induction motor in adjusting its stator or primary current with changes of current in its rotor or secondary circuit is very similar to the changes occurring in a transformer with changes in load.

The torque of an induction motor being due to the interaction of the rotor and stator fields is dependent on the strength of those fields and the phase relations between them. Mathematically,

$$T = K\phi I_r \cos \theta_r \qquad (4)$$

where $T$ = torque
  $K$ = a constant
  $\phi$ = rotating stator flux
  $I_r$ = rotor current
 $\cos \theta_r$ = rotor power factor

Throughout the normal range of operation, $K$, $\phi$, and $\cos \theta_r$ are substantially constant, the torque increasing directly with the rotor current $I_r$. The rotor current in turn increases in almost direct proportion to the motor slip.   The variation of torque with slip of a typical squirrel-cage motor of the standard type is shown in Fig. 13-7. Note that as slip increases from zero to about 10 per cent the torque increases in an almost straight-line relationship with the slip.

As was explained in Art. 13-6, an increase in slip causes an increase in rotor frequency and rotor reactance.  Since the rotor circuit resistance is constant, an increased rotor reactance means a decrease in rotor power factor (rotor power factor $= R_r/Z_r$).   However, in the standard motor the change in slip is so small as load is increased from zero to full load, or even considerably above full load, that the change in rotor impedance is almost negligible.

However as load and slip are increased much beyond the rated or full-load values, the increase in rotor reactance becomes appreciable.   The increasing value of rotor impedance not only decreases the rotor power factor, but also lowers the rate of increase of rotor current so that the torque does not continue to increase directly with the slip.   With the decreasing power factor and the lowered rate of increase in rotor current, the torque increase becomes less rapid and finally reaches maximum value at about 25 per cent slip in the standard squirrel-cage motor.   This maximum value of torque is called the *pull-out* or *breakdown torque* of the motor.   If load is increased beyond the breakdown point, the decrease in rotor power factor is greater than the increase in rotor current, resulting in a decreasing torque, and the motor quickly comes to a stop.

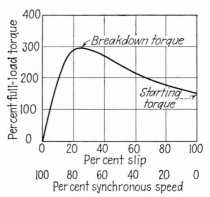

FIG. 13-7. Variation of torque with slip for a standard squirrel-cage motor.

The value of breakdown torque varies with the design of the motor but ranges from 200 to 300 per cent of full-load torque in standard squirrel-cage motors.   The value of slip at which the breakdown torque occurs depends on the value of rotor resistance; the higher the resistance, the higher the value of slip at breakdown.   Some squirrel-cage motors for special applications are designed with high-resistance rotors so that the maximum torque occurs at 100 per cent slip or at starting.

**13-8. Effect of Load on Power Factor**   The current drawn by an induction motor running at no load is largely a magnetizing current, the no-load current lagging the applied voltage by a large angle.

Thus the power factor of a lightly loaded induction motor is very low. Because of the air gap, the reluctance of the magnetic circuit is high, resulting in a relatively large value of no-load current as compared with a transformer.

As load is added, the active or power component of the current increases, resulting in a higher power factor. However because of the large value of magnetizing current, which is present regardless of load, the power factor of an induction motor even at full load seldom exceeds 90 per cent.

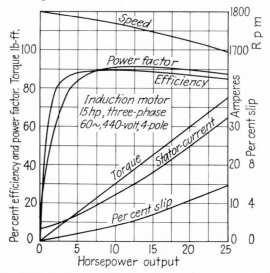

Fig. 13-8. Performance curves of a squirrel-cage motor.

The variation of the power factor of a typical motor with load is shown in Fig. 13-8. Other performance curves also shown are variations of speed, slip, efficiency, stator current, and torque for different values of load.

**13-9. Starting Conditions**  As stated in Art. 13-6, the rotor frequency and reactance are high under starting conditions, that is, with 100 per cent slip. Thus in the highly reactive rotor circuit, the rotor currents lag the rotor emf by a large angle. This means that the maximum current flow occurs in a rotor conductor at some time after the maximum density of the stator flux has passed that conductor. This results in a high starting current at low power factor, which results in a low value of starting torque.

As the rotor accelerates, the rotor frequency, and hence the rotor reactance, decreases, causing the torque to increase up to its maximum value. As the motor accelerates further, the torque decreases to the value required to carry the load on the motor at a constant speed.

The change in torque during the starting period is shown in Fig. 13-7, the starting torque being the value at the right-hand end of the curve, or at 100 per cent slip.

The high rotor reactance compared with the rotor resistance at starting results in a poor starting torque with a high starting current. One method of correcting this condition is to design the rotor circuit with a high resistance. This increases the rotor power factor and improves the motor starting characteristics, but under the running conditions, the motor operates at a reduced efficiency because of the high $I^2R$ loss in the rotor circuit. Another effect of a high rotor resistance, which may or may not be a disadvantage, is the increased speed regulation. Standard squirrel-cage motors are a compromise design; that is, they have a rotor resistance high enough to provide fair starting characteristics but which causes the motor to operate at a slightly reduced efficiency.

The standard or normal-torque normal-starting-current squirrel-cage motor has a starting torque of 150 to 200 per cent of full-load value with a starting current of 500 to 900 per cent of full-load current.

**13-10. The Double-squirrel-cage Motor** The double-squirrel-cage motor is designed to provide a high starting torque at a low starting current. The rotor is so designed that the motor operates with the advantages of a high-resistance rotor circuit during starting and a low-resistance rotor circuit under running conditions.

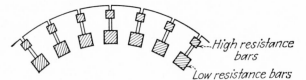

FIG. 13-9. The rotor of a double-squirrel-cage motor.

As the name denotes, the double-squirrel-cage motor has two rotor windings, one inside the other. A sectional view of this type of rotor is shown in Fig. 13-9. The outer cage winding has a high resistance and, being close to the rotor surface, has a low inductance. The inner cage is a low-resistance winding and, being nearly surrounded by iron, has a high inductance.

During the starting period with the high rotor frequency, the impedance of the outer winding is less than that of the inner winding, resulting in a large proportion of the rotor currents flowing in the outer high-resistance winding. This provides the good starting characteristics of a high-resistance cage winding. As the motor accelerates, the rotor frequency decreases, thereby lowering the reactance of the inner winding, allowing it to carry a larger proportion of the total rotor current. At the normal operating speed of the motor, the rotor frequency is so low that nearly all the rotor current flows in the low-resistance inner cage, resulting in good operating efficiency and speed regulation.

Thus the outer winding produces the high starting and accelerating torque, while the inner winding provides the running torque at good efficiency.

The starting torque of the double-squirrel-cage motor ranges from 200 to 250 per cent of full-load torque, with a starting current of 400 to 600 per cent of full-load value. It is classed as a high-torque low-starting current motor.

**13-11. The Wound-rotor Motor**   The rotor of a wound-rotor or slip-ring motor is wound with insulated windings similar to the stator winding. This three-phase winding is wye-connected with the open

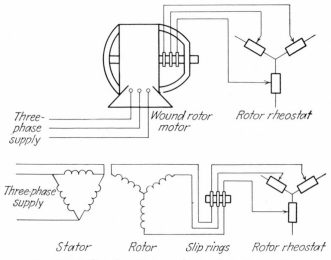

Fig. 13-10. Circuits of a wound-rotor induction motor.

ends of each phase winding being connected to three slip rings. Connected to the rotor circuit through the slip rings is a wye-connected external variable resistance. Figures 13-3 and 13-4 show the construction of the wound-rotor motor, the connection diagrams being shown in Fig. 13-10.

The rotor rheostat provides a means of increasing the rotor-circuit resistance during the starting period, resulting in a high value of starting torque.   As the motor accelerates, the rheostat is gradually cut out, thereby lowering the rotor resistance as the rotor reactance decreases.   By this means, the torque of the motor is controlled so that a maximum value of torque is provided throughout the accelerating period.   The slip rings are short-circuited when the motor reaches full speed, its operation under running conditions being the same as the squirrel-cage motor.

Because the rotor-circuit resistance may be varied during operation, a means is provided for controlling the speed of a wound-rotor motor. As the rotor-circuit resistance is increased, a given torque is developed at a larger slip.   Thus with the control rheostat cut in, the motor operates at a reduced speed.

The effects of operating a motor with external resistance in the rotor circuit on the motor performance are a decreased efficiency due to the $I^2R$ losses in the rheostat and a lowered value of speed regulation.

### 13-12. Speed Control of Squirrel-cage Motors

From the formula for the synchronous speed of a motor [Eq. (1)], it is evident that the supply frequency and the number of stator poles are the only variable factors determining synchronous speed.   A variation of frequency is impossible when a motor is connected to ordinary commercial supply lines, since such supplies are constant-frequency systems.   However, when an a-c generator supplies but one motor, as in the electric propulsion systems used in some ships, the supply frequency may be varied by varying the speed of the generator prime mover.

Multispeed squirrel-cage motors, designed to be operated on constant-frequency systems, are provided with stator windings that may be reconnected to form different numbers of poles.   Two-speed motors usually have one winding that may be switched through suitable control equipment to provide two speeds, one of which is half of the other.   Four-speed motors are equipped with two separate stator windings each of which provides two speeds.   While such motors do not have continuously adjustable speeds as do d-c motors, they are suitable for such applications as ventilating fans, conveyors, machine tools, or other applications requiring several definite speeds but not necessarily a continuously adjustable speed drive.

### 13-13. Starting Induction Motors

In general, induction motors may be started either by connecting the motor directly across the supply circuit or by applying a reduced voltage to the motor during the starting period.    Controllers used for starting motors by either method may be operated either manually or magnetically.

Unlike d-c motors, induction motors may be connected directly across the line without damage to the motor.   However, because of the voltage disturbance created on the supply lines by their heavy starting currents, motors larger than $7\frac{1}{2}$ to 10 hp are often started at a reduced voltage.   The maximum allowable horsepower rating to be started on full voltage depends, however, on the motor design, the supply capacity, and the regulations of the owners of the supply lines.

A greater starting torque is exerted by a motor when it is started on full voltage than when it is started on reduced voltage.   In fact, it may be shown that the torque of an induction motor is proportional to the square of the applied voltage.   Thus if the voltage is reduced to 80 per cent of its rated value during starting, the starting torque is reduced to only 64 per cent of that obtained by full-voltage starting.   The reduced voltage applied to the motor during the starting period lowers the starting current but, at the same time, increases the accelerating time because of the reduced value of the starting torque.   The type of load being started, then, also has a bearing on the method of starting to be used.   If, for example, a particular load might be damaged by sudden starting and should be accelerated slowly, then reduced-voltage starting must be used.

Commonly used starters and those to be described here are the following:

1. Full-voltage or across-the-line starters
2. Reduced-voltage starters
    a. Primary-resistor starters
    b. Autotransformer starters or compensators

**13-14. Across-the-line Starters**    Motors are started on full line voltage by means of across-the-line starters.    A magnetically operated across-the-line starter is shown in Fig. 13-11, and a connection diagram of the starter, using three-wire push-button control, is shown in Fig. 13-12.    The operation is the same as that of the d-c magnetic contactor with three-wire push-button control described in Art. 7-18, with the exception that a three-pole contactor is used in the a-c starter.

Across-the-line starters are generally equipped with thermal overload relays and when used with the three-wire push-button control as shown in Fig. 13-12 also provide undervoltage protection for the motor.

**13-15. Primary-resistor Starters**    Reduced voltage is obtained in the primary-resistor starter by means of resistances that are connected in series with each stator lead during the starting period. The voltage drop in the resistors produces a reduced voltage at the motor terminals. At a definite time after the motor is connected to the line through the resistors, accelerating contacts close which short-circuit the starting resistors and apply full voltage to the motor.

A magnetically operated primary-resistor starter with the cover removed is shown in Fig. 13-13, and an elementary wiring diagram is shown in Fig. 13-14. When the start button is closed, the main contactor $M$ is closed, connecting the motor to the line through the starting resistors. At the same time, a mechanical escapement timer is started. After a definite time has elapsed during which the motor has accelerated, the time-delay contacts $TC$ close.

FIG. 13-11. Three-pole magnetic across-the-line starter for three-phase 220-volt motors up to 15 hp and 440-volt motors up to 25 hp. (*Courtesy of Westinghouse Electric Corporation.*)

This energizes the accelerating

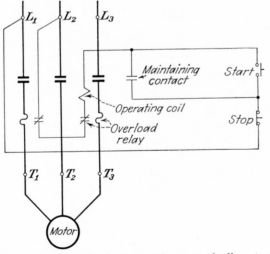

FIG. 13-12. Connection diagram of a magnetic across-the-line starter controlled by a three-wire push-button control circuit.

FIG. 13-13. Primary-resistor-type reduced-voltage starter rated 50 amp and 600 volts.   (*Courtesy of General Electric Company.*)

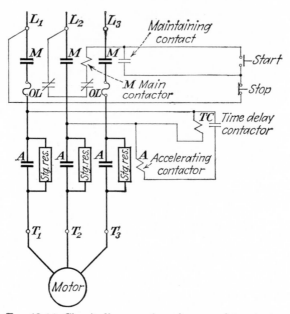

FIG. 13-14. Circuit diagram of a primary-resistor starter.

contactor $A$ which short-circuits the starting resistors and applies full voltage to the motor.

In the starter just described, the starting resistance is cut out in one step. To obtain smoother acceleration with less line disturbance, starters are available in which the starting resistance is cut out in several steps.

Overload and undervoltage protection are provided in the same manner as in the across-the-line starter.

Fig. 13-15. Manually operated autotransformer starter. (*Courtesy of General Electric Company.*)

**13-16. Autotransformer Starters**   Autotransformer starters, sometimes called starting compensators, employ autotransformers for reducing the voltage applied to the motor during the starting period.   Autotransformer starters may be either manually or magnetically operated; a typical manual type with the cover removed is shown in Fig. 13-15. The wiring diagram is shown in Fig. 13-16.

The manual autotransformer starter is essentially a multipole double-throw switch. In Fig. 13-16, three rows of contacts are shown: the starting, running, and movable contacts. The starting and running contacts are stationary, and the movable contacts are attached to the operating handle. When the operating handle is moved to the START position, the movable contacts are moved against the starting contacts. This connects the wye-connected autotransformers to the line and the motor to the secondary side of the transformers. The value of the secondary voltage of the transformers is determined by

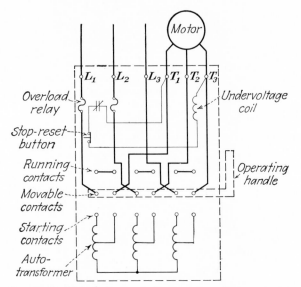

FIG. 13-16. Circuit diagram of an autotransformer starter.

the tap setting of the transformer but is usually either 80 or 65 per cent of the line voltage.

After the motor accelerates at reduced voltage, the operating handle is moved to the RUN position; this operation disconnects the transformers from the line and connects the motor directly to the line through the running contacts. The operating handle is held in the RUN position by the undervoltage device. If the supply voltage fails or drops to a low value, the handle is released and returned to the OFF position. Overload protection is provided by thermal overload relays.

**13-17. Induction-motor Losses, Efficiency, and Ratings** Induction-motor losses include stator and rotor copper losses, stator and rotor core losses, and friction and windage losses. As in the transformer, the core losses are practically constant for all loads. For practical purposes, the friction and windage losses are also considered to be constant. The copper losses, of course, vary with the load.

The efficiency curve of a typical 15-hp squirrel-cage motor is shown in Fig. 13-8. Note that the efficiency increases with load up to about three-fourths full load; above this point it begins to decrease because of the relatively larger values of $I^2R$ loss.

In general, the larger the motor, the higher the full-load efficiency. Average values of full-load efficiencies of squirrel-cage motors are about as follows: 5 hp, 82 per cent; 25 hp, 88 per cent; and 100 hp, 90 per cent. Wound-rotor motor efficiencies are slightly lower.

Motor nameplate data usually includes the following in addition to the manufacturer's serial, frame, and type numbers: horsepower, speed, voltage, frequency, and temperature rise in a specified time. If a motor is designed to be used on more than one voltage or to operate at more than one speed by reconnecting the windings, a connection diagram is also often included on the nameplate.

The standards of the National Electrical Manufacturers Association require that motors have a code letter stamped on the nameplate which designates the value of kilovolt-amperes per horsepower required by the motor at starting (rotor at a standstill).

Squirrel-cage motors are designed to have a wide variety of starting and operating characteristics, the different characteristics being attained by different designs of the rotor circuits. The motor referred to in this chapter as the standard motor is a normal-torque normal-starting-current motor and is a general-purpose motor. Other types of motors designed for special applications include the following: the normal-torque low-starting-current motor, the high-torque low-starting-current (double-squirrel-cage) motor, the low-torque low-starting-current motor, and the high-starting-torque high-slip motor. The operating characteristics of each are denoted by the name.

## REVIEW QUESTIONS

**1.** What are the two parts of an induction motor? How are the two circuits of an induction motor similar to the circuits of a transformer?

**2.** How does the construction of the squirrel-cage motor differ from that of the wound-rotor motor? Describe the rotor construction of each.

**3.** Describe briefly how the rotating magnetic field is produced by the three-phase stator currents. In a two-pole winding, how many revolutions does the rotating magnetic field make in one cycle of the current?

**4.** In general, what factors determine the synchronous speed of a motor?

**5.** How may the direction of rotation of a three-phase motor be reversed?

**6.** Upon what basic principle does the induction motor, like the d-c motor, depend for its operation?

**7.** Describe briefly how torque is produced in an induction motor. Is the direction of rotation of the rotor the same as or opposite to that of the rotating field?

**8.** Why does an induction motor run at less than synchronous speed? What is the difference between synchronous and rotor speed called?

**9.** Show why the rotor frequency is equal to the slip multiplied by the stator frequency. To what is the rotor frequency equal when the rotor is at a standstill with the stator excited?

**10.** What effect does slip have on rotor reactance?

**11.** What is the order of magnitude of the full-load slip of a standard squirrel-cage motor?

**12.** Describe the changes in speed, rotor currents, and torque as load is added to an induction motor. How is the motor able to adjust its stator current with changes in mechanical load?

**13.** Upon what factors does the torque of an induction motor depend?

**14.** What is the effect of the change in rotor frequency as load is increased from no load to full load? What is its effect when the load is increased considerably above full load?

**15.** What is meant by pull-out or breakdown torque? If load is increased beyond the breakdown torque, what happens to the speed of the motor?

**16.** In the standard squirrel-cage motor, at about what value of slip does breakdown torque occur? How does the value of rotor resistance affect the point at which breakdown torque occurs?

**17.** Why is the power factor of a lightly loaded induction motor very low? What happens to the power factor as load is increased on the motor?

**18.** As load is increased from no load to full load on an induction motor, what happens to the slip, speed, torque, stator current, power factor, and efficiency of the motor?

**19.** Why does a squirrel-cage motor have a poor starting torque?

**20.** What are objections to building a squirrel-cage motor with high enough rotor resistance to provide good starting torque?

**21.** Describe the action of the double-squirrel-cage motor. How does its starting torque and current compare with the standard squirrel-cage motor?

**22.** How is the rotor circuit of a wound-rotor motor excited?

**23.** Why does the wound-rotor motor have better starting characteristics than the squirrel-cage motor? What might be some reasons for the fact that wound-rotor motors are used less extensively than squirrel-cage motors?

**24.** How may the speed of a wound-rotor motor be varied? What are disadvantages of this method of speed control?

**25.** In what way may a squirrel-cage motor be made to operate over a wide range of continuously adjustable speeds? What are the limitations of this method of speed control?

**26.** How may the same squirrel-cage motor be made to operate at two definite speeds?

**27.** What are two general methods of starting squirrel-cage motors?

**28.** What determines the maximum size of a squirrel-cage motor that can be started on full voltage?

**29.** It is desired that an air-compressor motor be started automatically by an across-the-line starter that is controlled by a pressure switch on the air tank. Draw a connection diagram showing the starter and control wires. Use a two-wire control and include a thermal overload relay in the diagram.

**30.** Describe the operation of the magnetically operated primary-resistor starter.

**31.** Describe the operation of the manual autotransformer starter. Draw a simplified or elementary diagram of the connections.

**32.** Two motors are started at 50 per cent of line voltage, one with a primary-resistor starter, and the other with an autotransformer starter. The starting current taken by each motor is 100 amp per terminal. What is the value of the current on the line side of the starters in each case?

**33.** List the losses of an induction motor. Which are considered constant, and which are variable?

**34.** What would be the difference in design between a normal-torque normal-starting-current motor and a high-starting-torque high-slip motor?

## PROBLEMS

**1.** Find the synchronous speed of a 60-cycle motor that has an eight-pole stator winding.

**2.** Make a table showing the synchronous speeds of 2-, 4-, 6-, 8-, and 12-pole induction motors for frequencies of 25, 50, and 60 cps.

**3.** A six-pole 60-cycle induction motor has a full-load slip of 5 per cent. What is the full-load rotor speed?

**4.** A squirrel-cage-motor stator winding is wound for four poles. At full load, the motor operates at 1,720 rpm with a slip speed of 80 rpm. What is the supply frequency?

**5.** What is the rotor frequency of an eight-pole 60-cycle squirrel-cage motor operating at 850 rpm?

**6.** How much larger is the rotor reactance of a squirrel-cage motor at starting (with the rotor at a standstill) than it is when the motor operates at 5 per cent slip?

**7.** The three-phase induction motors driving an aircraft carrier have stators wound for either 22 or 44 poles. The frequency of the supply may be varied from 20 to 65 cps. What are the maximum and minimum speeds obtainable from the motors?

**8.** A 50-hp 220-volt three-phase motor requires a full-load current of 125 amp per terminal at a power factor of 88 per cent. What is its full-load efficiency?

**9.** A 10-hp 440-volt three-phase squirrel-cage motor at three-fourths rated load operates at an efficiency of 85 per cent and at a power factor of 85 per cent. What is the line current per terminal?

**10.** What are the rated full-load speeds of a 60-cycle motor that may be connected for either four- or eight-pole operation, assuming the motor to operate with a full-load slip of 5 per cent for either connection?

**11.** What is the percentage of full-voltage starting torque developed by a motor when it is started at 65 per cent of full voltage?

# CHAPTER 14

## SYNCHRONOUS MOTORS AND
## SELF-SYNCHRONOUS APPARATUS

Just as d-c generators may be operated as motors, a-c synchronous generators may be operated as motors. If, when two synchronous generators are operating in parallel, the prime mover is disconnected from one, it will continue to rotate, drawing power from the line to supply its losses. When mechanical load is added, the machine continues to operate at a constant speed. When operated in this manner, the machine is called a *synchronous motor*. The construction of a synchronous motor, except for slight modifications, is the same as synchronous generator construction. Salient-pole field construction is nearly always used in synchronous motors, the rotor of a typical slow-speed motor being shown in Fig. 14-1.

The three-phase synchronous motor is discussed in this chapter. Single-phase synchronous motors are discussed in Chap. 15.

**14-1. Operation of the Synchronous Motor** When an induction motor is connected to a three-phase supply, a rotating magnetic field is established which induces currents in the rotor windings, thereby producing a torque. The rotor can never turn at synchronous speed, since there must be relative motion between the rotating magnetic field and the rotor in order that currents can be induced in the rotor circuit.

When the stator windings of a synchronous motor are excited with three-phase voltages, a rotating magnetic field is established as in the induction motor. However, in the synchronous motor, the rotor circuit is not excited by induction but by a source of direct current as in the a-c generator. If the rotor is brought up to synchronous speed by some means, with the rotor poles excited, the poles of the rotor are attracted by the poles of the rotating magnetic field and the rotor continues to turn at synchronous speed. In other words, the rotor is locked into step magnetically with the rotating magnetic field.

If for any reason the rotor is pulled out of step with the rotating stator flux, the attraction is lost, no torque is developed, and the motor stops. Therefore, a synchronous motor develops torque only when running at synchronous speed. It follows, then, that a synchronous motor is not in itself self-starting, some auxiliary device being necessary to bring the rotor to synchronous speed.

FIG. 14-1  Rotor of a slow-speed synchronous motor.  (*Courtesy of Fairbanks, Morse & Co.*)

**14-2. Starting a Synchronous Motor**  As stated previously, the synchronous motor is not self-starting.  With the rotating magnetic field revolving at synchronous speed, and the rotor at a standstill, the rotor poles are first attracted in one direction and then in the other, resulting in a net torque of zero.

A synchronous motor may be started with a small auxiliary motor mounted on the main motor shaft and used only during the starting period.  When a synchronous motor normally drives a direct-connected d-c generator, the generator may be operated as a motor during the starting period.  Most synchronous motors, however, are started by means of a squirrel-cage winding embedded in the face of the rotor poles as shown in Fig. 14-1.  The motor is then started as an induction motor and is brought to about 95 per cent of synchronous speed by this means. At the proper instant, d-c field excitation is applied and the motor pulls into synchronism.

The amount of torque that a motor is able to exert when pulling into synchronism is called the *pull-in torque*. The value of pull-in torque developed by a synchronous motor varies widely with the application for which the motor is designed. For reciprocating compressors, a common application for synchronous-motor drive, the motor is designed to have a pull-in torque of about 50 per cent of full-load value. Motors for other applications may be designed to have pull-in torques as high as 150 per cent of full-load torque.

During the starting period, while the rotor is at a standstill, or is rotating at a speed much lower than synchronous speed, the rotating magnetic field rapidly cuts across the d-c field coils, inducing an emf in them. Since each field coil is wound with many turns and the several coils are connected in series, the induced emf may become dangerously high. One way of eliminating this hazard is to divide the field winding into several sections during the starting period. While emf is still induced in the field coils, the number of coils in series is reduced, so that the value of emf in any section is kept within safe limits. Sectionalizing the field winding may be accomplished by a centrifugally operated switch that keeps the field circuit sectionalized until the rotor revolves at near synchronous speed.

Another method of limiting the value of emf induced in the field during starting is to short-circuit the field through a resistance. The alternating current that flows in the field circuit is limited in value by the high reactance of the circuit. The resistance is removed as the motor nears synchronous speed.

Low-speed synchronous motors equipped with squirrel-cage starting windings are usually started on full voltage. Reduced-voltage starting, using autotransformer or resistor-type starters, is very often used on high-speed motors, or on other motors that require large amounts of starting current or where voltage fluctuations on the supply circuits must be kept to a minimum.

Modern synchronous motor controllers have automatic field control, the a-c power being manually or magnetically controlled. Field-control relays are used to energize the field circuit at the correct instant to ensure maximum pull-in torque. The field relay also acts immediately to open the field circuit should the motor pull out of synchronism. In the magnetic controllers, the motor is connected to the a-c supply by means of magnetic contactors that are operated from push buttons, float or pressure switches, or other automatic devices.

In addition to automatic field control, synchronous motor controllers generally include overload and undervoltage protective devices.

### 14-3. Effect of Load on a Synchronous Motor

In d-c motors and induction motors, an addition of load causes the motor speed to decrease. The decrease in speed reduces the counter emf enough so that additional current is drawn from the source to carry the increased load at a reduced speed. In the synchronous motor, this action cannot take place, since the rotor is locked into step magnetically with the rotating magnetic field and must continue to rotate at synchronous speed for all loads.

The relative positions of a stator pole and a d-c field pole of a synchronous motor running at no load are shown in Fig. 14-2a. The center

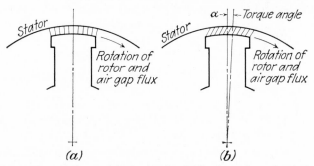

FIG. 14-2. (a) The relative positions of a d-c field pole and a pole of the rotating magnetic field of a synchronous motor at no load. (b) As load is added, the d-c field pole drops behind the rotating magnetic field.

lines of the two poles coincide. However, when load is added to the motor, there is a backward shift of the rotor pole relative to the stator pole, as shown in Fig. 14-2b. There is no change in speed; there is merely a shift in relative positions of the two poles, both of which continue to rotate at synchronous speed. The angular displacement between the rotor and stator poles is called the *torque angle*.

When a synchronous motor operates at no load or with a torque angle of practically 0°, the counter emf of the motor is equal and opposite to the applied or terminal voltage (neglecting the motor losses). With increasing loads and torque angles, the phase position of the counter emf changes with respect to the applied voltage which allows more stator current to flow to carry the additional load. This can best be shown by vector diagrams.

The vector diagram in Fig. 14-3a represents the condition in a synchronous motor at no load, the counter emf $E_g$ being equal and opposite to the applied voltage $E_t$. In Fig. 14-3b, enough load has been added to cause $E_g$ to drop behind its no-load position by the angle $\alpha$, corresponding to the change in torque angle similar to that shown in Fig. 14-2. The applied and counter voltages are no longer in direct opposition, their resultant being the voltage $E_r$ as shown. The resultant voltage $E_r$ causes a current $I$ to flow in the stator windings; $I$ lags $E_r$ by nearly 90° owing to the high inductance of the stator windings. The power input to the motor is thus $E_t I \cos \theta$ (for one phase), $\theta$ being the angle between the terminal voltage $E_t$ and the stator current $I$.

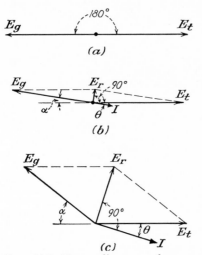

(a)

(b)

(c)

Fig. 14-3. Vector diagrams of a synchronous motor for three different load conditions, all at the same field excitation.

A further increase in load results in a larger torque angle, which in turn increases the value of $E_r$ and $I$ as shown in Fig. 14-3c. Thus a synchronous motor is able to supply increasing mechanical loads, not by a decrease in speed, but by a shift in relative positions of the rotor and the rotating magnetic field. Note in Fig. 14-3, that for increasing loads with a constant value of $E_g$ the phase angle $\theta$ increases in the lagging direction.

If too great a mechanical load is placed on a synchronous motor, the rotor is pulled out of synchronism, after which it comes to a stop; or if it has a squirrel-cage winding it continues to operate as an induction motor. The maximum value of torque that a motor can develop without losing its synchronism is called its *pull-out torque*. Pull-out torque, like pull-in torque, may be designed for widely varying values, depending on the application of the motor. These values range from 125 to 350 per cent of full-load torque values.

## 14-4. Power Factor; Effect of Changing Field Excitation

One of the outstanding characteristics of a synchronous motor is the fact that it may be made to operate over a wide range of power factors by adjustment of its field excitation.

Figure 14-4a shows the vector diagram of a synchronous motor with a mechanical load which results in the torque angle $\alpha$ and with the field excitation adjusted so that the motor operates at unity power factor.    If while the motor is carrying the same mechanical load, the field excitation is increased, the counter emf $E_g$ increases to the value shown in Fig. 14-4b.    This results in a change in phase position of the stator current $I$ with respect to the terminal voltage $E_t$ so that the motor then operates at a leading power factor.    Since the power output is unchanged, the value of $I$ must increase with the decrease in power factor.    Further increases in field excitation cause the motor to operate at a still more leading power factor with corresponding increases in stator current.

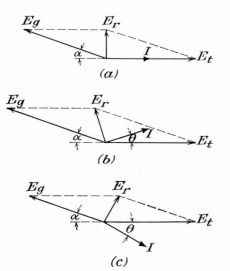

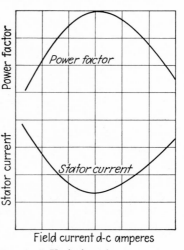

FIG. 14-4. Vector diagrams of a synchronous motor with a constant mechanical load but with different amounts of field excitation.    (a) Field excitation is adjusted for unity power-factor operation.    (b) Field is overexcited.    (c) Field is underexcited.

FIG. 14-5. Variation of stator current and motor power factor with a variation of field excitation at a constant load.

Figure 14-4c shows what happens if the field excitation is reduced below the value represented in Fig. 14-4a.    A reduction in excitation changes the power factor in the lagging direction, and as the excitation is further reduced it becomes still more lagging with corresponding increases in stator current.

Hence for a given load, the power factor of a synchronous motor may be varied from a low lagging value to a low leading value.    Figure 14-5 shows the variation of armature current and power factor of a synchronous motor with a variation of field excitation and for a constant load.

The normal value of field current for a given load is that value which results in unity power factor and a minimum stator current at that load.

When the motor is overexcited, it operates at a leading power factor; when it is underexcited, it operates at a lagging power factor.

**14-5. Efficiency and Ratings**   The efficiency of synchronous motors is in general higher than that of induction motors of the same horsepower and speed rating.   The losses are identical with those of synchronous generators.

Synchronous motors are divided into two distinct classifications as to speed: motors with speeds above 500 rpm are classed as high-speed motors, and those with speeds less than 500 rpm are classed as low-speed motors.

Synchronous motors are rated as unity-power-factor, 90 per cent leading-, or 80 per cent leading-power-factor motors.   Other power-factor ratings may be used for special applications.   While leading-power-factor motors provide more power-factor correction, they are more expensive than unity-power-factor motors since they must have larger current-carrying capacities.

Unity-power-factor motors may be operated at leading power factors but with less than rated horsepower output.   This is because more than rated stator current must flow to carry the rated horsepower load at a reduced power factor.   Likewise field current must be increased above normal value.

Synchronous-motor nameplate data include the same items found on a-c generator nameplates with the kilovolt-ampere rating being replaced with a horsepower rating.

**14-6. Application of Synchronous Motors**   Synchronous motors are used for constant-speed power applications in sizes above 20 hp and more often in sizes larger than 100 hp.   A very common application is for driving air or gas compressors.   It is especially desirable that compressors be driven at a constant speed since their output and efficiency vary considerably with the speed at which they are operated.   Another common application is for driving d-c generators where a source of direct current is needed, such as for electrolytic processes or for an excitation supply for alternators and other synchronous motors.

Other common applications are in public-works pumping, for driving fans, blowers, and pulverizers.

**14-7. Power-factor Correction**   An outstanding advantage of synchronous motors is the fact that they operate at unity or leading power factors.   When operated on the same electrical system with induction motors, or other devices that operate at lagging power factors, the leading reactive kilovolt-amperes, or kilovars (kvar), supplied by the synchronous motors compensate for the lagging reactive kilovolt-amperes, or kilovars, of other devices, resulting in an improvement in the over-all power factor.

Low power factors are undesirable for several reasons. Generators, transformers, and supply circuits are limited in ratings by their current-carrying capacities. This means that the kilowatt load that they can deliver is directly proportional to the power factor of the loads that they supply. For example, a system can deliver only 70 per cent of the kilowatt load at 0.7 power factor that it can deliver at a unity power factor.

The voltage regulation of generators, transformers, and supply lines is also poorer at low power factors than at unity power factor.

Since line and equipment losses are proportional to $I^2R$, these losses are higher in an electrical system for a given kilowatt load at low power factors than at unity power factor. Thus any improvement in power factor releases supply capacity, increases efficiency, and in general improves the operating characteristics of the system. For this reason power companies often include power-factor clauses in industrial power contracts which place a penalty on a consumer for operating at a power factor below a certain value.

To gain some of the above-mentioned benefits from high power factors, very often synchronous motors are used to compensate for the lagging reactive kilovolt-amperes taken by induction motors. The following example will be used to illustrate how a synchronous motor when used on the same system with induction motors improves the over-all power factor.

**Example 1** The load of an industrial concern is 400 kva at a power factor of 75 per cent, lagging. An additional motor load of 100 kw is needed. Find the new kilovolt-ampere load and the power factor of the load, if the motor to be added is (a) an induction motor with a power factor of 90 per cent, lagging, and (b) an 80 per cent power factor (leading) synchronous motor.

Original load, 400 kva at 75 per cent power factor.

$$kw = 400 \times 0.75 = 300 \text{ kw}$$
$$(kva)^2 = (kw)^2 + (kvar)^2$$
$$kvar = \sqrt{(kva)^2 - (kw)^2}$$
$$= \sqrt{400^2 - 300^2} = 264.6 \text{ kvar, lagging}$$

(a) Induction motor, 100 kw at 90 per cent lagging power factor

$$kva = \frac{kw}{\text{power factor}} = \frac{100}{0.9} = 111.1 \text{ kva}$$
$$kvar = \sqrt{(111.1)^2 - (100)^2} = 48.4 \text{ kvar, lagging}$$

$$\text{Resultant kilowatt load} = 300 + 100 = 400 \text{ kw}$$
$$\text{Resultant kilovar load} = 264.6 + 48.4 = 313 \text{ kvar}$$
$$\text{Resultant kilovolt-ampere load} = \sqrt{(\text{kw})^2 + (\text{kvar})^2}$$
$$= \sqrt{(400)^2 + (313)^2} = 507.8 \text{ kva}$$
$$\text{Resultant power factor} = \frac{\text{kw}}{\text{kva}} = \frac{400}{507.8}$$
$$= 0.787 = 78.7 \text{ per cent, lagging}$$

Since the relation between kilowatts, kilovars, and kilovolt-amperes of any load may be represented by a right triangle, the solution of the above problem may be made graphically as shown in Fig. 14-6. The triangle $OAE$ represents the original load; $OE = 300$ kw, $EA = 264.6$ kvar, and $OA = 400$ kva. The angle $\theta_1$ is the power-factor angle of the original load. Triangle $ABC$ represents the added induction-motor load, sides $AC$, $CB$, and $AB$ representing

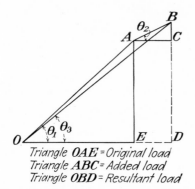

*Triangle OAE = Original load*
*Triangle ABC = Added load*
*Triangle OBD = Resultant load*

Fig. 14-6. Graphical solution for Example 1a.

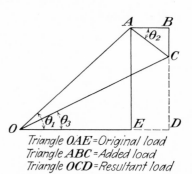

*Triangle OAE = Original load*
*Triangle ABC = Added load*
*Triangle OCD = Resultant load*

Fig. 14-7. Graphical solution for Example 1b.

100 kw, 48.4 kvar, and 111.1 kva, respectively, with the phase angle represented as $\theta_2$. Triangle $OBD$ represents the resultant load with sides $OD$, $DB$, and $OB$ representing 400 kw, 313 kvar, and 507.8 kva, respectively. The resultant power-factor angle is $\theta_3$.

(b) Synchronous motor, 100 kw at 80 per cent leading power factor.

$$\text{kva} = \frac{\text{kw}}{\text{power factor}} = \frac{100}{0.8} = 125 \text{ kva}$$
$$\text{kvar} = \sqrt{(125)^2 - (100)^2} = 75 \text{ kvar leading}$$
$$\text{Resultant kilowatt load} = 300 + 100 = 400 \text{ kw}$$
$$\text{Resultant kilovar load} = 264.6 \text{ (lagging)} - 75 \text{ (leading)}$$
$$= 189.6 \text{ kvar (lagging)}$$
$$\text{Resultant kilovolt-ampere load} = \sqrt{(\text{kw})^2 + (\text{kvar})^2}$$
$$= \sqrt{(400)^2 + (189.6)^2} = 442.5 \text{ kva}$$
$$\text{Resultant power factor} = \frac{\text{kw}}{\text{kva}} = \frac{400}{442.5} = 0.903 = 90.3 \text{ per cent, lagging}$$

The graphical solution is shown in Fig. 14-7, with triangles $OEA$, $ABC$, and $OCD$ representing the original load, the added load, and the resultant load, respectively.

Synchronous motors when operated without mechanical load and for the purpose of improving power factor are called *synchronous condensers*. By considerably overexciting its field, a synchronous condenser is made to operate at a very low leading power factor, the only kilowatt input required being that necessary to supply its losses. When used at the end of a long transmission line, the synchronous condenser neutralizes the effects of lagging power-factor loads, thereby improving the regulation of the transmission line.

## SELF-SYNCHRONOUS APPARATUS

Self-synchronous devices are used to transmit motion electrically between two points. Self-synchronous indicating systems are used for transmitting messages or orders between two points, such as between the bridge and engine room of a ship. They are also used to provide an indication of some mechanical motion at distant points such as indications of wind direction, wind velocity, speed of a rotating shaft, the difference in speed of two rotating shafts, or the angular position of some mechanical device. Automatic control of operations remote from the point of control may also be accomplished by self-synchronous apparatus. As power-transmission devices, self-synchronous systems are used to maintain synchronism between several driving units such as between the driving units at each end of a lift bridge or between the many units of large newspaper presses.

**14-8. Self-synchronous Indicators**  Self-synchronous indicators are very similar in construction to small synchronous motors. A simple indicating system consists of a self-synchronous generator or transmitter, and a self-synchronous motor or receiver. The stators of each have three uniformly distributed windings very similar to the three-phase windings used in synchronous motors and generators. The rotors are of two-pole salient-pole construction. The transmitter and receiver rotors are similar in construction except that the receiver is equipped with a damper ring mounted on the shaft to prevent excessive oscillations and to prevent the receiver from starting as an induction motor. Figure 14-8 shows the wound rotor and damper of a typical receiver.

The rotor or primary circuits of both transmitter and receiver are excited from a single-phase a-c supply, and the stator or secondary windings of the transmitter are connected to those of the receiver as shown in Fig. 14-9.

When the primary circuits are energized, emfs are induced in the secondary windings by transformer action. The value of the emf induced in each of the three secondary windings of both the transmitter and receiver depends on the angular positions of the rotors. When the

Fig. 14-8. Wound rotor of a self-synchronous receiver with damper ring mounted on the shaft. Front and rear views of damper shown at the left. (*Courtesy of General Electric Company.*)

rotors of the transmitter and receiver are in the same relative position, the secondary emfs induced in the transmitter are equal and opposite to those of the receiver and no secondary current flows. However, if the position of the transmitter rotor is changed, the secondary emfs are no longer balanced, resulting in the flow of current through the secondary circuits of both the transmitter and receiver. The action

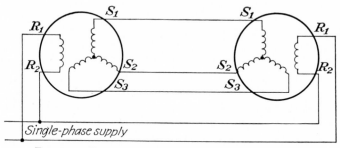

Fig. 14-9. Circuits of a simple self-synchronous system.

of the secondary currents is to produce torque in both the transmitter and receiver. The torque in the transmitter is a restraining torque, opposing the motion of the rotor, while that in the receiver attempts to move the receiver rotor to a new position where the secondary emfs are again balanced. Hence if the receiver rotor is free to turn, it will follow any motion of the transmitter. If the transmitter rotor is moved, say, 30° clockwise, the receiver rotor also moves 30° in the clockwise direction. If the rotor of the transmitter is rotated at a speed of, say, 20 rpm, the receiver rotor follows in synchronism at 20 rpm. Thus either angular motions or rotation may be transmitted by the system.

The transmitter rotor may be moved automatically by means of gears from some mechanical motion or may be moved manually by an operator. The transmitter and receiver of a manually operated signal indicator are shown in Fig. 14-10. When the pointer on the transmitter is set at a given signal, the pointer of the receiver takes up a corresponding position.

(a)                                        (b)

FIG. 14-10. (a) Hand-operated self-synchronous transmitter. (b) Self-synchronous indicator. (*Courtesy of General Electric Company.*)

The simple indicating system shown in Fig. 14-9 may be extended so that one transmitter may be made to operate several receivers simultaneously. Selective operation may also be provided, with the transmitter being connected to any one of several receivers one at a time.

**14-9. Self-synchronous Power Drives**  Self-synchronous motors used for synchronized power drives are very similar in construction to three-phase wound-rotor induction motors. The primary windings are excited from a three-phase supply, and the secondary windings are interconnected.

The respective units of the system are synchronized by first applying single-phase excitation, the three-phase excitation being applied after a time delay of a few seconds. This is necessary since if three-phase excitation were applied when the rotors were not in synchronous positions the unbalanced secondary emfs might allow enough secondary current to flow to allow the motors to start as induction motors. Once synchronized, the various units all rotate at the same speed or at definite speed ratios over the required speed range.

## REVIEW QUESTIONS

**1.** How does the construction of a synchronous motor compare with that of a synchronous generator?

**2.** Describe the principle of operation of a synchronous motor. How does the principle of operation of a synchronous motor differ from that of an induction motor?

**3.** What determines the speed of a synchronous motor? How may the speed be varied?

**4.** How would it be possible to reverse the direction of rotation of a synchronous motor?

**5.** Why is a synchronous motor not self-starting? Name some ways in which they are started.

**6.** What is pull-in torque?

**7.** What precaution must be taken in regard to the field circuit of a synchronous motor during the starting period?

**8.** What types of controllers are used for starting synchronous motors? What forms of motor protection are generally provided?

**9.** How does a synchronous motor adjust its electrical input with changes in mechanical output?

**10.** For a constant field excitation, what is the effect on the motor power factor of an increasing load?

**11.** What is meant by the pull-out torque of a synchronous motor?

**12.** For a constant mechanical output, how may the power factor at which a synchronous motor operates be changed?

**13.** Compare the method of adjusting the power factor of a synchronous motor with the method of adjusting the power factor of a synchronous generator operating in parallel with other synchronous generators.

**14.** When is a synchronous motor said to be (a) overexcited; (b) underexcited?

**15.** How are synchronous motors classified as to speed?

**16.** What are the standard power-factor ratings of synchronous motors?

**17.** What precaution must be taken in operating a synchronous motor at a power factor that is more leading than its rated power factor?

**18.** Under what operating condition would the field circuit be apt to heat abnormally?

**19.** What are some applications of synchronous motors?

**20.** Why is a low power factor undesirable?

**21.** Explain how a synchronous motor can improve the power factor of a load with a low lagging power factor.

**22.** What is a synchronous condenser?

**23.** What are some uses of self-synchronous devices?

**24.** Describe the construction of the self-synchronous receiver. How does it differ from the transmitter?

**25.** Describe the operation of the simple self-synchronous indicating system. Compare its operation with that of two single-phase transformers operating in parallel.

## PROBLEMS

**1.** What is the speed of a 30-pole 60-cycle 440-volt synchronous motor? Is this motor classed as a high- or low-speed motor?

**2.** What is the per cent speed regulation of the motor in Prob. 1?

**3.** A motor-generator set used for frequency conversion consists of a 10-pole 25-cycle synchronous motor and a direct-connected 24-pole synchronous generator. What is the generator frequency?

**4.** If a six-pole induction motor electrically connected to the generator terminals in Prob. 3 has a full-load slip of 5 per cent, what is its full-load speed in rpm?

**5.** The propulsion motors used on a naval vessel are rated 5,900 hp, three phase, 2,400 volts, 62.5 cycles, and 139 rpm.   How many poles do they have?   The speed of the above motors may be varied by a variation of the supply frequency between 16 and 62.5 cycles.   What are the maximum and minimum speeds?   Assuming a full-load efficiency of 85 per cent and unity power factor, what is the full-load current input per terminal?

**6.** In Example 1, Art. 14-7, what must be the power factor of the added 100-kw load if it improves the over-all plant power factor to 100 per cent?

**7.** A transmission line delivers a load of 7,500 kva at a power factor of 70 per cent, lagging.   If a synchronous condenser is to be located at the end of the line, to improve the load power factor to 100 per cent, how many kilovolt-amperes must it draw from the line, assuming it to operate at 0 per cent leading power factor?

# CHAPTER 15

# SINGLE-PHASE MOTORS

Single-phase motors may be divided into three general classes: (1) commutator motors, (2) induction motors, and (3) synchronous motors. The more common commutator motors are the series motor, the repulsion motor, and the repulsion-induction motor, with various modifications and combinations of these types being in use.

Single-phase induction motors require a special starting means. Because of this it has been customary to classify these motors according to the starting method used. Thus, single-phase induction motors are classed as split-phase motors, repulsion-start induction motors, and shaded-pole motors.

**15-1. The A-C Series Motor** Direct-current shunt or series motors rotate in the same direction regardless of the polarity of the supply. Thus, it might be expected that either motor would operate on alternating current. It has been found, however, that the shunt motor develops but little torque when it is connected to an a-c supply. The high inductance of the field winding causes the field current to lag the armature current by such a large angle that a very low net torque results. However, in the series motor, the field and armature currents are the same, so that the main field and armature field are in phase. Therefore, about the same torque is developed with a given alternating current as with a like amount of direct current in a series motor.

However, some changes must be made in a d-c series motor that is to operate satisfactorily on alternating current. When an ordinary d-c series motor is connected to an a-c supply, the current drawn by the motor is limited to a relatively low value by the high series-field impedance. Consequently, the power developed is small. To reduce the field reactance to a minimum, a-c series motors are built with as few field turns as possible, sufficient field flux being obtained by using a low-reluctance magnetic circuit. The effect of armature reaction in the series motor is overcome by the use of compensating windings in the pole faces. The compensating winding may be short-circuited on itself, in which case the motor is said to be *inductively* compensated, or it may be connected in series with the armature and field, in which case the motor is *conductively* compensated. All parts of the magnetic circuit of an a-c series motor must be laminated to reduce the eddy-current losses.

The operating characteristics of the a-c series motor are very similar to those of d-c series motors. The speed increases to a high value with a decrease in load. In the very small series motors, the losses are usually large enough at no load to limit the speed to a definite value. The torque is high for high armature currents, thus giving the motor a good starting torque.

Since inductive reactance is directly proportional to frequency, a-c series-motor operating characteristics are better at lower frequencies. Some series motors are built in large sizes for traction service and are designed to operate at low frequencies, 25 cps or less. However, fractional horsepower sizes may be designed to operate satisfactorily at 60 cycles. For some applications, it is desirable to use a motor that will operate on either a-c or d-c circuits. By a compromise design, fractional-horsepower series motors may be built to operate satisfactorily on either 60 cycles or direct current at 115 or 230 volts. These motors are called *universal* motors. Common applications for the universal motor are in vacuum cleaners, sewing machines, and portable tools.

**15-2. The Repulsion Motor**  The field or stator winding of a repulsion motor is connected directly to a single-phase source. The armature or rotor is similar to a d-c motor armature, with a drum-type winding connected to a commutator. However, the brushes are not connected to the supply, but are connected to each other or are short-circuited. The armature winding is excited by induction; that is, the alternating field flux induces currents in the armature circuit. The principle of operation is illustrated in Fig. 15-1 which shows a two-pole repulsion motor with its two short-circuited brushes. The three drawings of Fig. 15-1 represent a time at which the field current is increasing in the direction shown so that the left-hand pole is north and the right-hand pole is south at the instants shown.

As the field flux increases through the ring armature winding represented in Fig. 15-1, emf is induced in both the upper and lower halves of the armature winding. The direction of the emf is such that the magnetic effect of the resulting armature currents will oppose the increase in flux. As shown by the arrows on the armature winding in Fig. 15-1*a*, emf is induced to cause current to flow from brush *A* to brush $B$ through the two armature paths $ACB$ and $ADB$. With the short-circuited brushes set in line with the centers of the field poles as shown in Fig. 15-1$a$, current will flow from brush $B$ through the short-circuiting bar to brush $A$ where it enters the armature and flows back to brush $B$ through the two paths provided by the armature winding. With the brushes set in this position, half of the armature conductors

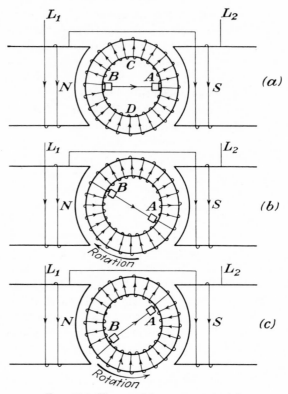

Fig. 15-1. The repulsion-motor principle.

under the north pole carry current inward and half carry current outward. The same is true under the south pole. Therefore, as much torque is developed in one direction as in the other and the armature remains stationary.

Figure 15-1$b$ represents the motor at the same instant as that in Fig. 15-1$a$, but the brushes have been shifted to a position that is about 20° in a clockwise direction from the center line of the field poles. Electromotive force is still induced in the directions indicated in Fig. 15-1$a$, and current flows through the two paths of the armature winding from brush $A$ to brush $B$.  However, because of the new brush positions, the greater part of the conductors under the north pole carry current in one direction, while the greater part of the conductors under the south pole carry current in the opposite direction.  With the brushes in this position, torque is developed in a clockwise direction. If the brushes are shifted in the counterclockwise direction as in Fig. 15-1c, the armature current under the pole faces is reversed and torque is developed in the counterclockwise direction.  Thus a repulsion motor may be made to rotate in either direction, depending on the direction in which the brushes are shifted.

The repulsion motor has operating characteristics very similar to those of a series motor; that is, it has a high starting torque and a high speed at light loads.  The most general application of the repulsion-motor principle is in the starting of induction motors, which in themselves do not possess a starting torque.

**15-3. The Repulsion-Induction Motor**  The *repulsion-induction* motor has two separate rotor windings, one inside the other, in a manner similar to the double-squirrel-cage three-phase rotor.  The inner winding is a squirrel-cage winding with the rotor bars permanently short-circuited.  Placed over the squirrel-cage winding is a repulsion winding similar to a d-c armature winding.  The repulsion winding is connected to a commutator on which ride short-circuited brushes.  The outer winding is active during the starting periods as in the double-squirrel-cage rotor, thus giving the motor the good starting characteristics of the repulsion motor.  As the motor speed increases, the current shifts from the outer to the inner winding, owing to the decreasing impedance of the inner winding with increasing speed, so that at the running speeds the squirrel-cage winding carries the greater part of the rotor current. This shifting from the repulsion- to the induction-motor characteristics is thus done without any switching arrangement.  This type of motor is used for applications requiring a high starting torque with an essentially constant running speed.  The common sizes are $\frac{1}{4}$ to 5 hp, although larger sizes are made.

**15-4. The Single-phase Induction-motor Principle**  In a two-phase induction motor, the phase coils are spaced 90 electrical degrees apart on the stator surface.  When these coils are excited by two-phase voltages, that is, voltages which differ in time phase by 90°, the resulting phase currents are out of phase by 90°.  Each of the two currents establishes a pulsating or alternating field, but these fields combine to produce a single rotating field as in the three-phase motor (Chap. 13).

The rotating field sweeping across the rotor conductors induces a current in these conductors that causes a torque to be developed in the direction of the rotation of the field.  This is the basic principle of operation of the polyphase motor.  It is briefly reviewed here because conditions in a single-phase motor are similar to those of a two-phase motor.

If a single-phase voltage is applied to the stator winding of a single-phase induction motor, alternating current will flow in that winding. This stator current establishes a field similar to that shown in Fig. 15-2. During the half-cycle that the stator current is flowing in the direction indicated, a south pole is established on the stator surface at $A$ and a north pole at $C$.  During the next half-cycle, the stator poles are

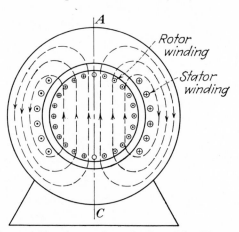

FIG. 15-2. The stator field pulsates along the line $AC$.  No torque is developed.

reversed.  Although the stator field strength is varying and reversing its action periodically, its action is always along the line $AC$.  This field, then, does not rotate but is a pulsating stationary field.

As in a transformer, voltages are induced in the secondary circuit, in this case the rotor.  Since single-phase induction-motor rotors are of the squirrel-cage type similar to those of polyphase motors, rotor currents are caused to flow as shown in Fig. 15-2.  These rotor currents establish poles on the rotor surface, but since these poles are always in direct line (along the line $AC$) with the stator poles, no torque is developed in either direction.  Therefore, *a single-phase induction motor is not self-starting* and requires some special starting means.

When, however, the single-phase stator winding in Fig. 15-2 is excited and the rotor is made to turn by some auxiliary device that will be described later, the rotor conductors cut across the stator field, causing

an emf to be generated in them.    This is illustrated in Fig. 15-3 which
shows the rotor being turned in a clockwise direction.    If the stator
flux is upward at the instant shown, the direction of the generated
rotor emfs, as determined by Fleming's right-hand rule, will be outward
in the upper half of the rotor and inward in the lower half of the rotor,
as indicated by the dots and crosses.    One-half cycle later the direction
of the generated emfs will be reversed.    The generated rotor emfs

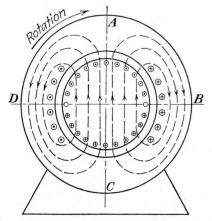

Fig. 15-3. The motor of Fig. 15-2, with the rotor turning, generates an emf in the
rotor conductors in the direction shown by the dots and crosses.

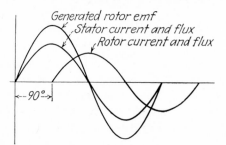

Fig. 15-4. Phase relations of the stator current and flux, the generated rotor emf,
and the rotor current and flux.    The rotor flux lags the stator flux by 90°.

vary *in phase* with the stator current and flux.    Because of the low
resistance and high inductance of the rotor, however, the resulting
rotor current *lags* the generated rotor emf by nearly 90°.    Figure 15-4
shows the phase relations of the stator current and flux, the rotor emf,
and the rotor current and flux.
    The maximum value of the field produced by the rotor currents, as
shown in Fig. 15-5, occurs nearly one-fourth cycle after the generated
rotor emf has reached its maximum value.    Because this rotor field is

at right angles to the stator field, it is called a *cross field*. Since the rotor currents are caused to flow by an alternating emf, the field resulting from these currents also alternates and its action is always along the line $DB$, Fig. 15-5. The cross field is very similar to a field that would be produced by another coil placed on the stator in the spaces at $A$ and $C$ in Fig. 15-5 and excited by a voltage 90° behind the voltage applied to the coil in place, as in a two-phase motor. Since the cross field acts at right angles to the stator field and also lags the stator field by 90° in *time phase*, the two fields combine to form a resultant rotating field that revolves at synchronous speed.

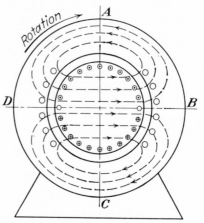

FIG. 15-5. The cross field established by the rotor currents one-fourth cycle later than the stator field shown in Fig. 15-3.

It should be kept in mind, however, that the cross field is produced by a *generator action* and therefore is present only when the rotor is turning. It also follows that the strength of the cross field must be proportional to the rotor speed. At synchronous speed the cross field is nearly the same strength as the stator field. But since an induction motor must operate at some speed lower than synchronous speed, the cross field is somewhat weaker than the stator field at actual operating speeds. This means that the rotating field in a single-phase induction motor is irregular and is not of constant strength as is the field of a polyphase motor. Therefore, the torque developed by a single-phase induction motor is irregular or pulsating. This is the reason why many single-phase motors are set on rubber or spring mounts to reduce the vibration and noise which are inherent in such motors.

**15-5. Split-phase Starting** It was shown in the preceding article that, when two windings are spaced 90 electrical degrees apart on the stator of a motor and are excited by two alternating emfs that are 90° displaced in time phase, a rotating magnetic field is produced.   If two windings so spaced are connected in parallel to a single-phase source, the field produced will alternate but will not revolve since the two windings are equivalent to but one single-phase winding.   If, however, an impedance is connected in series with one of these windings, the currents may be made to differ in time phase.   By the proper selection of such an impedance, the currents may be made to differ by as much as 90°, thereby producing a rotating field very much like the field of a two-phase motor.   This is the principle of *phase splitting*.

When two similar motor stator windings that are spaced 90 electrical degrees apart are connected in parallel to a single-phase source, the currents through the two windings lag the applied voltage by the same

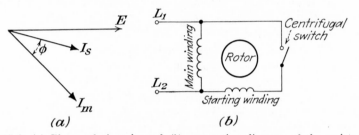

FIG. 15-6. (a) Phase relations in and (b) connection diagram of the resistance-start split-phase motor.

angle.   By connecting a resistance in series with one winding, the current through that winding is caused to be more nearly in phase with the applied voltage.   Since the current in the first winding is not affected by the addition of the resistance, the currents through the two windings are displaced in time phase.   This is the condition necessary to produce a revolving field.   A motor using this method of phase splitting is called a *resistance-start motor*.   The resistance-start split-phase motor is commonly known as the *split-phase motor* even though there are other forms of split-phase motors.

In practice, instead of using an external series resistor, one winding is designed to have a higher resistance and lower reactance than that of the other winding.   The high-resistance winding is called the *starting* or *auxiliary winding*, and the low-resistance winding is called the *main winding*.

The phase relations of the applied voltage $E$, the main-winding current $I_m$, and the starting-winding current $I_s$ at the instant of starting are shown in Fig. 15-6a.   The angle $\phi$ between the main and starting winding currents is small, being of the order of 30°, but this is enough phase difference to provide a weak rotating magnetic field. Since the currents in the two windings are not equal in magnitude, the rotating field is not uniform and the starting torque so produced is small.

It was shown in the preceding article that a single-phase induction motor develops a torque once it has been started. For this reason, the starting winding of the resistance-start motor is disconnected when the motor reaches a predetermined speed, usually 70 to 80 per cent of synchronous speed. This is accomplished by a centrifugally operated switch. A connection diagram showing the main and starting windings of a resistance-start motor is shown in Fig. 15-6b.

The resistance-start split-phase motor is very widely used for easily started loads. Common applications are for driving washing machines, woodworking tools, grinders, oil burners, and various other low starting-torque applications. Because of its low starting torque, this motor is seldom used in sizes larger than ⅓ hp.

An improvement can be made in the starting characteristics of a split-phase motor by connecting a capacitor in series with the starting

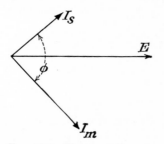

FIG. 15-7. Phase relations in the capacitor-start motor.

winding. A motor of this type is called a *capacitor-start motor*. The current through the main winding lags the applied voltage as in the resistance-start motor. By choosing a capacitor of the proper size, the current in the starting winding may be made to *lead* the voltage. Thus, the time-phase difference $\phi$ in the currents of the two windings at starting may be made nearly 90° as is shown in Fig. 15-7. This more nearly approximates the action of the two-phase revolving field than did the resistance-start motor, thereby resulting in a relatively higher starting torque.

The capacitor-start motor, like the resistance-start motor, has the starting winding disconnected by means of a centrifugal switch as the motor approaches synchronous speed. The centrifugally operated switch may be seen on the right-hand end of the rotor in the sectional view of the capacitor-start motor shown in Fig. 15-8. This type of motor has become popular because of the development of a cheap, reliable electrolytic condenser. It is commonly used on refrigerators or compressors or for other applications involving a hard starting load. The usual size range is from ⅛ to ¾ hp, but larger sizes are available.

Some split-phase motors are designed to operate with the auxiliary winding and its series capacitor permanently connected to the line. This type of motor is called the *capacitor motor*. The capacitance in series with the auxiliary winding may have one fixed value, or it may be of one value for starting and another value for running. One method of obtaining two values of capacitance is shown in Fig. 15-9. As the motor approaches synchronous speed, the centrifugal switch

FIG. 15-8. A capacitor-start motor. (*Courtesy of Wagner Electric Corporation.*)

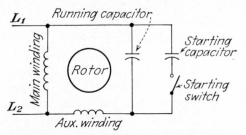

FIG. 15-9. Capacitor motor with a starting and running capacitor.

disconnects one section of the capacitor. The capacitor motor operates in essentially the same way as a two-phase motor, thereby producing a constant torque and not a pulsating torque as in other single-phase motors. For this reason, it is often used in applications where a quiet-operating motor is desired.    The permanently connected capacitor also causes the motor to operate at a good power factor.

The capacitor-start and capacitor motors have become increasingly popular and are now manufactured in the larger sized single-phase motors where previously only the repulsion-start motors were available.

### 15-6. The Repulsion-start Induction Motor

The repulsion-start induction motor is built for applications requiring a high starting torque.    The usual range of sizes is from ½ to 15 hp but, for special applications, ratings as high as 40 hp are available.    This type of motor has a better starting torque than the split-phase types, although the

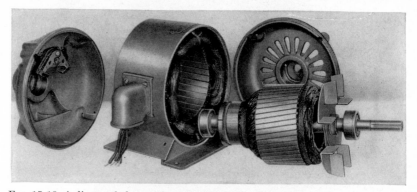

Fig. 15-10. A dismantled repulsion-start induction motor.    (*Courtesy of Robbins & Myers, Inc.*)

capacitor-start motor has nearly the same starting characteristics in the fractional horsepower sizes.    The repulsion-start induction motor is often erroneously referred to as the repulsion-induction motor.

As the name implies, the repulsion-start induction motor starts as a repulsion motor and runs as an induction motor.    The rotor of a repulsion motor is built like that of a d-c motor; that is, the windings are connected to a commutator.    To convert such a rotor to an induction-motor rotor, it is necessary to short-circuit the commutator segments. This is done in the repulsion-start induction motor by a centrifugal device that operates as the motor nears full speed to press a conducting ring against the commutator.    In some motors of this type, the brushes are lifted from the commutator at the same time that the commutator is short-circuited.    Figure 15-10 shows the various parts of the repulsion-start induction motor.    Note the short-circuiting ring at the end of the commutator.

The repulsion-start induction motor combines the desirable starting characteristics of the repulsion motor with the good operating characteristics of the induction motor.

### 15-7. The Shaded-pole Motor

A shading coil is a low-resistance short-circuited copper loop which is placed around a part of each pole of a motor. Figure 15-11 shows one pole of a motor which is equipped with shading coils. As the flux begins its increase at the beginning of the cycle, an emf is induced in the short-circuited coil which causes a current to flow. The field produced by the flow of current is in such direction as to oppose the change in the main field flux. Thus, the increase in flux is less rapid through the shading coil than in the main part of the pole, as is shown in Fig. 15-11$a$. Figure 15-11$b$ represents

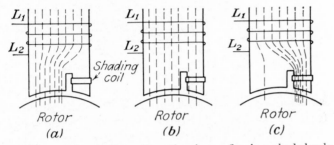

Fig. 15-11. Effect of the shading coil on the air-gap flux in a shaded-pole motor.

the same pole when the flux has reached a maximum value and is not changing in value. The flux is distributed uniformly across the pole face, since no current is flowing in the shading coil. As the flux decreases, the induced current in the coil is in a direction such that its magnetic effect opposes the decrease in flux. Consequently, the flux decreases less rapidly through the coil than through the other part of the pole as shown in Fig. 15-11$c$.

The effect of the shading coil is to cause the field flux to shift across the pole face from the unshaded to the shaded portion. This shifting flux, somewhat like a rotating magnetic field, produces a small starting torque. This method of motor starting is used only on very small motors up to about $\frac{1}{25}$ hp in size, such as may be used for driving small fans and relays.

### 15-8. Synchronous Motors

There are several types of nonexcited single-phase synchronous motors that are used to drive electric clocks, phonograph motors, and timing devices, all of which require an absolutely constant speed drive.

One type of small synchronous motor, called the Warren synchronous motor, is shown in Fig. 15-12. A shifting field is produced by the use of shading coils on the pole faces in a manner similar to that produced in the shaded-pole induction motor. The rotor is built of a hardened magnet steel. A starting torque is developed from the effects of the flow of eddy currents in the rotor iron and by the effect of hysteresis. When the rotor reaches synchronous speed, the rotor steel

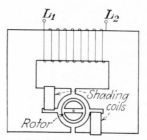

Fig. 15-12. The Warren synchronous motor.

becomes magnetized in one direction since it completes the magnetic circuit for the stator flux. The rotor iron being so magnetized is pulled into synchronism with the rotating stator flux, and the motor operates as a synchronous motor. The torque so developed is very small, but when the rotor is geared down through a gear train, enough torque is available for driving timepieces or other such devices.

## 15-9. Summary of Single-phase Motor Types
Single-phase motor types may be summarized in outline form as follows:

    I. Commutator motors
        A. Series motor
            1. Alternating-current series
            2. Universal
        B. Repulsion motor
        C. Repulsion-induction motor
    II. Induction motors (classified as to starting methods)
        A. Split-phase motors
            1. Resistance-start motor
            2. Capacitor-start motor
            3. Capacitor motor
        B. Repulsion-start induction motor
        C. Shaded-pole motor
    III. Synchronous motors

## REVIEW QUESTIONS

**1.** What are the three general classes of single-phase motors?

**2.** Name three types of single-phase induction motors.

**3.** Why is the shunt motor unsatisfactory for a-c operation?

**4.** How does an a-c series motor differ in construction from a d-c series motor?

**5.** Is an a-c series motor classed as a constant- or variable-speed motor?

**6.** What is a universal motor?

**7.** What type of armature is used on a repulsion motor? How are the brushes connected?

**8.** Why is there no torque developed when the brushes of a repulsion motor are set on the center line of the field poles? Will torque be developed when the brushes are moved 90° from the above position?

**9.** Describe the operating characteristics of a repulsion motor.

**10.** Describe the rotor construction of a repulsion-induction motor.

**11.** Why does the starting current flow in the outer winding of a repulsion-induction motor?

**12.** What are the operating characteristics and applications of the repulsion-induction motor?

**13.** Does a single-phase induction motor develop torque when the rotor is stationary? Why?

**14.** What causes the rotating magnetic field to be established in a single-phase induction motor? What determines its direction of rotation?

**15.** What is the split-phase method of motor starting? Name two methods of phase splitting.

**16.** Why is the starting winding of a split-phase motor disconnected after the motor has been started?

**17.** Which has the better starting characteristics, the resistance-start or the capacitor-start induction motor?

**18.** What is a capacitor motor?

**19.** Describe briefly the construction of the repulsion-start induction motor.

**20.** Describe briefly the operating characteristics of the repulsion-start induction motor.

**21.** What is the effect of the shading coil when used in starting induction motors? Motors using this method of starting are built in sizes up to about what horsepower rating?

**22.** Why does the rotor of a Warren synchronous motor stay in synchronism?

# CHAPTER 16

# CIRCUIT-PROTECTIVE AND SWITCHING EQUIPMENT

Protective and switching equipment plays a very important part in the operation of a modern electrical system. Since modern economy is so dependent upon the availability of electric energy, it is the goal of those who design, operate, and maintain electrical supply systems to provide as nearly as possible a continuous, uninterrupted supply of electric energy to all consumers at a reasonable price. To provide this service, heavy investments must be made in generating, transmitting, and distributing equipment. Protective and switching equipment is necessary to protect this investment, to provide flexibility in operation of the system, and to assure a dependable supply of energy to all consumers.

**16-1. Short Circuits and Interrupting Capacity**   Short circuits are the greatest hazard to the continuity of service. Since protective and switching equipment must either isolate or withstand the effects of short circuits, it is desirable to know what short circuits are, what causes them, and what their effects are.

All circuits consist of conductors that are isolated from other conductors by insulating materials. Conductors are necessary to carry the current, and insulators are necessary to confine the current to the conductor. Conductor materials commonly used are copper and aluminum. Insulating materials may be air, rubber, porcelain, thermoplastic materials, and other similar materials.

Conductors used indoors are usually insulated with rubber, varnished cambric, or thermoplastic materials coated directly over the conductor material so that the conductor may be placed in a confined area such as a conduit or raceway. Conductors used on outdoor overhead lines are very often bare and are supported on glass or porcelain insulators. Such circuits depend upon physical separation in air for their insulation, air being the insulator.

Regardless of the construction of an electric circuit, the two basic components are present, the conductor and the insulator.  However, regardless of the care used in constructing an electric circuit, the circuit is subject to damage such that the insulator between two or more conductors is destroyed and a *short circuit* or a *fault* is said to exist.  A short circuit is then merely an insulation failure in an electric circuit; this failure in insulation provides a low-resistance current path in the circuit.

Insulation failures or short circuits in an electric circuit may be caused by inherent defects or by external causes.  Inherent defects result from improper design or installation of equipment.  Insulation may fail because of external causes such as lightning surges, switching surges, mechanical damage, or operating errors.  Many short circuits

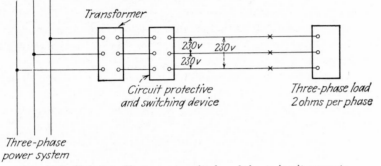

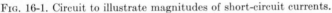

FIG. 16-1. Circuit to illustrate magnitudes of short-circuit currents.

are the result of overloads.  Overloads cause a deterioration of insulation and if sustained may cause a complete failure of insulation resulting in a short circuit.

The amount of current flowing in a circuit is determined by the applied voltage and the impedance of the circuit.  This is true in a normal circuit as well as in a faulty circuit.  In the circuit shown in Fig. 16-1, the normal load current is the phase voltage divided by the phase impedance, or

$$I_{\text{norm}} = \frac{230}{1.73 \times 2} = 66 \text{ amp}$$

However, if a three-phase short circuit should occur at the point $X$, the flow of current in the circuit will be much larger since the only impedance to limit the flow of current is then the impedance of the system itself.  If the system and the transformer have an impedance of 0.1 ohm per phase, the short-circuit current will be

$$I_{sc} = \frac{230}{1.73 \times 0.1} = 1{,}330 \text{ amp}$$

The larger the supply system and supply transformer, the lower the system impedance becomes. If the circuit in Fig. 16-1 were supplied by a larger transformer so that the system and transformer impedance were only 0.01 ohm per phase, then the short-circuit current would be

$$I_{sc} = \frac{230}{1.73 \times 0.01} = 13{,}300 \text{ amp}$$

As may be seen from the foregoing examples, insulation failures cause abnormally high currents to flow. Such high values of current may damage equipment or property unless the faulty circuit or equipment is removed from the supply system. Furthermore, the amount of damage to equipment or property is somewhat proportional to the length of time that a short circuit is allowed to exist on an electrical system. It is, therefore, imperative that short circuits be removed as quickly as possible. It is further desirable to remove only the faulty circuit or equipment from the system so that service may be maintained to the remainder of the system.

A circuit-protective and switching device such as the one shown in Fig. 16-1 has two purposes:

1. It carries the normal load current and when necessary is used to open and close the circuit.

2. It is used to open the circuit to interrupt the flow of abnormal or short-circuit current.

Circuit-protective and switching devices in general have two ratings: a *continuous* rating and an *interrupting* rating. The continuous rating is usually in amperes and is the amount of current that a device can carry continuously without overheating. The interrupting rating of a device is based on the ability of that device to interrupt the flow of short-circuit current. Interrupting ratings of low-voltage devices are usually in amperes and of high-voltage devices either in amperes or in kilovolt-amperes at a given voltage.

**16-2. Electrical Distribution Systems** The distribution of electric energy is accomplished by dividing and subdividing large-capacity feeders into feeders of smaller and smaller capacity. At each change in circuit capacity on an electrical system there is a distribution center at which is grouped circuit-protective and switching equipment. In general, this is true throughout a system from the generators to the loads.

The system represented in one-line-diagram form in Fig. 16-2 is a simple radial system in which all circuits radiate from the generating station. Typical groups of protective and switching equipment are

shown in the diagram. An assembly of metal-clad switchgear and a
step-up outdoor substation are shown at the generating station.
Another section of metal-clad switchgear is shown at the 34,500- to
4,160-volt step-down substation. At the load are shown the load-
center unit substation, low-voltage metal-enclosed switchgear (which

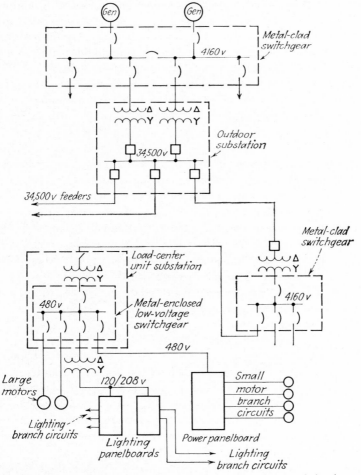

Fig. 16-2. Electrical system one-line diagram to illustrate the use of circuit-protective and switching equipment.

is a part of the unit substation), and lighting and power panelboards.
Some of the more commonly used protective and switching equipment
as shown in Fig. 16-2, and the part this equipment plays in the functioning of the modern electrical system are discussed briefly in this
chapter. This equipment has been grouped here into two main groups:

low-voltage equipment for circuits operating at 600 volts and below, and high-voltage equipment for circuits operating at voltages above 600 volts.

## LOW-VOLTAGE PROTECTIVE AND SWITCHING EQUIPMENT

The classification of low-voltage protective and switching equipment as used here applies to that equipment used on circuits rated at 600 volts or less. This voltage classification includes a large percentage of the utilization systems such as in homes, commercial establishments, and industries since most of these systems utilize power at 120, 208, 240, 480, or 550 volts. Protective and switching equipment used on such systems is used for normal-load switching, for protection of circuits and equipment against overload, and for protection against short circuits.

**16-3. Low-voltage Fuses** A fuse is an overcurrent protective device that has a circuit-opening fusible member directly heated and destroyed by the passage of overcurrent through it. As indicated by the definition, a fuse contains a current-carrying element so sized that the heat created by the flow of normal current through it is not sufficient to fuse or melt the element. However, when short-circuit or overload currents flow through the fuse, the fusible element melts and opens the circuit. The fusible element of an indoor fuse is enclosed in a protective housing to prevent the heat generated during the clearing of a short circuit from damaging adjacent equipment. Some representative types of fuses are shown in Fig. 16-3.

The *plug fuse* is used on circuits rated 125 volts or less to ground. This fuse consists of a zinc or alloy strip fusible element enclosed in a porcelain or Pyrex housing which is fitted with a screw base. The maximum continuous current-carrying capacity of plug fuses is 30 amp, and the commonly used standard sizes are 10, 15, 20, 25, and 30 amp. These fuses do not have published interrupting capacities since they are ordinarily used on circuits that have relatively low values of available short-circuit current.

*Cartridge fuses* are used on circuits with voltage ratings up to 600 volts, the standard voltage ratings of these fuses being 250 and 600 volts. The nonrenewable cartridge fuse is constructed with a zinc or alloy fusible element enclosed in a cylindrical fiber tube. The ends of the fusible element are attached to metallic contact pieces at the ends of the tube. The tube is filled with an insulating porous powder resembling chalk which surrounds the fusible element. On overloads or short circuits, the fusible element is heated to a high temperature, causing it to vaporize. The powder in the fuse cartridge cools and condenses the vapor and quenches the arc, thereby interrupting the flow of current.

Cartridge fuses are also available in a renewable type in which the fusible element may be replaced after it has operated. The ends of the cartridge are removable so that the fuse link is readily replaceable. This feature minimizes fuse expense where a great many fuses must be

Fig. 16-3. Some representative types of plug and cartridge fuses. (*Courtesy of General Electric Company.*)

replaced. However, this type of fuse is not generally considered to be as reliable as the nonrenewable type.

Cartridge fuses both in the 250- and 600-volt ratings are made to fit standardized fuse-clip sizes. These are 30-, 60-, 100-, 200-, 400-, and 600-amp sizes. Each fuse-clip size has several continuous current ratings. For example, the 100-amp size is available in the continuous ratings of 70, 80, 90, and 100 amp. Standard National Electrical Code type cartridge fuses do not have published interrupting ratings since these ratings have not been standardized. However, for application on systems having high values of available short-circuit current there are fuses available which have published interrupting ratings of as high as 100,000 amp.

*Time-lag fuses* are made in both the plug and cartridge types. These fuses are constructed so as to have a much greater time lag than ordinary fuses, especially for overload currents. They do operate, however, to clear short-circuit currents in about the same time as do the standard fuses. Time-lag fuses have two parts, a thermal-cutout part and a fuse link. The thermal cutout with its long time lag operates on overload currents up to about 500 per cent of normal current. Currents above this value are interrupted by the fuse link. Time-lag fuses find their greatest application in motor circuits where it is desirable that the fuse provide protection for the circuit and yet not operate because of a momentary high current during the starting period of the motor.

Since a fuse is a device that is destroyed in the process of interrupting the flow of abnormal current, it must be easily replaceable. Plug fuses have a screw-type base and can be inserted into sockets designed for their use. Cartridge fuses are inserted into fuse clips which make contact with the two ends of the fuse. Fuse sockets and clips usually are assembled into a supporting insulating base provided with means for connecting the fuse into the circuit. The assemblies of fuse, fuse clips, and supports are manufactured and used in many different ways. Two devices in which fuses are commonly used are *safety switches* and *panelboards*.

**16-4. Safety Switches**  A *switch* is a device for isolating parts of an electric circuit or for changing connections in a circuit or system. When a switch is mounted in a metal enclosure and is operable by means of an external handle, it is called a *safety switch*. The switch itself is not designed for interrupting the flow of short-circuit currents. However, switches and fuses are often incorporated into a single device called a *fusible safety switch*.

Safety switches are made in two-, three-, four-, or five-pole assemblies, either fused or unfused. They are made in single-throw and double-throw units; and, depending upon their use, they have a variety of constructional features. One type known as type A has a quick-make, quick-break mechanism so arranged that regardless of the speed at which the operating handle is moved, a spring-loaded arrangement causes the contacts to open or close with a quick motion. This type of switch also has a door interlock to prevent the opening of the enclosure door when the switch is closed. A type A three-pole fusible safety switch with the door open and the fuses removed is shown in Fig. 16-4.

Enclosed switches, either fusible or nonfusible, are used as disconnecting devices for main services into buildings, for feeder and branch circuit-protective and switching devices, and for motor protection and switching.

Safety switches are available in two voltage ratings: 230 and 575 volts a-c.    Current ratings are the same as the standard fuse-clip sizes.

FIG. 16-4. A three-pole safety switch.    (*Courtesy of Square D Company.*)

## 16-5. Low-voltage Air Circuit Breakers    A circuit breaker is a device designed for interrupting a circuit between separable contacts without injury to itself.    Air circuit breakers are circuit breakers in which the circuit interruption occurs in air.    The circuit breakers to be discussed here are the so-called low-voltage circuit breakers suitable for application on circuits rated 600 volts or lower.    Circuit breakers intended for application on high-voltage circuits are called *power circuit breakers* and are discussed in Art. 16-10.

One commonly used low-voltage air circuit breaker is the *molded-case breaker*. The breaker is assembled as an integral unit in a housing of insulating material. The external appearance of a three-pole

molded-case breaker is shown in Fig. 16-5, and a cutaway view of the same breaker is shown in Fig. 16-6.

An electric circuit is completed or interrupted manually with a circuit breaker by moving the operating handle to the ON or OFF position. In all except the very small breakers, the linkage between the operating handle and the contacts is arranged for a quick-make, quick-break contact action regardless of the speed at which the handle is moved. The handle is also trip-free so that the contacts cannot be held closed against a short circuit or overload.

FIG. 16-5. A three-pole molded-case air circuit breaker of the 100-amp frame size. (*Courtesy of Square D Company.*)

The breaker automatically trips when the current through it exceeds a certain value. In the lower current ratings, automatic tripping is accomplished by a thermal tripping device. The thermal trip consists of a bimetallic element so calibrated that the heat from the normal current through it does not cause it to

FIG. 16-6. Cutaway view of the circuit breaker shown in Fig. 16-5. (*Courtesy of Square D Company.*)

deflect. However, an abnormally high current caused either by an overload or by a short circuit causes the element to deflect and trip the linkage holding the circuit-breaker contacts closed. The breaker contacts are opened by spring action.

The bimetallic tripping element, being responsive to heat from the current flowing through it, has an inverse-time characteristic. It operates quickly for heavy currents such as those resulting from short circuits and operates more slowly for moderate overload currents. This is a desirable characteristic for an overcurrent protective device that is used for protecting circuit conductors against overheating. The current-carrying ability of a conductor is limited by the temperature at which its insulation may be operated safely. The operating temperature of the conductor is the sum of the temperature of the air in which the conductor is operating and the temperature rise due to the $I^2R$ loss in the conductor. A circuit breaker that uses a thermal element for tripping depends upon these same two sources of heat for its operation and, therefore, affords good conductor protection. Thus, when circuit-breaker sizes are properly selected, they have approximately the same response to temperature as do the conductors which they protect, and they will act to trip the circuit before dangerous overheating can occur in the conductors.

In the larger current ratings of molded-case breakers, the thermal trip element is supplemented by a magnetic trip element. The magnetic unit uses the magnetic force surrounding the conductor to operate the breaker-tripping linkage. Breakers which have the combination thermal-magnetic trip have inverse-time tripping characteristics for overcurrents up to about ten times the nameplate rating of the breaker and instantaneous tripping for currents above that value. Stated another way, these breakers have inverse-time thermal tripping for overload currents and instantaneous magnetic tripping for short-circuit currents.

Arc interruption in an air circuit breaker takes place between the separable contacts. Many variations in design and arrangement of contacts and the surrounding chamber are used by different manufacturers. One commonly used design is the placing of the contacts in an arc chute made in such a way that the arc formed as the contacts part is drawn out into the arc chute. As the arc is drawn into the chute it is divided into small segments and quenched.

Molded-case breakers are manufactured in a wide range of sizes and ratings. Six frame sizes, 50-, 100-, 225-, 400-, 600-, and 800-amp frames are available, each with a standard range of continuous-current ratings. The physical size, rating of the contacts, and interrupting rating are the same for all breakers of a given frame size. The continuous-current rating of any breaker is determined by the rating of its trip elements. Voltage ratings available range from 120 to 600 volts and interrupting capacities range as high as 35,000 amp.

*Large air circuit breakers* are used in industrial and large commercial distribution systems since these breakers are available in higher current and interrupting ratings than are the molded-case breakers. Circuit breakers of this type are available with continuous current ratings

FIG. 16-7. A three-pole large air circuit breaker. (*Courtesy of Westinghouse Electric Corporation.*)

as high as 4,000 amp and interrupting ratings as high as 100,000 amp. A typical electrically operated breaker of this type with an interrupting rating of 50,000 amp is shown in Fig. 16-7.

Large air circuit breakers with interrupting ratings of 50,000 amp or lower may be either electrically or manually operated. All larger breakers are electrically operated. The contact assembly of an electrically operated breaker is linked mechanically to a movable iron core in a solenoid. When current is passed through the solenoid, the core is magnetized and moves the linkage to close the breaker. Electrical closing of circuit breakers ensures quick and positive closing of the breaker. This is especially desirable when a breaker is closed on a short circuit. Electrically operated circuit breakers are also used when remote operation of breakers is required. The operation of a push-button or control switch mounted at a convenient location remote from the breaker completes the control circuit for the solenoid mechanism on the breaker, which causes the breaker to close. Closing and tripping of manually operated breakers is accomplished by means of a direct mechanical linkage from an operating handle on the front of the breaker to the contact-operating mechanism.

When large air circuit breakers are closed, the operating mechanism is latched closed. The breakers are tripped by operating the latch in the operating mechanism either by the manual operating handle or by an electrically operated trip coil that is energized from a control power source through a push-button or control switch.

Automatic tripping of large air circuit breakers is usually accomplished by a series overcurrent tripping device. The operating coil of the tripping device is connected in series with the circuit in which the breaker is installed. The flow of abnormal current in the circuit causes a plunger of the tripping unit to come in contact with the latch of the breaker-operating mechanism to open the breaker.

Several types of overcurrent tripping devices are available for large air circuit breakers. The device used on many breakers is a dual device having a long time-delay element for moderate overload currents and an instantaneous element for short-circuit and severe overload currents. The tripping characteristics of these devices are similar to those of tripping devices used with molded-case breakers. One other tripping device often used has both a long time-delay and a short time-delay element. Moderate sustained overloads cause the breaker to trip after a relatively long time delay and short circuits cause the breaker to trip after an intentional short time delay. This device is used in selective systems.

By the proper selection of ratings and types of tripping units, a completely selective system may be designed. On such a system, the breaker nearest the fault is caused to trip and remove the faulty circuit or equipment from service while the other breakers on the system, closer to the source, remain closed to carry normal load current to the unfaulted parts of the system.

Arc extinction in large air circuit breakers during the interruption of short circuits is accomplished by different methods by different manufacturers. The method used by one manufacturer is the deionization or physical removal of the conduction particles from the arc path.   In breakers using this principle, the arc is forced upward into an arc chute by strong magnetic fields so that rising gas blasts carry the ionized air particles out of the arc path.

Large air circuit breakers are manufactured in various physical sizes as determined by their interrupting capacity.   These interrupting capacities are 15,000, 25,000, 50,000, 75,000, and 100,000 amp.   This method of rating should be contrasted with the ratings of molded-case breakers, the frame sizes of which are designated by continuous-current ratings.   Each interrupting rating of large air circuit breakers does have a definite range of continuous-current capacities, however.   For example, the continuous-current ratings of the 25,000-amp breakers are from 35 to 600 amp.   The physical construction and, usually, the contact rating are the same for all ratings of breakers that have the same interrupting capacity.

In general, overcurrent protection is required by the National Electrical Code at every point in a distribution system where wire sizes are reduced.   As a consequence, circuit breakers are used at service entrances, on feeder circuits, and on branch circuits for the protection and switching of the various components of the system.

Circuit breakers used for the protection and switching of motor circuits are selected from breaker-application tables prepared by the circuit-breaker manufacturers.   In general, such breakers are selected to have a continuous-current rating not to exceed approximately 250 per cent of the full-load current of the motor.   For circuits other than motor circuits, circuit breakers are selected to have the same rating as the continuous rating of the conductor used in the circuit they are protecting.

Large air circuit breakers are often assembled in groups together with other control and metering equipment into *metal-enclosed low-voltage air-circuit-breaker switchgear*.   This type of switchgear is discussed in Art. 16-7.

**16-6. Panelboards**   A *panelboard* consists of a group of overcurrent-protective devices, with or without switches, including buses, assembled into a cabinet which is accessible only from the front.   As shown in Fig. 16-2, panelboards are located between the secondary feeders and the branch circuits that supply the utilization equipment.   So located, they are the means of control and protection for lighting and power circuits and the equipment supplied by them.

Panelboard overcurrent-protective devices may be fuses, either plug or cartridge type, or circuit breakers.   Fusible panelboards used for lighting and small-appliance loads often have a tumbler switch in series with each of the branch-circuit fuses and are called *switch-and-fuse panelboards*.

Cabinet enclosures for panelboards are usually made of galvanized sheet steel. Cabinets are large enough to provide ample wiring space around the panel assembly. Knockouts of various sizes are provided in the sides, top, and bottom of the cabinet for terminating the conduit for the main-supply and branch-circuit conductors which terminate at the panel assembly. Cabinets are constructed so that the panelboard may be either flush or surface mounting. The flush-mounting type is installed so that the front of the panelboard is flush with the wall surface and all wiring is concealed in the wall.

The trim of a panelboard consists of a door and the framework to which the door is attached. All wiring is done in the panelboard with the trim removed. After wiring is complete, the trim is set in place and all wiring is concealed. Most modern panelboards are of the dead-front type in which no live parts are exposed when the door is open.

The panel assembly itself consists of a set of bus bars to which the several branch circuits are connected through the overcurrent or switching devices. The main-supply conductors for the panelboard may connect directly to lugs on the bus bars or may connect to the bus bars through a main circuit breaker, main fuses, or a fused disconnect switch.

Fusible and circuit-breaker lighting panelboards are available in several voltage ratings. Two of the more common ratings are the 120/240-volt three-wire single-phase grounded neutral and the 120/208-volt four-wire three-phase grounded neutral panelboards. Panelboards with these ratings are supplied from four-wire delta or wye-connected transformers, as described in Art. 11-15. A 120/240-volt three-wire panelboard with cartridge fuses and tumbler switches for the branch circuits is shown in Fig. 16-8. The partially assembled panelboard shown in Fig. 16-9 is a circuit-breaker lighting panelboard for use on a 120/208 four-wire system.

For distribution or power circuits with voltage ratings up to 600 volts, both fusible and circuit-breaker-type panelboards are available. One commonly used panelboard of this type is the convertible distribution panelboard. Convertible panelboards are of the sectionalized type made up in multiples of standardized circuit-breaker dimensions so that it is possible to interchange circuit breakers with different ratings or with different numbers of poles. With this type of panelboard it is possible to provide space in the panelboard cabinet for future additional circuits. These panelboards will accommodate circuit breakers in frame sizes up to 600 amp.

## 16-7. Metal-enclosed Low-voltage Air-circuit-breaker Switchgear

"A metal-enclosed low-voltage air-circuit-breaker switchgear is a switching structure containing dead-front air circuit breakers, bare

FIG. 16-8. A typical lighting panelboard with tumbler switches and cartridge fuses in the branch circuits. (*Courtesy of Square D Company.*)

buses, and connections, with an enclosure on ends, back, and top. The air circuit breakers are contained in individual compartments and controlled remotely or from the front of panel. The structures are of two types, stationary and drawout. The stationary-type switchgear contains air circuit breakers which are mounted rigidly on bases and have no special arrangement for quick removal from the structure. The drawout-type switchgear contains air circuit breakers so arranged that they may be easily drawn out of their housing and disconnected from the buses by means of self-coupling disconnecting devices."*

The drawout-type switchgear is more extensively used than the stationary type because it is more flexible and is more easily maintained than the stationary type. Service interruptions are minimized by the use of drawout switchgear since a breaker in need of maintenance can be replaced by a spare breaker in a very short time.

FIG. 16-9. Circuit-breaker lighting panelboard assembly. (*Courtesy of Westinghouse Electric Corporation.*)

A section of low-voltage metal-enclosed switchgear consisting of eight drawout air circuit breakers is shown at the right-hand end of the load-center unit substation in Fig. 16-10. The housing of the switchgear includes the breaker compartments, breaker supporting rails, buses, connections, and instrument transformers. Control switches and instruments when used are mounted on the front panels of the switchgear. This switchgear is dead front; that is, no live parts are

* Definition is from National Electrical Manufacturers Association's "Standards for Power Switchgear Assemblies."

exposed at any time. Interlocks are provided to prevent inadvertent access to the live parts.

The circuit breakers and associated auxiliary apparatus are all mounted on an assembly which may be inserted or withdrawn from the housing of the switchgear. As the removable element is inserted into its connected position, the main power and control connections are made by means of self-aligning primary and secondary contacts. Interlocking is provided so that breakers cannot be inserted into or withdrawn from the connected position when the breaker is closed. Breakers may be withdrawn to a test position or to a disconnected

Fig. 16-10. A load-center unit substation with high- and low-voltage circuit breakers and a liquid-filled transformer section. (*Courtesy of General Electric Company.*)

position. In the test position, the main power or primary circuit is disconnected but the control or secondary circuits remain intact. In this position, the breaker may be opened or closed to check its operation and the functioning of the control apparatus. In the disconnected position, all connections between the stationary structure and the circuit breaker are opened, and the breaker can be removed completely from the structure.

Both manually operated and electrically operated circuit breakers are used in metal-enclosed low-voltage switchgear. The application of circuit breakers in switchgear is the same as when the breakers are used individually, as described in Art. 16-5. The rating of switchgear is dependent upon the rating of the circuit breakers used in the switchgear.

**16-8. Load-center Unit Substations**  Load-center unit substations are combinations of transformers and metal-enclosed switchgear assembled as a unit.  These substations may have switchgear either on the high-voltage or low-voltage side, or on both sides of the transformer. The unit substation shown in Fig. 16-10 has a high-voltage switchgear section consisting of a metal-clad circuit breaker, a liquid-filled transformer section, and a low-voltage metal-enclosed switchgear section consisting of eight drawout air circuit breakers.  The usual voltage ratings of unit substations are 15,000 volts or less for the high-voltage section and 600 volts or less for the low-voltage section.  Transformers are usually rated 2,000 kva or less.

Modern practices in power-system design include the extensive use of the load-center system of power distribution with distribution voltages of from 2,400 to 13,800 volts.  In this system of distribution, power is distributed to the point of utilization at the distribution voltage, where it is stepped down to utilization voltage by the load-center unit substation and distributed by short low-voltage feeders.  In this way, good system voltage regulation is obtained with relatively small conductor sizes.  The use of several small transformers at the load centers rather than one large transformer centrally located on the system also allows the use of smaller circuit breakers at the utilization-voltage level.  Breakers are smaller for the load-center type of system because less load current is carried by the breakers, and the available short-circuit current is less because of the higher impedance of the small transformers.  Another advantage of the load-center system of distribution is its adaptability to changes in loads.  Since the unit substation is factory-assembled as a compact unit, it is readily moved if load centers change.

Load-center unit substations find their greatest application in manufacturing plants and other large, industrial, power-distribution systems.

## HIGH-VOLTAGE PROTECTIVE AND SWITCHING EQUIPMENT

**16-9. High-voltage Fuses**  High-voltage fuses are used both indoors and outdoors for the protection of circuits and equipment with voltage ratings above 600 volts.  There are many types of fuses and they are mounted in many different ways.  Some of the more commonly used fuses and mountings are mentioned briefly in the following paragraphs.

*Expulsion fuses* consist of a fusible element mounted in a fuse tube and depend upon the vaporization of the fuse element and fuse-tube liner to expel conducting vapors and metals from the fuse tube, thereby extinguishing the arc formed when current is interrupted.  Another type of fuse, called the *liquid fuse*, depends on a spring mechanism to separate quickly the ends of the melted fuse element in a noninflam-mable liquid to extinguish the arc.   Still another type of fuse is the *solid-material fuse*, in which the arc is extinguished in a hole in a solid material.   In one type of solid-material fuse a spring mechanism simi-lar to that of the liquid fuse is used to separate the arcing terminals when the fuse blows.   In this fuse, overload and low fault currents are interrupted in a small cylindrical chamber in the solid arc-extinguishing

FIG. 16-11. Combination disconnect switches and solid-material fuses, rated 15,000 volts, in metal cubicle.   (*Courtesy of S & C Electric Company.*)

material, and large fault currents are interrupted in a larger chamber in the same fuse holder.

   High-voltage fuse mountings when used indoors are usually enclosed in a metal housing with insulating barriers placed between fuses of the different phases of the circuit.   High-voltage fuses are often mounted in the same enclosure with disconnect switches to provide short-circuit protection and switching facilities for circuits and equipment.   A typi-cal installation of this type is shown in Fig. 16-11.   The equipment shown is for use on 13,800-volt circuits and consists of two enclosures, each with a three-pole disconnect switch above and three solid-material fuses below.  The outgoing cable pothead is in front of the fuses in each compartment.

Outdoor high-voltage fuses for low-capacity overhead lines are mounted in distribution fuse *cutouts*.  Cutouts consist of a fuse support and fuse holder in which the fuse link is installed.  One commonly used type of fuse cutout is the drop-out enclosed cutout.  In this type of cutout, the fuse holder is enclosed within a porcelain housing.  The

Fig. 16-12. A typical installation of high interrupting-capacity solid-material fuses on a 23,000-volt circuit.  (*Courtesy of S & C Electric Company.*)

fuse holder which contains the fuse link is mounted on the inside of the hinged enclosure door and is so arranged that it is connected into the circuit when the cutout door is closed.  When the fuse link melts in clearing a short circuit, the cutout door drops open, thereby providing an indication of the blown fuse.  The cutout is placed back in service by inserting a new fuse link in the fuse holder and closing the cutout door.

Fuse mountings for high interrupting-capacity high-voltage outdoor fuses are mounted on insulators, as shown in Fig. 16-12.  The size of the insulators and the spacing between phases is dependent upon the voltage rating of the circuit. These fuses are used for the protection of circuits, transformers, and other equipment where the system short-circuit currents are high.

**16-10. Power Circuit Breakers** The term *power circuit breaker* applies to circuit breakers intended for service on circuits rated 600 volts and higher and includes both air and oil circuit breakers. Power circuit breakers have standard voltage ratings of from 2,500 to 345,000 volts and three-phase interrupting ratings of from 25,000 to 25,000,000 kva. Breakers with even higher ratings are being developed.

During the early development of electrical systems, the vast majority of power circuit breakers used were oil circuit breakers. However, air circuit breakers of the magnetic and compressed-air types have been developed and are now in common use in ratings up to 34,500 volts. Compressed-air breakers are used to a lesser extent at even higher voltages.

The *magnetic air circuit breaker* is available in ratings up to and including 750,000 kva at 13,800 volts. In this type of breaker the current is interrupted between separable contacts in air with the aid of magnetic blowout coils. As the main current-carrying contacts part during the interruption of a fault, the arc is drawn out in a horizontal direction and transferred to arcing contacts. At the same time, the blowout coil is connected into the circuit to provide a magnetic field to draw the arc upward into arc chutes. The arc accelerates upward, aided by the magnetic field and natural thermal effects, into the arc chutes where it is elongated and divided into small segments. The arc resistance increases until, as the current passes through zero, the arc is broken; after this it does not reestablish itself.

The general construction of the magnetic power circuit breaker is somewhat similar to the large air circuit breaker used on low-voltage circuits except that they are all electrically operated. These breakers are used extensively in metal-clad switchgear assemblies in industrial plants, steel mills, and small power plants.

*Compressed-air breakers* (sometimes called *air-blast breakers*) depend upon a stream of compressed air directed toward the interrupting contacts of the breaker to interrupt the arc formed when current is interrupted. This type of breaker was introduced by American manufacturers in 1940, but since that time it has become universally accepted for use in heavy-duty indoor applications. Maximum standard ratings for indoor use are 2,500,000 kva at 34,500 volts.

*Oil circuit-breaker* contacts are immersed in oil so that the current interruption takes place under oil which by its cooling effect helps quench the arc. Since oil is an insulator, the live parts of oil circuit breakers may be placed closer together than they could be in air. The poles of small oil circuit breakers are all placed in one oil tank, but in the large high-voltage breakers each pole is in a separate oil tank. Tanks of small breakers are suspended from a framework so that the tanks may be lowered for inspection of the contacts. The tanks of

FIG. 16-13. A frame-mounted 69,000-volt outdoor oil circuit breaker. (*Courtesy of Westinghouse Electric Corporation.*)

very large oil circuit breakers rest directly on a foundation and have handholes for access to the contact assembly.

The oil tanks of oil circuit breakers are usually sealed, the electrical connections between the external circuit and the contacts in the tank being made through porcelain bushings. The breaker contacts are opened and closed by means of insulated lift rods on which the movable contacts are mounted. The lift rods are connected to the operating mechanism by means of a mechanical linkage, so that the contacts of all poles of the breaker are opened and closed together.

Only the very small oil circuit breakers are manually operated. The larger oil circuit-breaker mechanisms are solenoid operated, pneumatically operated, or spring operated. Solenoid operators are similar in principle to those used for air circuit breakers. Pneumatic operators obtain the closing and tripping energy from compressed air provided by a small, automatically controlled air compressor that maintains enough compressed air for several operations of the breaker in an air receiver. Spring operators derive their energy from a spring that is compressed by a small electric motor.

Indoor oil circuit breakers are generally assembled into metal-clad switchgear units, although oil breakers are being replaced in many cases by air circuit breakers. Oil circuit breakers are used under adverse atmospheric conditions such as in oil refineries where there is danger of explosion from any open arc. Outdoor oil circuit breakers are usually frame-mounted and are set individually on concrete footings, with open overhead connections being made to the breaker bushings. A typical frame-mounted outdoor oil circuit breaker is shown in Fig. 16-13. In this photograph, the breaker-operating mechanism housing is shown at the near end of the breaker.

**16-11. Protective Relays**  Low-voltage air circuit breakers ordinarily have self-contained series trip coils either of the instantaneous or time-delay types. The tripping energy is supplied by the flow of the short-circuit current through the trip coil. Power circuit breakers seldom use series trip coils but are equipped with trip coils designed to operate from a storage battery or a reliable source of alternating current. Auxiliary devices called *protective relays,* designed to detect the presence of short circuits on a system, are used to connect the breaker trip coils to the source of tripping power and thereby trip the breaker.

Protective relays are said to be selective when they trip only the circuit breakers directly supplying the defective part of the system and no other circuit breakers. When relays and circuit breakers are selective, short circuits are removed from a system with a minimum of service interruption. Of course it is also desirable to isolate the defective system element as quickly as possible. To this end, relays and circuit breakers have been developed that will clear a short circuit in less than 0.1 sec. However, selectivity being more important than speed, the tripping of some circuit breakers on a system is delayed intentionally to gain selectivity in clearing faults at certain locations on a system.

Protective-relay operating elements are connected to high-voltage circuits by means of current and potential transformers so that they in effect "measure" the quantities of current, voltage, or phase angle or combinations of these quantities to determine whether or not an abnormal condition exists in the circuit being protected. Relays with widely different operating characteristics have been developed for specific applications in protective schemes for rotating machines, transformers, buses, and lines. Two of the more commonly used types of protective relays to be described here are *overcurrent* and *differential* relays.

Overcurrent relays, as the name indicates, operate to close their contacts when current through the relay operating coil exceeds a predetermined value. Overcurrent relays are connected to the protected circuit through current transformers so that the current-transformer secondary current through the relay is proportional to the current in the primary circuit.

The most generally used overcurrent relay is the induction overcurrent relay. This relay is similar in principle to the induction watthour meter and has a movable disk driven by an electromagnet. However, the induction overcurrent relay disk is not free to revolve continuously as in the watthour meter since the operating torque is opposed by a restraining spring. Furthermore, a movable contact is attached to the disk shaft so that after a partial revolution the movable contact makes contact with the stationary contact and further rotation is impossible.

The pickup current of an overcurrent relay is the current that will just cause the contacts to close. The operating coil of the relay is tapped to provide a means for adjusting the relay for different values of pickup current. Several tap ranges are available for induction relays, a commonly used range being from 4 to 16 amp.

Induction overcurrent relays have inverse-time characteristics; that is, the contact-closing time is fast for high operating-coil currents and slow for low operating-coil currents. Moreover, the operating time for a given current is adjustable, the time of operation being proportional to the distance that the disk is allowed to travel before the contacts close.

With both the pickup current and the operating time being adjustable, induction overcurrent relays may be applied in selective systems, with relays close to the generator adjusted for long operating times and with progressively shorter time settings for relays farther away from the generator. Induction overcurrent relays are relatively inexpensive, are reliable, and are easily calibrated and maintained. Consequently, they are widely used for the protection of transmission and distribution lines and equipment. A typical induction overcurrent relay completely assembled in its case is shown in Fig. 16-14a. The rear view of this relay removed from its case in Fig. 16-14b shows the tapped operating coil or electromagnet, the induction disk, and the general construction of the relay.

Differential relays, like induction relays, have an induction disk assembly on which is mounted a movable contact. However, the differential relay has, in addition to its operating electromagnet, a restraining electromagnet so connected that the flow of current through it provides a restraining torque or a contact-opening torque on the relay during the normal functioning of the equipment being protected by the relay.

Differential relays are commonly used for the protection of rotating machines, transformers, and buses. Differential relays compare the

(a)                                              (b)

FIG. 16-14. Induction overcurrent relay: (a) front view in case; (b) rear view out of case. (*Courtesy of General Electric Company.*)

currents entering and leaving each phase winding of the apparatus being protected. Normally the currents entering and leaving the apparatus are equal or are directly proportional to each other. However, on the occurrence of an internal fault in the apparatus, the two currents are no longer equal or proportional, since short-circuit current is fed into the apparatus from one or both sides. Under this condition, the difference of the two currents passes through the operating coil of the relay, causing the relay to close its contacts and trip the necessary circuit breakers to isolate the apparatus from the system. An elementary diagram showing typical connections for a transformer differential relay is shown in Fig. 16-15a. A typical differential relay removed from its case is shown in Fig. 16-15b. The relay shown is suitable for the protection of two-winding transformers.

A complete installation of three-phase transformer differential relays consists of three relays, one for each phase. For simplicity the diagram in Fig. 16-15a shows the connections for only one relay. The flow of normal currents is shown in the diagram, the current on the 69,000-volt

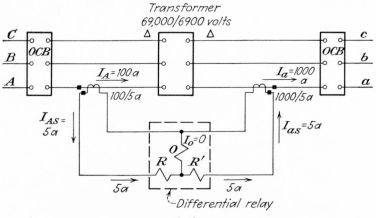

(b)

FIG. 16-15. (a) Circuit to illustrate connections of transformer differential relays. (b) Front view of differential relay removed from case. (*Courtesy of General Electric Company.*)

side of the transformer being 100 amp and on the 6,900-volt side being 1,000 amp. With current-transformer ratios as shown, the secondary currents are balanced, each being 5 amp. The 5 amp then circulates in the series circuit consisting of the two current transformers and the two relay-restraining windings $R$ and $R'$. For this normal condition, there is no current in the relay-operating winding $O$, and the current in the two restraining windings creates a torque that holds the relay-operating contacts open.   However, when a fault develops within the transformer, short-circuit current is fed into the transformer from one or both sides, depending upon the system arrangement.   This causes the current in one restraining winding either to reverse or to increase out of proportion to the current in the other restraining winding.   The restraining winding currents are no longer balanced, and the unbalanced current flows through the operating winding of the relay, developing a contact-closing torque which causes the relay contacts to close.

Differential relays for the protection of generators and motors are similar to transformer differential relays except that they are ordinarily more sensitive and will operate on a smaller unbalanced current than will transformer relays.   Bus differential relays are also similar to transformer relays except that the current transformer secondaries of all incoming lines to the bus are paralleled and connected to one relay-restraining winding, and the current transformer secondaries of the outgoing lines are paralleled and connected to the other restraining winding.

**16-12. Metal-clad Switchgear**   *Metal-clad switchgear* is a type of switchgear assembly in which all parts are completely enclosed in

Fig. 16-16. A typical installation of metal-clad switchgear.   (*Courtesy of General Electric Company.*)

grounded metal enclosures.   Circuit breakers used in metal-clad switchgear are either air or oil breakers of the removable type, equipped with self-coupling primary and secondary disconnecting devices.   All buses, connections, and joints are insulated and are completely isolated from the secondary wiring and control devices.   Instruments, relays, and control switches are mounted on the front panels of the switchgear.

Metal-clad switchgear is available in both indoor and outdoor types for use on circuits with voltage ratings below 15,000 volts, the standard voltage ratings being 4,160, 7,200 and 13,800 volts.   Interrupting- and continuous-current ratings are based on the ratings of the circuit breakers used in the switchgear.

A typical installation of metal-clad switchgear is shown in Fig. 16-16. The installation shown includes the circuit breakers and control equipment for several generator and feeder circuits in an industrial plant. The various instruments, relays, and control switches may be seen on the front of the switchgear with the synchronizing panel on the extreme right-hand end of the assembly.

**16-13. Outdoor Substations**   Outdoor substations consist of structural frameworks on which switches, fuses, buses, and lightning arresters are mounted and from which connections are made to circuit breakers, transformers, and other heavy equipment installed on the ground under the structure.   Structures are usually constructed of galvanized structural steel, but some low-voltage structures are of wood.   Buses, jumpers, and connections are supported on insulators which are attached to the structural framework.

There are no limitations to electrical capacity in outdoor substations since equipment of almost any rating or capacity can be installed in stations of this type.   Spacings of buses and equipment and arrangement of station are dependent upon the voltage of the station.   Arrangement, of course, is also influenced by the function for which the station is intended.   Substations are usually designed to fit individual requirements, although some standardization is possible in certain types of substations.

A typical outdoor substation with a voltage rating of 34,500 volts is shown in Fig. 16-17.   This substation is a step-up substation at a generating plant with the step-up transformer shown at the right.   The station is designed for three outgoing 34,500-volt feeders which may be seen at the left.   The frame-mounted oil circuit breakers are installed below the structure, and two bus potential transformers are mounted on a steel stand in the foreground.   The potential transformer high-voltage fuses are shown mounted on the structure above the potential transformers.   Lightning arresters are mounted on the structure just below the dead-end insulators for the outgoing circuits.

Outdoor substations may be of the step-up type or they may be step-down stations for supplying loads from a high-voltage transmission line.  Step-down stations for supplying loads or distribution systems at 15,000 volts or less often consist of an open-type steel framework for terminating the high-voltage circuit, a three-phase transformer, and an assembly of outdoor metal-clad switchgear for the protection and switching of the low-voltage circuits.

Voltage transformations are not always involved in outdoor substations.  Switching stations in which only circuit breakers and other

FIG. 16-17. A typical outdoor substation rated at 34,500 volts.  (*Courtesy of Stanley Engineering Company.*)

switching equipment are installed are used at junctions and taps in transmission systems.

**16-14. Lightning Arresters**  Lightning is a major cause of short circuits on overhead transmission and distribution lines.  Transient voltages on the lines caused by lightning strokes may exceed the insulation level of the line, causing a flashover which may result in a line-to-ground or line-to-line short circuit.  It is the function of lightning arresters to provide a path by which lightning surges are conducted to ground before a flashover on the line can occur.

The *valve-type lightning arrester*, a commonly used type, may be likened to a normally open circuit breaker connected from the protected circuit to ground, which closes when a high-voltage surge appears and then reopens when the surge disappears.  This arrester consists of two elements, a series gap and a valve assembly, both enclosed in a porcelain housing.   The spacing of the series gap is such that it will withstand normal circuit voltage.   However, an overvoltage such as may be caused by a lightning surge causes the gap to break down, with a resulting flow of current through the valve assembly to ground.   The valve assembly is constructed of a ceramic compound that has the

Fig. 16-18. Installation of valve-type lightning arresters rated at 60,000 volts in an outdoor substation.   (*Courtesy of General Electric Company.*)

peculiar property of offering a high resistance to current flow when normal system voltage is applied, but a low resistance to the flow of high-surge currents.   Thus it operates as a current valve and allows the surge current to pass but assumes its former high resistance to stop the flow of current as soon as the voltage drops to its normal value. An installation of heavy-duty station-type valve arresters is shown in Fig. 16-18.

## REVIEW QUESTIONS

**1.** What is a short circuit?

**2.** What are two commonly used automatic circuit-protective devices?

**3.** In general, where is circuit-protective and switching equipment grouped on an electrical system?

**4.** What is a fuse? What are two types of low-voltage fuses?

**5.** What are the standard fuse-clip sizes for cartridge fuses?

**6.** Describe a time-lag fuse.

**7.** What is a safety switch? Where is it used?

**8.** Describe the operation of a molded-case circuit breaker.

**9.** What is meant when it is said that a circuit breaker has a thermal-magnetic trip element?

**10.** What are the standard frame sizes of molded-case circuit breakers?

**11.** When is electrical operation of a circuit breaker desirable?

**12.** What type of automatic tripping is used on large low-voltage air circuit breakers?

**13.** How do the ratings of large low-voltage air circuit breakers differ from the ratings of molded-case breakers?

**14.** What is a panelboard? What types of overcurrent devices are used in panelboards?

**15.** What are two types of construction used in metal-enclosed low-voltage air-circuit-breaker switchgear? What are some advantages of draw-out switchgear?

**16.** What is a load-center unit substation?

**17.** Name three types of high-voltage fuses.

**18.** What is a fuse cutout? Where is it used?.

**19.** Name two types of air circuit breakers. In general where are they used?

**20.** What are the different types of operating mechanisms used with outdoor oil circuit breakers?

**21.** What is the function of protective relays?

**22.** Describe the principle of operation of overcurrent and differential relays.

**23.** What is metal-clad switchgear? What are the maximum standard current, voltage, and interrupting ratings?

**24.** What are the essential features of outdoor substations?

**25.** Describe briefly the operation of the valve-type lightning arrester.

# CHAPTER 17

## ELECTRICAL INSTRUMENTS AND
## ELECTRICAL MEASUREMENTS

The methods of measurement of electrical quantities are so many and varied that only the more commonly used methods of measurements can be discussed here. For further details on instruments and meters, the student is referred to the many excellent texts available on electrical measurements.

**17-1. Galvanometers** As was learned from the study of electric motors, when a current-carrying conductor is placed in a magnetic field, a force is developed on the conductor which tends to move the

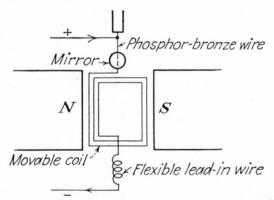

FIG. 17-1. Diagram of the essentials of a galvanometer. The deflection of the movable coil is proportional to the current flowing.

conductor at right angles to the field. This principle is used in current-detecting instruments. A sensitive current-detecting instrument called a *galvanometer* and operating on this principle is shown diagrammatically in Fig. 17-1.

A coil of very fine insulated wire, usually wound on an aluminum frame or bobbin, is suspended as shown between the poles of a permanent magnet. The coil is suspended by a phosphor-bronze filament which acts as one lead-in wire for the coil. The other lead-in wire is a very flexible spiral wire at the bottom of the coil. When current flows through the coil, a deflecting force proportional to the flux density, the current, and the dimensions of the coil rotates the coil on its vertical axis. The deflecting force is opposed by the restraining force of the suspension filament so that the coil does not continue to rotate as in a motor but turns until the deflecting force is balanced by the restraining force of the suspension filament. Since the deflecting force is directly proportional to the current flowing in the coil, the amount of angular rotation may be used as an indication of the value of the current flowing in the coil.

The amount of deflection and hence the amount of current flowing through the coil may be indicated by a pointer which is attached to the moving element and moves over a calibrated scale.

On the more sensitive galvanometers a mirror is attached to the moving coil as shown in Fig. 17-1. A light beam is reflected from the mirror onto a ground-glass scale. As the coil is deflected, the light beam moves over the scale.

The restoring force of the suspension filament acts to return the coil and indicating system to the normal or zero position when the current flow through the coil is interrupted.

After a reading is taken and the restoring force acts to return the coil to its normal position, the coil tends to oscillate about the normal position for some time before coming to rest. To prevent excessive oscillation of the coil, a system of damping must be employed. The aluminum frame upon which the coil is wound provides the damping force in the galvanometer just described. Whenever the frame moves in the magnetic field, induced currents are produced which flow around the closed circuit formed by the frame. The induced currents oppose the motion that produces them, thereby bringing the moving element immediately to a standstill.

## 17-2. The Permanent-magnet Moving-coil Instrument

The permanent-magnet moving-coil instrument is universally used for the measurement of direct currents and voltages. It is essentially a galvanometer made in portable form. The movable coil is wound of fine insulated wire on a light aluminum frame. The coil is pivoted on steel pivots that rotate in jeweled bearings. A light pointer that moves over a graduated scale is attached rigidly to the movable coil. Current is brought into the coil by means of spiral springs, one at each end of the coil. The springs also provide the restoring force for the instrument. The movable coil, springs, and pointer of a Weston permanent-magnet moving-coil instrument are shown in Fig. 17-2.

The magnetic circuit consists of a permanent horseshoe magnet to which are attached soft-iron pole pieces. To form a uniform air gap

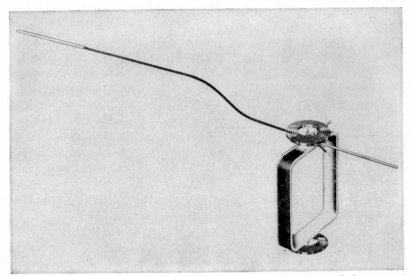

FIG. 17-2. Moving element of a permanent-magnet moving-coil instrument. (*Courtesy of Weston Electrical Instrument Corporation.*)

FIG. 17-3. The permanent-magnet moving-coil mechanism. (*Courtesy of Weston Electrical Instrument Corporation.*)

through which the coil may turn, a cylinder of soft iron is supported between the pole pieces. The method of assembly of the magnetic circuit and moving element is shown in Fig. 17-3. Note in Fig. 17-3 that a uniform air gap is provided for the coil for a wide range of deflection of the coil. The use of the uniform air gap results in a deflection of the pointer that is almost directly proportional to the current flowing in the coil. Thus the scale used with this type of instrument may be made very uniform.

The aluminum frame upon which the coil is wound provides the damping force.

### 17-3. D-C Voltmeters

A voltmeter must be designed to be connected *across* the line. Since the coil of a permanent-magnet moving-coil instrument has a low resistance, it must have in series with it a high value of resistance when it is used as a voltmeter. The value of the series resistance must be high enough that the rated current of the coil is not exceeded. In portable testing voltmeters, several voltage ranges may be provided by using different values of series resistance for each range. The series resistance is usually contained in the instrument case itself.

So that the voltmeter will read upscale, the positive (+) terminal of the voltmeter must be connected to the positive line.

### 17-4. D-C Ammeters

An ammeter is connected in *series* with the line in which current is to be measured. Since the moving coil and the spiral springs used as coil connections can be designed for a maximum of only about 50 ma (0.05 amp), the permanent-magnet moving-coil instrument when used for the measurement of current higher than this value must be equipped with a *shunt*. A shunt is merely a low resistance that is placed in parallel with the coil circuit. The greater part of the current in the main circuit is then diverted around the coil through the shunt.

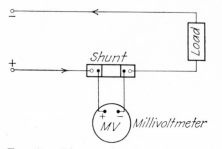

Fig. 17-4. Diagram showing the method of connecting a shunt and a millivolt-meter for measuring current.

Portable testing ammeters are equipped with self-contained shunts in ranges up to about 50 amp. For measurement of higher values of current, millivoltmeters are used with external shunts. The millivoltmeter together with the shunt then constitute the ammeter. Shunts used with millivoltmeters are usually designed so that when rated current flows through them the voltage drop across the shunt is 50 mv (0.05 volt). Millivoltmeters used with 50-mv shunts are designed to give a full-scale reading at 50 mv. Switchboard-type instruments or portable instruments always used with the same shunt are generally scaled to read directly in amperes.    The method of connecting a shunt and millivoltmeter for measuring current is shown in Fig. 17-4.    Note the polarity marking of the millivoltmeter with respect to the line polarity.

**17-5. Moving-iron Vane Instruments**    When two soft-iron bars are placed parallel to each other inside a current-carrying coil, the bars become magnetized, with adjacent ends of the bars having like magnetic poles.    The bars being similarly magnetized repel each other, the amount of repulsion being dependent on the amount of magnetizing

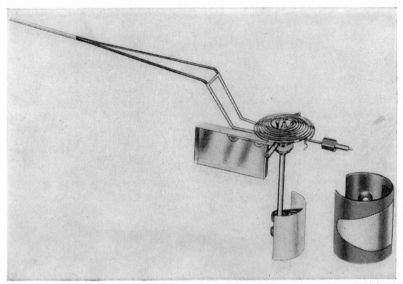

FIG. 17-5. The moving element of the moving-iron vane instrument with the stationary vane shown at the right.    (*Courtesy of Weston Electrical Instrument Corporation.*)

force of the coil.    Repulsion occurs between the bars for either direction of current through the coil and thus they are repelled when an alternating current is passed through the coil.

The moving-iron vane instrument, widely used for the measurement of alternating currents and voltages, operates on the above-described principle.    Two iron vanes, one stationary and one securely attached to the central shaft of the moving element, are placed inside the coil through which the current to be measured is passed.    In one type of moving-iron vane instrument, the vanes are concentric, the movable vane being placed inside the stationary vane.    This type of construction is shown in Fig. 17-5.    Another version of this type of instrument uses flat vanes, one attached to the shaft like a flag, the other one fixed.

This so-called *radial vane* type of instrument has certain advantages in sensitivity and scale distribution.

When current flows in the coil surrounding the vanes, the movable vane being repelled by the stationary vane moves the entire moving element clockwise, the amount of movement being dependent on the amount of current flowing in the coil. Restraining action is provided by the spiral spring at the top of the moving element. It should be noted that in this instrument the springs do not carry current. The damping device is an aluminum vane attached to the moving element,

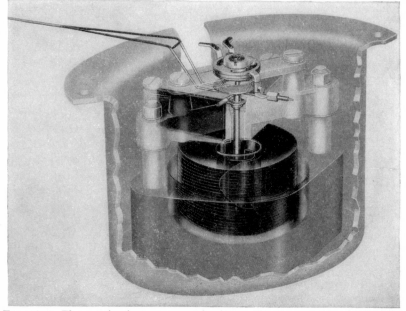

Fig. 17-6. The moving-iron vane mechanism. (*Courtesy of Weston Electrical Instrument Corporation.*)

as shown in Fig. 17-5, which moves in a closed chamber. The motion of the vane against the air in the chamber prevents excessive oscillation of the pointer. Figure 17-6 shows a phantom view of an assembled moving-iron vane mechanism.

When used as a voltmeter, the moving-iron vane instrument is used with a series resistance. Portable voltmeters are made with self-contained resistors in ranges up to 750 volts. Higher ranges may be obtained by using external multipliers or, as is usually the case, potential transformers (Art. 11-9). Since the standard low-voltage rating of potential transformers is 115 or 120 volts, voltmeters when used with potential transformers generally have a full-scale value of 150 volts.

When used as an ammeter, the moving-iron vane instrument is wound with wire heavy enough to carry the rated current.   Usual practice, however, is to use a 5-amp ammeter in conjunction with a current transformer for measuring values of current larger than 5 amp.

### 17-6. Electrodynamometer Voltmeters and Ammeters   The electrodynamometer instrument operates on the same principle as the permanent-magnet moving-coil instrument in that deflection of the moving element is obtained from the interaction of two magnetic fields.   However, in the electrodynamometer instrument, two stationary coils are used in place of the permanent magnet.   The movable coil is attached

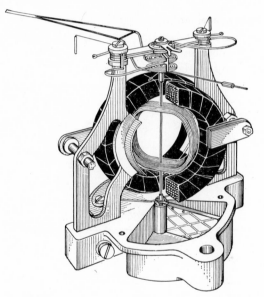

FIG. 17-7. The electrodynamometer mechanism.   (*Courtesy of Weston Electrical Instrument Corporation.*)

to the central shaft so that it may rotate inside the two stationary coils as shown in Fig. 17-7.   Connections are made to the movable coil through the two spiral springs at the top of the mechanism.   The springs also provide the restoring force for the moving element.   Air damping is obtained by means of the aluminum vanes that move in the enclosed chambers shown at the bottom of the mechanism.

When used as a voltmeter, or as an ammeter for measuring small values of current, the stationary and movable coils are connected in series.   Since the polarity of the fields produced by both the stationary and movable coils is reversed by a reversal of current, the deflection of the moving element is always in the same direction, regardless of the direction of current through the coils. For this reason, electrodynamometer instruments may be used with practically equal precision for either d-c or a-c measurements.

Since the movable coil and its flexible connections can be made to carry but a small amount of current, the electrodynamometer-type instrument is seldom used as an ammeter except for low current ranges. Higher current ranges are obtained by means of current transformers. The permanent-magnet moving-coil and the moving-iron vane instruments are more commonly used for the measurement of direct and alternating currents, respectively.

**17-7. Power Measurements** Power is measured by means of the wattmeter. Since power is a function of both current and voltage, two elements are necessary in a wattmeter. For this reason, wattmeters are generally of the electrodynamometer type. The movable

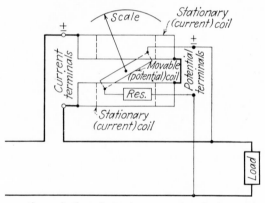

Fɪɢ. 17-8. Connection of the electrodynamometer instrument for use as a wattmeter.

coil with a series resistance forms the potential element, while the stationary coils are used as the current element. Connection is as shown in Fig. 17-8, with the potential and current elements in parallel and series, respectively, with the circuit in which the power is to be measured.

Electrodynamometer wattmeters may be used for the measurement of either a-c or d-c power. Since power in a d-c circuit is always a product of current and voltage, however, it is seldom necessary to use a wattmeter in a d-c circuit. The power can be calculated easily from the voltmeter and ammeter readings.

Power in an a-c circuit depends on the power factor of the circuit as well as the current and the voltage.   At unity power factor, the current in both the current and potential coils of a wattmeter reverses at the same time, resulting in a deflecting force on the moving element which is always in the same direction.   However, at power factors less than unity, the current in one element reverses before the current reverses in the other element, resulting in a reverse torque during the time that the two currents are in opposite directions.   The inertia of the moving element prevents its following the torque reversals, however, so that the resulting indication of the instrument is a resultant of the two torques.   For a phase angle of 90°, the two torques are equal and the wattmeter indicates zero power.   Thus the wattmeter indicates the true or actual power of an a-c circuit.

Power in a three-phase three-wire circuit may be measured by means of two wattmeters $W_1$ and $W_2$ connected as shown in Fig. 17-9.   The

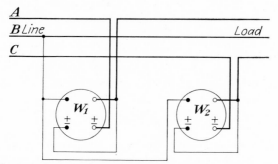

Fig. 17-9. Diagram of connections of two wattmeters for measuring power in a three-wire three-phase circuit.

algebraic sum of the readings of the two wattmeters will be the total three-phase power of the circuit for either balanced or unbalanced loads or voltages.   For balanced loads at unity power factor, the readings of the two wattmeters will be identical.   When the load power factor is 50 per cent, $W_2$ will read zero and $W_1$ will read the total three-phase power.   At power factors between 50 and 100 per cent, $W_1$ will read higher than $W_2$.   At power factors lower than 50 per cent, the reading of $W_2$ will be negative and the total three-phase power will be $W_1 - W_2$. At zero power factor, the wattmeters will have identical readings but of opposite signs, indicating zero power.   Thus there is a definite ratio of $W_1$ to $W_2$ for each value of circuit power factor.

The two-element or polyphase wattmeter may be used in place of the two single-phase wattmeters shown in Fig. 17-9.   Two complete elements are mounted on the same shaft and connected in the same manner as two single-phase wattmeters.    The deflection of the pointer indicates total three-phase power directly.

In a three-phase four-wire system, three wattmeters connected as shown in Fig. 17-10 are necessary for a true indication of power under all conditions of unbalance.    Total three-phase power is the sum of the readings of the three wattmeters.    In general, power may be measured

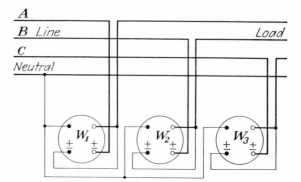

FIG. 17-10. Connection of three wattmeters to measure power in a four-wire three-phase circuit.

in any polyphase system with the number of wattmeters one less than the number of wires in the system.

### 17-8. Energy Measurements in A-C Circuits    Energy is measured by means of the watthour meter.    Since energy is a product of power and time, both quantities must be taken into account in energy measurements.    Watthour meters are small motors in which the speed of rotation at any time is proportional to the power at that time.    The total number of revolutions made by the rotating element in a given time is then a measure of the energy consumption during that time.

The induction watthour meter is used for measuring and recording energy in a-c circuits.    The essential parts are an electromagnet, a rotating element, a damping or retarding system, and a register.    A modern watthour meter is shown in Fig. 17-11.

The induction watthour meter operates essentially as a split-phase induction motor.    The rotating element is an aluminum disk mounted on a vertical shaft.    Friction is reduced to a minimum by the use of jeweled bearings.    Driving torque is obtained from the electromagnet which consists of a potential coil and two current coils mounted on an iron core but mechanically displaced from each other.    The arrangement of the coils of a typical electromagnet is shown in Fig. 17-12. The current coils, being connected in series with the line, are wound

Fig. 17-11. Single-phase induction watthour meter. (*Courtesy of Westinghouse Electric Corporation.*)

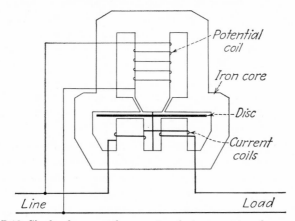

Fig. 17-12. Single-phase watthour-meter electromagnet and connections.

with a few turns of relatively heavy wire since they must carry the full line current. Flux produced by the current coils is proportional to and in phase with the line current.

So that it may be connected directly across the circuit in which the energy is to be measured, the potential coil is wound with many turns of fine wire. Because of the high inductance of the coil, the current lags behind the applied voltage by nearly 90°. To cause the potential coil flux to be exactly 90° behind the current coil flux, a short-circuited coil is placed around the core below the potential coil. Induced currents in this coil act to retard the potential coil flux to the desired phase position.

The flux produced by the potential and current coils, being displaced both in space and time phase, as in the split-phase motor, induce eddy currents in the disk of the rotating element. The motor action so produced is greatest at unity power factor and is zero at zero power factor and, for given values of current and voltage, is proportional to any value of power factor. Hence the speed of the rotating element is proportional to $EI \cos \theta$.

To prevent the armature from racing at a high speed when a torque is applied and to make the speed proportional to the power supplied the meter, a retarding torque is necessary. This is obtained by placing a permanent magnet near the rotating element so that the disk rotates in the field established by the magnet. Eddy currents induced in the disk produce a field that reacts with the field of the magnet, thereby causing a damping action that is proportional to the speed of the disk; that is, the faster the disk is turned, the greater the eddy currents and the greater the retarding action. Hence, the speed of the rotating element of a watthour meter is made directly proportional to the power in the circuit.

Since the speed of the rotating element is proportional to the power, every revolution represents a definite amount of energy. Geared to the rotating element is a register, the reading of which is an indication of the energy consumed over any given period. Register dials are calibrated to read directly in kilowatthours.

Friction compensation is obtained by means of a shading coil placed in the air gap of the magnetic circuit so as to produce a forward torque sufficiently great to overcome the friction normally encountered by the rotating element.

Single-phase watthour meter connections are the same as single-phase wattmeter connections in that the potential coil is connected in parallel and the current coil in series with the circuit in which energy is being measured.

Polyphase energy measurements are similar to polyphase power measurements; that is, the number of watthour meters required for correct energy measurements is one less than the number of wires in the system.   Multielement watthour meters are generally used, however, the required number of electromagnets being mounted so as to drive one rotating element that records the total polyphase energy on one register.

Several schemes of metering polyphase energy are in use whereby the number of elements is less than required for absolutely correct measurement.   For reasonably balanced loads and voltages, these meters are sufficiently accurate for commercial measurements.

**17-9. Power-factor Meter**   The electrodynamometer-type instrument when made with two movable coils set at right angles to each other may be used to measure power factor.   The method of connection of this type of power-factor meter in a three-phase circuit is shown in

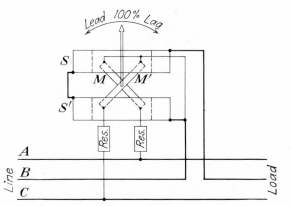

Fɪɢ. 17-13. Connection diagram of a three-phase power-factor meter of the electro-dynamometer type.

Fig. 17-13.   The two stationary coils $S$ and $S'$ are connected in series in line $B$.   Mounted on the central shaft and free to move without restraining or control springs are coils $M$ and $M'$.   Coils $M$ and $M'$ are connected with their series resistors from lines $B$ to $A$ and $B$ to $C$, respectively.   At unity power factor, one potential-coil current leads and one lags the current in line $B$ by 30° so that the coils are balanced in the position shown in Fig. 17-13.   A change in power factor causes the current of one potential coil to become more in phase and the other to be more out of phase with the current in line $B$ so that the moving element and pointer take a new position of balance to indicate the new power factor.

The power-factor meter shown in Fig. 17-13, when used with a special reactance-resistance network auxiliary, may be used to measure power factor in a single-phase circuit.

**17-10. Measurement of Resistance; Voltmeter-Ammeter Method**    A very simple method of measuring resistance is by the voltmeter-ammeter method.    A direct current is passed through the unknown resistance, the current being measured by an ammeter and the voltage drop across the resistance being measured by a voltmeter.    By Ohm's law, the resistance is

$$R = \frac{E}{I}$$

Although this method of resistance measurement is relatively simple, care should be taken so that the currents taken by the instruments

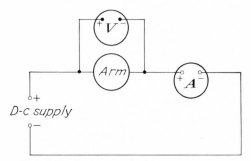

Fig. 17-14. Connection of a voltmeter and ammeter for measuring a low value of resistance.

themselves do not introduce errors in the results of the measurements. When low values of resistance, such as an armature-circuit resistance, are being measured, the connections for the least amount of error are as shown in Fig. 17-14.    To ensure that the voltage drop across the armature is large enough to be read on the voltmeter, a large value of current must be used, care being taken, of course, not to exceed the current rating of the armature.    For the connection shown in Fig. 17-14, the ammeter reads the sum of the currents through the armature and the voltmeter.    However, the current taken by the voltmeter is so small compared with the current through the armature that the error introduced is practically negligible.

When higher values of resistance are being measured and where the value of test current is quite small, the instrument connections should be as shown in Fig. 17-15.    Note that the voltmeter is connected across both the ammeter and the unknown resistance.    The ammeter reads the true value of the current through the resistance, but the voltmeter reading includes the $IR$ drop in the ammeter.    Since the test current required is quite low, the ammeter $IR$ drop is very low, resulting in an almost negligible error in the measurements.

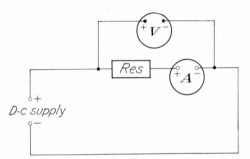

FIG. 17-15. Connection of a voltmeter and ammeter for measuring a high value of resistance.

For precise measurements with either of the two above methods of resistance determination, corrections should be made for the currents taken by the instruments.    This is not necessary in most ordinary commercial measurements, however.

**17-11. Wheatstone Bridge**    The most commonly used device for accurate resistance measurements in the range of 1 to 100,000 ohms is

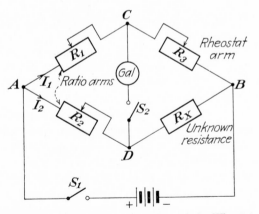

FIG. 17-16. Schematic diagram of connections of the Wheatstone bridge.

the Wheatstone bridge.    As shown in Fig. 17-16, it is composed of resistances $R_1$, $R_2$, and $R_3$, which are accurately known adjustable resistances.    The unknown resistance $R_x$ is connected between points

$D$ and $B$. The resistors are arranged in two parallel circuits through which current from the battery can flow. A galvanometer is bridged across the two circuits between the points $C$ and $D$.

Balancing the bridge consists of closing the battery switch $S_1$ and adjusting $R_1$, $R_2$, and $R_3$ to such values that when the galvanometer switch $S_2$ is closed the galvanometer shows no deflection.

With the bridge balanced, the points $C$ and $D$ are at the same potential. This means that the voltage drops from $A$ to $C$ and $A$ to $D$ must be equal and that the drops from $C$ to $B$ and $D$ to $B$ are also equal. Hence

$$I_1 R_1 = I_2 R_2 \tag{1}$$

and
$$I_1 R_3 = I_2 R_x \tag{2}$$

Dividing Eq. (1) by Eq. (2) and solving for $R_x$ results in

$$R_x = \frac{R_2}{R_1} R_3 \tag{3}$$

**Example 1** The Wheatstone bridge represented in Fig. 17-16 when used for determining the value of an unknown resistance $R_x$ is balanced when $R_3$ is 124 ohms, $R_1$ is 10 ohms, and $R_2$ is 100 ohms. What is the value of $R_x$?

$$R_x = \frac{R_2}{R_1} R_3$$

$$= \frac{100}{10} \times 124 = 1{,}240 \text{ ohms}$$

Resistances $R_1$ and $R_2$ are called the ratio arms of the bridge and are usually made to equal a definite ratio such as 1 to 1, 10 to 1, or 100 to 1. Resistance $R_3$ is called the rheostat arm and is made continuously variable from 1 to 1,000 or from 1 to 10,000 ohms. When the bridge is balanced, the value of the unknown resistance is equal to the value of $R_3$ multiplied by the ratio of $R_2$ to $R_1$.

On commercial "dial" type bridges such as the type shown in Fig. 17-17, the ratio of $R_2$ to $R_1$ is selected by means of a rotary switch, the setting being indicated on a dial. The rheostat arm $R_3$ is adjusted by four or more rotary switches, one of which varies the resistance in steps of 1 ohm, another in steps of 10 ohms, another in steps of 100 ohms, and so on. The value of the rheostat arm $R_3$ then may be read directly from the setting of the several dials on the rotary switches when the bridge is balanced.

The best accuracy is obtained with a Wheatstone bridge when all four resistances are equal; that is, with the ratio arms set for a 1-to-1 ratio and the rheostat arm adjusted to equal the unknown resistance.

Fig. 17-17. Dial-type Wheatstone bridge. (*Courtesy of Leeds & Northrup Company.*)

**17-12. Insulation Resistance**    Insulating materials are materials that offer a high resistance to the flow of an electric current.    The materials and the dimensions of the materials used for insulating electric circuits must be such that a very high resistance, usually in the order of megohms,* is offered to the flow of current.    For example, the armature coils of a generator must have sufficient insulation to prevent the leakage of current to adjacent coils or to the iron armature core.    The operation of electric equipment such as transformers, motors, generators, and cables depends on the maintenance of the proper value of insulation resistance for the circuits involved.

In many cases it is desirable to measure periodically the insulation resistance of electric circuits, so that defective insulation may be found before it causes failure of the equipment.    Defective insulation may

* One megohm is equal to 1,000,000 ohms.

occur from the effects of heat, the presence of moisture, mechanical injuries, chemical action, or other causes. Of the several known methods for measuring insulation resistance, the voltmeter method and the Megger method are the most commonly used and are described in the following articles.

**17-13. Measurement of Resistance; Voltmeter Method**   A voltmeter may be used for measuring insulation resistance or other high resistances. A high-resistance voltmeter is preferable, and the voltmeter resistance $R_v$ must be known. A reading is first taken with the voltmeter across a constant source of voltage $E$. The voltmeter and the unknown resistance are then connected in series to the same source of voltage $E$, as in Fig. 17-18, and a second reading is taken. From these readings, the value of the unknown resistance may be calculated as shown below.

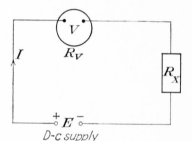

FIG. 17-18. The voltmeter method of measuring resistance.

In Fig. 17-18 the current is

$$I = \frac{E}{R_v + R_x} \quad (4)$$

The voltmeter reading $V$ when the voltmeter is connected in the circuit of Fig. 17-18 is the voltage drop in its own resistance, **or**

$$V = IR_v \quad (5)$$

Substituting Eq. (4) in Eq. (5) and solving for $R_x$ results in

$$R_x = R_v \left(\frac{E}{V} - 1\right) \quad (6)$$

The value of the unknown resistance $R_x$ may thus be calculated by substituting the two voltmeter readings in Eq. (6).

**Example 2**   It is desired to measure the resistance of the insulation between a motor winding and the motor frame. A 300-volt 30,000-ohm voltmeter is used in making the measurements. The voltmeter when connected across the source reads 230 volts and when connected in series with the insulation reads 5 volts. Find the insulation resistance.

$$R_x = R_v \left(\frac{E}{V} - 1\right)$$

$$= 30,000 \left(\frac{230}{5} - 1\right) = 30,000 \times 45$$

$$= 1,350,000 \text{ ohms, or } 1.35 \text{ megohms}$$

**17-14. The Megger Insulation Tester**   The Megger insulation tester is very commonly used for measuring insulation resistance.   An exterior view of one model of this line of insulation testers is shown in Fig. 17-19.

FIG. 17-19. The Megger insulation tester.   (*Courtesy of James G. Biddle Co.*)

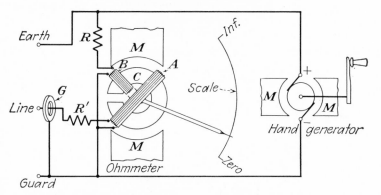

FIG. 17-20. Simplified circuit diagram of the Megger insulation tester.   (*Courtesy of James G. Biddle Co.*)

Essentially the Megger insulation tester consists of a hand-driven d-c generator and a direct-reading true ohmmeter.   A simplified diagram of the electrical connections of the instrument is shown in Fig. 17-20.   Permanent magnets provide the field for both the generator and the ohmmeter.

The moving element of the ohmmeter consists of two coils, *A* and *B*, which are mounted rigidly to a pivoted central shaft and which are free to rotate over a stationary C-shaped iron core. The coils are connected to the circuit by means of flexible leads that exert no restoring force on the moving element. Hence the moving element may stand in any position over the scale when the generator is not in operation. Coil $B$ is connected in series with the resistance $R$ across the generator terminals, while coil $A$ is connected in series with the resistance $R'$ between one generator terminal and the test terminal marked LINE.

When current flows from the generator through coil $B$, the coil tends to set itself at right angles to the field of the permanent magnet. With the test terminals open, corresponding to infinite resistance, no current flows in coil $A$. Coil $B$ thus governs the motion of the rotating element, causing it to move to its extreme counterclockwise position. The point on the scale indicated by the pointer under this condition is marked infinite resistance.

Coil $A$ is wound to produce a clockwise torque on the moving element. With the test terminals marked LINE and EARTH short-circuited, corresponding to zero external resistance, the current flowing through coil $A$ is large enough to produce enough torque to overcome the counterclockwise torque of coil $B$. This moves the pointer to its extreme clockwise position, which point is marked zero resistance on the scale. The resistance $R'$ protects coil $A$ from the flow of excessive current when the test terminals are short-circuited.

When an unknown value of resistance is connected between the test terminals LINE and EARTH, the opposing torques of the coils balance each other so that the pointer comes to rest at some intermediate point on the scale. The scale is calibrated so that the pointer indicates directly the value of the resistance being measured.

The purpose of the guard ring $G$ is to prevent errors in reading due to leakage currents between the LINE and EARTH terminals of the instrument. The GUARD terminal is provided so that unwanted leakage currents in the apparatus under test may also be eliminated.

Generators rated at 500, 1,000, or 2,500 volts are used in Megger testers, the higher voltages being used in the instruments with the higher resistance ranges. Variations in generator voltage in a given instrument do not appreciably affect the readings except when the apparatus under test has considerable capacitance as, for example, a long length of lead-covered cable. To avoid the effect of the charging and discharging currents when a varying voltage is applied, Megger testers equipped with a friction clutch are available. When the generator is cranked faster than a certain speed, the clutch slips, thereby maintaining a constant generator speed and output voltage. The instrument shown in Fig. 17-19 is of the constant-voltage type.

**17-15. The Ohmmeter**   The series ohmmeter generally used in portable circuit analyzers makes use of the principle of using a voltmeter for measuring resistance as described in Art. 17-13.   Figure 17-21 shows the circuit of the series ohmmeter.   A battery, a current-detecting instrument $G$, and a series-resistance $R$ are connected in series between the two terminals $A$ and $B$. With the terminals $A$ and $B$ open (infinite resistance), the pointer of the instrument is at rest at the left-hand end of the scale. The value of the series resistance $R$ is chosen so that with the test terminals $A$ and $B$ short-circuited (zero resistance) the pointer comes to rest at the right-hand end of the scale.   Thus an inverse scale is used, zero resistance being indicated on the right-hand end with increasing values of resistance marked on the scale from right to left.

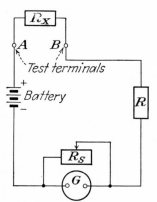

Fig. 17-21. Connections of the ohmmeter.

Fig. 17-22. Combination volt-ohmmeter.   (*Courtesy of Simpson Electric Company.*)

Before making a measurement of resistance, the test terminals are short-circuited and the instrument pointer is adjusted to the zero position by means of the variable-shunt resistance $R_s$. This is necessary since the battery voltage may vary from time to time and thus affect the readings. The resistance $R_x$ to be measured is then connected between terminals $A$ and $B$, the value of the resistance being read directly from the scale.

Ohmmeters are very often included as a part of a multirange test instrument. In the more complete multipurpose instruments, provision is made whereby alternating currents and voltages, direct currents and voltages, and resistance all may be measured with the same instrument. Such an instrument is shown in Fig. 17-22. Self-contained dry cells provide the source of emf for resistance measurements.

## REVIEW QUESTIONS

**1.** What is a galvanometer? What is the fundamental principle upon which it operates?

**2.** How is the restoring or restraining action produced in a galvanometer? How is damping accomplished?

**3.** Describe the construction of a permanent-magnet moving-coil instrument. For what kind of measurements is it used?

**4.** How are voltmeters and ammeters connected to a circuit?

**5.** How may the range of a voltmeter be extended so that high values of voltage may be measured?

**6.** How are high values of current measured with a permanent-magnet moving-coil instrument?

**7.** Describe the principle of the moving-iron vane instrument. How is damping provided? For what kind of measurements is it used?

**8.** What is an electrodynamometer instrument? Why can this instrument be used for either a-c or d-c measurements while the permanent-magnet moving-coil instrument is suitable only for d-c measurements?

**9.** How is the electrodynamometer instrument connected when used as a wattmeter? Will this instrument correctly measure power in a circuit in which the current and voltage are out of phase?

**10.** How many single-phase wattmeters are necessary for accurate measurements of power in a three-wire three-phase circuit? How are the wattmeters connected?

**11.** How is driving torque obtained in the induction watthour meter? How is retarding torque provided?

**12.** How do watthour-meter connections compare with wattmeter connections?

**13.** What type of instrument is commonly used for power-factor measurement?

**14.** Show how an ammeter and voltmeter should be connected for determining the resistance of a 115-volt 10-watt lamp. How does this connection differ from that used for measuring a motor armature resistance?

**15.** Draw a sketch showing the essential circuits of a Wheatstone bridge. Show the relation between the four resistances when the bridge is balanced.

**16.** What is meant by insulation resistance? Why is it important to know the value of insulation resistance?

**17.** Describe the method of measuring resistance with a voltmeter.

**18.** What are the essential parts of the Megger insulation tester?  Describe its operation.

**19.** How is a series ohmmeter adjusted for a zero reading?  Why is this adjustment necessary?

## PROBLEMS

**1.** A 150-volt d-c voltmeter has a resistance of 15,000 ohms.  Find the current flowing through the voltmeter when it is connected to a 120-volt line.  What will be the voltmeter current for full-scale (150 volts) deflection?

**2.** What must be the value of an external resistance used with the voltmeter in Prob. 1 if it is desired to use the voltmeter for measuring a maximum of 300 volts?

**3.** What is the resistance of a 50-amp shunt if the voltage drop across it is 50 mv at rated shunt current?

**4.** A 50-mv millivoltmeter is used with a 100-amp 50-mv shunt for measuring the current taken by a d-c motor.  What is the motor current when the instrument indicates 30 mv?  By what factor must any reading of the above millivoltmeter be multiplied to give the motor current in amperes?

**5.** If a 100-mv instrument is used with the shunt in Prob. 4, what will be the scale-multiplying factor?

**6.** A millivoltmeter used with a 200-amp 50-mv shunt has a 0 to 200 scale marked to read directly in amperes.  If the 200-amp shunt is replaced by a 100-amp 50-mv shunt, by what factor must the instrument readings be multiplied to obtain true values of current?

**7.** A permanent-magnet moving-coil instrument has a coil resistance of 2 ohms and requires a current of 0.025 amp for full-scale deflection.  The scale reads 0 to 300.  Find the value of a series resistance required to make the instrument suitable for use as a 300-volt voltmeter.

**8.** Three impedances having resistances of 5 ohms and inductive reactances of 8.66 ohms are wye-connected to a 480-volt three-phase three-wire system.  Three ammeters and two single-phase wattmeters are connected to read currents and power in the circuit.  Draw a circuit diagram showing the connections for the ammeters and wattmeters.  What will be the readings of each of the ammeters and of each wattmeter?

**9.** A 15,000-ohm voltmeter is to be used for an insulation-resistance measurement.  The supply voltage is 120 volts.  When connected in series with the supply and the insulation under test, the voltmeter reads 10 volts.  What is the resistance of the insulation?

**10.** With the ratio arms of a Wheatstone bridge set at a 10-to-1 ratio, the bridge balances with the rheostat arm set at 23 ohms.  What is the value of the unknown resistance?

# CHAPTER 18

# ELECTRON TUBES AND DEVICES

The field of application of electron devices is so wide and is expanding so rapidly that it will be possible to mention but a few of the applications here. Some of the fundamentals that are common to many electron devices are discussed in this chapter, however, together with a few typical applications.

**18-1. Electron-tube Types** An electron tube is a device designed for the production and control of the flow of free electrons (electric current) through an evacuated or gas-filled space. It is a relatively simple device, originally developed for use in communications circuits, and one which has found extensive application in industrial control circuits.

Electron tubes may be classified in several different ways:

1. They are either *vacuum* or *gas-filled* tubes, depending on the medium enclosed by the tube envelope.

2. If they are classified by the manner in which the free electrons are produced, they may be *thermionic, mercury-pool,* or *photoemissive.*

3. Using the number of electrodes within the tube envelope as a criterion, they may be two-, three-, four-, or five-electrode tubes, called *diodes, triodes, tetrodes,* or *pentodes,* respectively.

**18-2. Electron-tube Electrodes** The functioning of all electron tubes depends on the fact that under certain conditions, materials may be made to emit electrons. All tubes must, therefore, have an electron-emitting electrode which is called the *cathode.* In addition to the cathode, all tubes must have an electrode to collect the electrons that are liberated from the cathode. This electrode is called the *anode* or *plate.* To control the flow of electrons within the tube envelope, certain types of tubes have one or more additional electrodes called *grids* which are placed between the cathode and the anode.

The terminal connections from the electrodes to the external circuits are in the form of pins or prongs in the base of the tube. To meet shielding and insulation requirements, some tubes have cap terminals on the top or side of the envelope in addition to the terminals in the base.

**18-3. Thermionic Emission**   It was shown in Chap. 1 that all materials are thought to be composed of positive and negative electric charges. The negative charges, or electrons, are in a state of continual vibratory motion.   Some electrons are not bound securely and are relatively free to move from atom to atom within the material.   A drift of these free electrons along a conductor constitutes an electric current.

While some electrons may be free to move within the conductor, there exists at the surface of conductors a condition, similar to surface tension, which prevents the escape of the free electrons into the surrounding space.   Thus, normally the flow of electrons is confined to the metal conductor.   Under certain conditions, however, the electrons may be made to obtain enough energy to overcome the surface restraint and escape into the surrounding space.   When this happens, *electron emission* is said to take place.   The amount of energy represented by this escape of the electrons varies with different materials; that is, electron emission can take place more easily in some materials than in others.

A very common method of driving electrons out of a material is by the application of heat to the material.   The process of causing electrons to be released or emitted from a material by heating the material is called *thermionic emission*.

When a conductor is heated, the agitation of the free electrons is increased.   As the temperature of the conductor is increased, a point is reached at which some of the free electrons in the conductor acquire sufficient velocity (or energy) to escape into the surrounding space.   The process may be thought of as being similar to the vaporization of water; that is, the electrons seem to "boil off" the conductor when its temperature is raised to a certain level.

The thermionic-tube cathode may be made in the form of a filament, similar to a lamp filament, of a high-resistance material; this filament is heated by the passage of current through it.   When made in this form, it is called a *directly heated cathode* or *filament*.   Or the cathode may be made separate from and surrounding an electric heater in which case it is called an *indirectly heated cathode*.   Each type has its advantages and specific applications.   In either case the cathode is heated from a separate circuit and not by the electron emission.

Most pure metals melt before their temperature becomes high enough to emit any appreciable quantity of electrons.   Because of its high melting point and other desirable physical properties, however, tungsten is used as a cathode material in high-voltage electron tubes.

In medium-power tubes, a cathode material called *thoriated tungsten* is used. This material consists of tungsten with small amounts of thorium oxide added. After the filament has been formed, it is subjected to a high temperature for a short time. The action of the high temperature is to form a very thin layer of thorium on the filament surface. During normal operation, when the filament is held at the high temperature necessary for good emission, some of the layer evaporates from the surface. However, as fast as it evaporates it is replaced by further diffusion of the thorium to the surface from within the filament. Thoriated filaments cannot be used in high-voltage tubes since the thorium evaporates faster than it can be replaced from within the filament.

Cathodes in which good emission is obtained at relatively low temperatures are formed by coating tungsten or nickel-alloy wire with barium or strontium oxides. Indirectly heated cathodes are of the oxide-coated type since their temperatures do not become so high as those of the directly heated types. The oxide-coated cathode is used in low-voltage radio-receiver tubes and many industrial tubes.

The electron-receiving electrode, or plate, is made of a material that is a poor emitter of electrons, usually of nichrome, tungsten, nickel, or graphite. Its construction must be such that electrons striking it at a high velocity do not overheat it. Plates are usually in the form of a thin metal sheet surrounding the cathode.

**18-4. The Vacuum Diode**  When the cathode of an electron tube is heated sufficiently, an invisible cloud of electrons is set free in the space surrounding the cathode. If a voltage is applied between the plate and cathode so that the plate is made positive with respect to the cathode as shown in Fig. 18-1, the electrons are attracted to the plate. Inasmuch as a transfer of electrons constitutes a current flow, it can be said, then, that a current flows through the tube. The electron flow is from the cathode to the plate inside the tube. It should be kept in mind that the direction of electron flow is opposite to the assumed or conventional direction of current flow in a circuit.

The amount of current that flows through a tube, called the anode or plate current, is dependent on both the number of electrons emitted by the cathode and the ability of the plate to attract the electrons. In the thermionic tube, the number of electrons emitted from the cathode depends on its temperature, which in turn depends on the amount of current flowing through the cathode or its heater. The ability of the plate to attract the emitted electrons depends on the voltage between the cathode and plate or, as it is usually called, the plate voltage. Therefore, the plate current of a two-element electron tube may be varied by varying the filament or heater current or the plate voltage.

If the plate voltage of the tube shown in Fig. 18-1 is reversed so that the plate is negative with respect to the cathode, the emitted electrons are repelled by the plate and as a result no electron flow can take place. Thus the tube acts as a check valve in a circuit; that is, it can pass electrons in only one direction. For this reason, electron tubes are sometimes called valves.

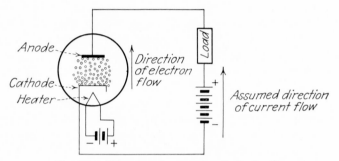

FIG. 18-1. Diagram of a vacuum-diode circuit.

It is this inherent property of an electron tube, its ability to allow the flow of current in only one direction, that makes it suitable for use as a rectifier.

## 18-5. Vacuum-diode Rectifiers

A rectifier is a device for changing alternating current to direct current. Electron tubes are inherently rectifiers since they pass current in one direction only.

When an alternating voltage is applied to a two-element vacuum tube as in Fig. 18-2, the plate is charged alternately positive and negative with respect to the cathode. When the plate is positive, during the positive half-cycle of the applied plate voltage, current can pass through the tube. During the next half-cycle, when the plate is negative, the tube is nonconducting. Thus the tube conducts current only during the positive half-cycles of the plate voltage, resulting in a pulsating

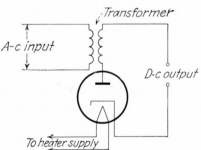

FIG. 18-2. Half-wave rectifier circuit.

d-c output with a waveshape like that shown in Fig. 18-3.    The plate voltage is shown for reference.    A rectifier producing an output current of this type is called a *half-wave rectifier*.

The pulsating output produced by a half-wave rectifier is suitable for some applications, but in most cases the pulsations must be reduced

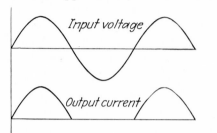

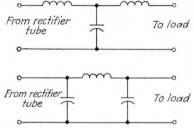

FIG. 18-3. Curves showing the action of the half-wave rectifier.

FIG. 18-4. Typical filter circuits used to reduce the pulsations of the output of rectifier tubes.

by means of filter circuits.    Filter circuits are combinations of inductance coils and capacitors arranged so that the pulsating energy is stored alternately in the coils and capacitors, resulting in a much smoother flow of current from the rectifier tube.    Two typical filter circuits are shown in Fig. 18-4.

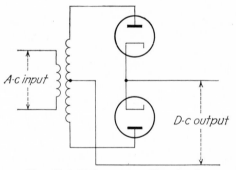

FIG. 18-5. Full-wave rectifier circuit.

So that current may flow during both halves of the cycle, thereby yielding a smoother current output, two diodes may be connected as shown in Fig. 18-5 to form what is known as a *full-wave rectifier*.    A center-tapped transformer winding supplies the plate voltage for both tubes.    With the plates supplied from the same source, the plate of one tube is positive at a time when the plate of the other tube is negative. One-half cycle later, the polarities are reversed.    Thus one tube is conducting during each half-cycle, and the output-current wave is as shown in Fig. 18-6.

The vacuum diode is widely used as a rectifier tube in radio receiving sets. Here the current requirements are small, usually 100 ma or less. A very common tube for this purpose is a twin-diode full-wave rectifier which consists of two diodes enclosed in the same envelope.

Where small amounts of direct current at high voltages are required, the vacuum-diode rectifier is also used. A typical application is in the provision of high voltages for electrostatic precipitators. Electrical precipitation is used for removing dust particles from air or for recovering valuable particles from flue gases. The air or gas to be cleaned is passed between a series of charged electrodes. The negative electrodes are in the form of wires or rods that are spaced between flat plates, the plates forming the positive electrodes. As the air passes between the electrodes, which are charged to voltages as high as 60,000 volts, the air becomes ionized, causing the

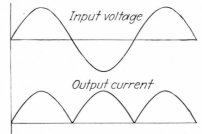

FIG. 18-6. Curves showing that the output current of a full-wave rectifier flows during both halves of the cycle.

suspended particles to become negatively charged. The charged particles accumulate on the positive electrodes from which they fall by gravity into hoppers below. The electric precipitator is effective in removing tiny particles that normally pass through other types of filters.

High-vacuum diodes are used also for supplying high voltages for testing purposes, X-ray apparatus, and other high-voltage applications.

**18-6. The Vacuum Triode: Action of the Grid** Triodes, or three-element tubes, contain a control element, or *grid*, which serves to control the flow of electrons in the tube. The grid is usually in the form of a wire-mesh screen so that when it is uncharged it does not obstruct the flow of electrons. However, when the grid is positively charged with respect to the cathode, its effect is to increase the flow of electrons from cathode to plate. If it is negatively charged, the flow of electrons is retarded. If it is made sufficiently negative, it can stop completely the electron flow.

By making small changes in the grid potential, it is possible to produce large changes in plate current. A change of 1 volt in grid potential will produce many times the change in plate current that a change of 1 volt in the plate voltage will produce. The grid thus provides a very effective means of controlling the plate current.

It is the action of the grid in an electron tube that enables it to act as an amplifier of small voltages or currents. If a small voltage is available (such as the voltage received in a radio antenna), but is too small to be used directly, it may be used as a signal voltage applied to the grid of a vacuum tube as shown in Fig. 18-7. Each change in the grid voltage produces a corresponding change in plate current except that all changes are greatly magnified. Thus the output of a vacuum

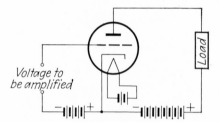

FIG. 18-7. Simple amplifier circuit using a vacuum triode.

tube may be varied in exactly the same manner as the input but with increased amplitude.

Amplifier tubes may be used as relays in a manner similar to that shown in Fig. 18-8. The switch $S$ represents the contacts of a sensitive contact-making device such as might be used on a voltmeter or pressure gauge. In such applications it is desirable that the contacts be made as light as possible and carry as little current as possible. For this

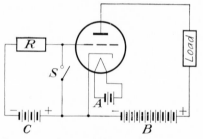

FIG. 18-8. An amplifier used as a relay.

reason the contacts cannot carry the load current directly. However, by the circuit arrangement shown in Fig. 18-8, the contact may be made to open and close the load circuit with very little current through the contacts themselves.

When the contacts are open and the grid potential is held several volts negative with respect to the cathode by the battery $C$, the grid prevents the flow of plate current even though the plate is positively charged. Therefore no current can flow through the load. However, when the contacts $S$ are closed, the grid is connected to the cathode and no longer has a negative potential. Plate current is thus allowed to flow through the load. To prevent the battery $C$ from causing excessive current flow when the contacts are closed, the resistor $R$ having a resistance of several megohms is placed in the circuit. A typical commercial electronic relay is shown in Fig. 18-9.

Fig. 18-9. An electronic relay for controlling a power circuit from a low-current contact. (*Courtesy of General Electric Company.*)

Triodes used as *oscillators* generate high frequencies for use in communications, power-line carrier equipment for relaying and remote control, high-frequency induction furnaces, and many other similar applications.

**18-7. Vacuum Tetrodes and Pentodes**   One of the limitations of the triode, when operated as an amplifier at high frequencies, is the capacitance of the capacitor formed by the control grid and the plate. The coupling of the input circuit to the output circuit through this capacitance in the triode can result in unstable operation.

The grid-plate capacitance of an electron tube can be reduced by the addition of another electrode called the *screen grid* between the control grid and the plate. Such a tube is called a *tetrode*. The screen grid is operated at a positive potential with respect to the cathode and its effect is to reduce the grid-to-plate capacitance by several hundred times when it is connected to the proper external components. The tetrode not only has a low grid-to-plate capacitance but also has a higher amplification factor than a triode.

In all electron tubes, electrons striking the plate at high velocity may dislodge other electrons, causing them to be emitted from the plate. This effect is called *secondary emission*. In diodes and triodes, secondary emission does not affect the operation of the tube appreciably because dislodged electrons are drawn back to the positively-charged plate. However, when a positively charged screen grid is present, some of these electrons are attracted to the screen grid. This effect lowers the plate current and limits the operating range of the tube.

To retain the advantages of the screen grid and minimize its disadvantages, a third grid called the *suppressor grid* may be added to an electron tube. A tube having three grids, control, screen, and suppressor, in addition to the plate and cathode is called a *pentode*.

The pentode is used extensively as an amplifier in communications work both at audio and radio frequencies. In addition to the advantage of its low grid-to-plate capacitance, it provides a much greater voltage amplification than does the triode.

**18-8. The Cathode-ray Oscilloscope**  The cathode-ray oscilloscope is a very useful general-purpose electronic measuring instrument. It is used for studying waveshapes of alternating currents and voltages

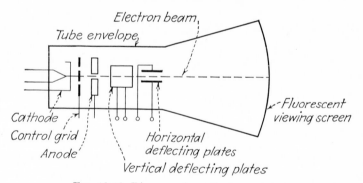

Fig. 18-10. Diagram of a cathode-ray tube.

as well as for measuring voltage, current, power, and frequency; in fact, almost any quantity that involves amplitude and waveform.

A simplified cross-sectional view of a cathode-ray tube of the type used in the oscilloscope is shown in Fig. 18-10. The cathode is usually of the oxide-coated type, indirectly heated. When the cathode is heated to its emitting temperature and the proper voltage is applied between the anode and cathode, electrons are drawn toward the anode as in any electron tube. However the anode of the cathode-ray tube has a small hole in it so that some of the electrons pass on through it. These electrons, because of the velocity attained by their movement from the cathode to the anode, continue to move through the highly evacuated tube until they strike the end wall of the tube. This part of the tube is covered with a fluorescent material that glows when it is struck by the stream of electrons and forms the viewing screen of the tube. A stream of electrons passing from the cathode through the opening in the anode and in a straight line to the screen appears as a stationary spot on the screen.

Between the anode and the viewing screen and adjacent to the electron stream are placed two pairs of deflecting plates, one horizontal pair and one vertical pair. By applying a voltage to either pair of plates, the electron stream may be deflected from its straight-line path, the amount of deflection being in proportion to the voltage applied. If, for example, an alternating voltage is applied across the two vertical deflecting plates, the electron stream is deflected back and forth along a horizontal line on the viewing screen as the voltage changes in magnitude and direction. Unless the frequency of the applied voltage is very low, the back-and-forth movement of the electron stream appears as a stationary horizontal line on the screen. Likewise, an alternating voltage applied to the horizontal plates appears as a stationary vertical line.

When the oscilloscope is being used to study the waveshape of, say, an alternating voltage, the voltage under test is applied to one set of plates while a second voltage, called a sweep voltage, is applied to the other set of plates. The sweep voltage is of special waveform and is generated in an oscillator that is usually a part of the oscilloscope. The sweep voltage is adjusted until it is synchronized with the voltage under test. With the two voltages properly synchronized, a stationary wave of the exact shape of the voltage under test appears in the form of a graph on the viewing screen. Thus both the waveshape and magnitude of the test voltage may be observed on the screen. The brilliance of the image on the screen may be controlled by means of a control grid placed between the cathode and the deflecting plates.

Because of its versatility in high-frequency measurements, the cathode-ray oscilloscope is almost indispensable in communications research work and in the servicing of communications equipment. It is used in the study of transient phenomena due to lightning and switching surges on power systems. It is also used in the studies of electric arcs and commutation; for the measurements of impedance, transformer ratios, and phase angle; for mechanical measurements; and in many other applications.

**18-9. Effect of Gas in Electron Tubes; Ionization**   When the cathode of a vacuum tube is heated to its emitting temperature, electrons are driven off and form an invisible cloud around the cathode.   This cloud of electrons has a negative charge and tends to repel the similarly charged electrons as they leave the cathode.   In effect, this cloud of electrons tends to neutralize the attraction of the positively charged plate for electrons in the space near the cathode.   This is called the *space-charge* effect.   The space-charge effect in vacuum tubes limits the amount of current that can be carried by the tube, and for this reason vacuum tubes can be used only for low-current applications, the plate currents being of the order of milliamperes.

The space-charge effect can be neutralized in an electron tube by the addition of a small amount of inert gas, such as argon or mercury vapor. Such an electron tube is called a *gas-filled* tube.

As electrons are emitted from the cathode of a gas-filled tube and move toward the positively charged plate, their passage is obstructed by their collision with the relatively large gas molecules.   If, when these collisions take place, the electrons have sufficient velocity, electrons are knocked completely out of the gas molecules.   A plate-to-cathode voltage of 10 to 30 volts, the actual value depending on the gas and its temperature and pressure, is sufficient to give the electrons this required velocity.   When the normally uncharged gas molecules lose electrons by this collision, they become positively charged and are called *ions*.   Once ions have started to form in a gas-filled tube the process is cumulative; that is, electrons knocked off the molecules move toward the plate, colliding with other molecules, and so on.   Large numbers of ions are formed in the space of a few millionths of a second. The gas is then said to be *ionized*.

The positive ions in an ionized gas of an electron tube are attracted to the cathode, but being relatively large they move very slowly.   Thus the space between the plate and cathode is filled with large numbers of ions.   Since the positive ions are practically stationary in the area around the cathode, their effect is to neutralize the effect of the space charge.   Ionization thus allows more of the emitted electrons to reach the plate and accounts for the fact that gas-filled tubes are able to carry very much larger currents than vacuum tubes of a similar size.

When the plate current of a gas-filled tube is interrupted, the electrons and ions recombine to form the natural uncharged gas molecules. This process is called *deionization* and, like ionization, takes place very rapidly.

When the gas in a gas-filled tube becomes ionized, a dull light or glow is emitted.   For this reason, gas-filled tubes are sometimes referred to as *glow-discharge tubes*.

**18-10. Gas-filled Diode**   The two-element gas-filled tube, sometimes called the *phanotron*, is widely used as a rectifier where the currents required are about 30 amp or less, at low voltages.   As such, it is used for charging storage batteries and other similar applications.   A typical self-regulated automatic battery charger using phanotron tubes is shown in Fig. 18-11.   This charger, known by the trade name of Phano-charger, has an adjustable d-c output voltage of from 120 to 140 volts

FIG. 18-11. A self-regulating electronic battery charger. (*Courtesy of General Electric Company.*)

at 12.5 amp and is used for maintaining the proper charge on 60-cell station batteries in generating plants.   The rectifier tubes are mounted on the panel in the cabinet, and the voltage and control tubes are in the assembly on the back of the cabinet door.

The gas-filled diode, or phanotron, is not satisfactory for use at high voltages or high frequencies.   One of the requirements of a good rectifier is that it should offer a very high impedance to the flow of current through it when the plate is negative.   The gas-filled tube does not have this property at high voltages.   The time required for ionization and deionization of the gas prevents the use of gas-filled tubes on frequencies above a few hundred cycles per second.

As the plate voltage is gradually raised on a vacuum tube for a given cathode temperature, the plate current gradually increases. As the plate voltage of a gas-filled tube is increased from zero, the tube is nonconducting until a certain critical voltage is reached. At this critical voltage, which is usually about 15 volts, the gas ionizes and the plate current immediately reaches its full value as determined by the impedance of the connected circuit. The tube is then said to be *ignited* or *firing*. If the voltage applied to the plate circuit is increased, the current flow increases causing a larger $IZ$ drop in the connected load, but the voltage drop across the tube remains constant at about 15 volts. Because of the lower voltage drop, the gas-filled tube has a higher efficiency than the vacuum tube.

### 18-11. The Grid-controlled Gas-filled Tube: the Thyratron The

*thyratron* is a gas-filled tube with one or more control grids. It is used extensively as an electronic switch and as a rectifier.

When the cathode of a thyratron is heated, electrons are emitted. Whether or not the electrons flow to the positively charged plate depends on the potential of the grid. When the grid is negative with respect to the cathode, no current can flow. As the grid potential is made more positive, a point is reached at which the gas ionizes and the flow of electrons suddenly begins. The action of the grid is that of a trigger, releasing the full flow of electrons almost instantly.

The thyratron differs from the grid-controlled vacuum tube in that once the tube has fired or begun conducting, the grid loses control of the plate current. The only way in which the plate current may be stopped is by lowering the plate voltage to zero. The grid then regains control and again prevents the flow of current until the grid potential is brought to its proper value.

A good picture of the difference in operation between a vacuum tube and a gas-filled tube may be formed by thinking of the vacuum tube as a current-throttling device or a rheostat in a circuit and of the gas-filled tube as a switch.

The thyratron finds wide use in timing and other control applications. The fact that its time of firing may be controlled makes the thyratron adaptable to heat control in resistance welding. By delaying or advancing the time during the cycle at which the tube fires, the average amount of welding current allowed to flow per cycle may be increased or decreased. In addition to this, the number of cycles that the welding current is allowed to flow may be controlled very accurately.

A system of electronic motor control using thyratron rectifiers is shown in Fig. 18-12.   Taking power from an a-c supply, this system supplies direct current for the operation of a d-c motor.   Provision is made for a wide range of speed control, automatic acceleration, automatic speed regulation, and various types of motor protection.   The

Fig. 18-12. A d-c motor operated from an a-c circuit.   (*Courtesy of General Electric Company.*)

armature power supply is a full-wave rectifier composed of two thyratrons.   Smaller thyratrons supply the motor field.   Speeds below the motor base speed are obtained by armature control, while those above base speed are obtained by field control.   Vacuum triodes are used to control the grids of the thyratrons.   The triodes in turn are supplied by vacuum-diode rectifiers.

**18-12. The Ignitron**    The *ignitron* is a gas-filled tube with a mercury-pool cathode.    The anode is made of graphite and is placed close to the cathode to keep the voltage drop in the tube low.    Instead of a grid as in the thyratron, the control element is an *igniter*.    The igniter, made of a crystalline substance, dips into the mercury pool but is not wet by the mercury.    When a current is passed through the igniter to the mercury, an intensely hot spot is formed at their junction, resulting in an ionization of the surrounding vapor.    If the anode is positive at

Fɪɢ. 18-13. An ignitron unit substation with the door of the rectifier section open. This type of substation converts alternating current to direct current for industrial, mining, and railway use.    (*Courtesy of Westinghouse Electric Corporation.*)

the instant that the cathode hot spot is formed, an arc is established between the cathode and anode.    Thus the time of firing of the tube may be very accurately controlled by means of the igniter.

As do other power tubes, the ignitron conducts current in only one direction.    By the proper control of the igniter, it is possible to delay the firing of the tube until any desired time has elapsed after voltage has been applied to the anode.

To dissipate the heat losses, the larger sized tubes have built-in water jackets for cooling.

Two important uses of the ignitron are in rectification and control.

It is widely used as a rectifier where large amounts of direct current are required as in railway service, in mines, and in the reduction of aluminum and magnesium ores. An ignitron rectifier unit assembled as part of a unit substation is shown in Fig. 18-13.

Ignitron rectifiers with ratings as high as 6,000 kw at 600 volts have been built. While installations have been made for as high as 12,000 volts direct current, the usual application is at the lower voltages.

The second important use of the ignitron is its use as a switch. Its ability to open and close circuits carrying thousands of amperes almost instantaneously makes it especially adaptable for use as a contactor for precision-welding operations. With the igniter controlled by a thyratron, very close control of welding time and the amount of heat is obtained.

**18-13. The Phototube** The *phototube* or *photocell* operates on the principle that certain substances emit electrons when light strikes them.

The phototube is a two-element tube and may be either of the high-vacuum or the gas-filled type. The cathode is made of the light-sensitive material. Common construction is to make the cathode in a semicylindrical shape, with the electron-emitting substance on the inside. The anode is usually a straight wire mounted on the axis of the cylinder so as to receive a maximum number of the emitted electrons without shading the cathode any more than necessary.

When the phototube is connected to a source of voltage so that the anode is positive, no current can flow through the tube if no light strikes the cathode. When light falls on the cathode, electrons are emitted and are attracted to the anode. In general, the amount of electron flow is proportional to the amount of light. The amount of emission is so small, however, that the current is not large enough to operate even the more sensitive relays, and for this reason it must be amplified by other electron tubes to be useful.

Phototubes are usually operated by the interruption of the beam of light striking them. They can be used, however, to detect the presence of light or to detect different degrees of intensity of light.

The industrial uses of the phototube are generally familiar. To mention a few applications, they are used in counting, sorting, color matching, starting and stopping machinery, and in burglar alarms. One application is the use of the phototube in detecting holes in tin plate so small that they cannot be seen with the naked eye. A light source is placed directly over the tin plate as it passes through the shearing line at a high rate of speed. The phototube is placed under the strip so that any light shining through an imperfection allows current to flow through the tube.    This impulse, when amplified, operates an automatic marker that marks the imperfections on the strip.

**18-14. Semiconductors**   Materials which have many free electrons are conductors.    Materials which have few free electrons are insulators. Materials which are neither good conductors nor good insulators are called *semiconductors*.   A semiconductor may act either as a conductor, allowing an easy flow of electric current, or as an insulator, blocking the flow of current, depending upon various physical influences.   Two materials used extensively in the manufacturing of semiconductor devices are germanium and silicon.

It is possible to change the electrical characteristics of germanium or silicon crystals during the manufacturing process by adding closely controlled amounts of impurities.   One type of impurity, called $N$-type impurity, when added to the semiconductor crystal, produces loosely bound electrons in the crystal.   Another type of impurity called $P$-type impurity, removes electrons or creates *holes* in the crystal.   The introduction of the impurities into the semiconductor crystalline structure may be thought of as the addition of mobile charge carriers and either positive or negative charge carriers may be added.   When $P$-type impurities are added, the resulting material has a surplus of holes or positively charged particles and is called $P$-type material.   Likewise, when $N$-type impurities are added, the resulting $N$-type material has a surplus of electrons or negatively charged particles.

In a conductor, the flow of electric current is considered to be the movement of free electrons.   In a semiconductor, the current may be considered to be either the movement of electrons or the movement of holes.   If the material is $P$-type material, that is, deficient in electrons, conduction is by holes.   If the material is $N$-type material, which has an excess of electrons, conduction is by electrons.

A *PN junction* is formed when a $P$-type material is joined to an $N$-type material with a distinct boundary between them.   This junction will pass current in one direction but will offer considerable resistance to the flow of current in the reversed direction; that is, it exhibits the properties of a rectifier.   A two-electrode semiconductor device having a $P$-type electrode and an $N$-type electrode with one junction is called a junction diode or diode rectifier and is electrically equivalent to the diode vacuum tube.

The action of the $PN$ diode may be explained by referring to Fig. 18-14$a$ which shows a battery connected with its positive terminal to the $P$-terminal of the diode and the negative terminal to the $N$-terminal of the diode.   Electrons are attracted across the diode junction by the positive terminal of the battery while the holes are attracted in the opposite direction across the junction by the negative terminal of the battery. Electrons constantly enter the *N*-terminal of the diode and leave the *P*-terminal and current flows in the circuit.

If the battery polarity is reversed as in Fig. 18-14*b*, the excess electrons in the *N*-type material are attracted away from the junction by the positive terminal of the battery. Likewise, the holes are attracted away from the diode junction. This leaves the section of the diode

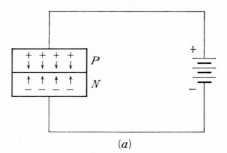

(*a*)

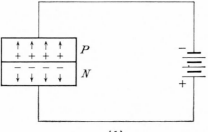

(*b*)

Fig. 18-14. Diagram to illustrate *PN* diode rectifier action: (*a*) diode conducting; (*b*) diode nonconducting.

near the junction practically void of charge carriers and current cannot flow through the junction or the circuit. Since the diode will pass current in one direction and not in the other, it constitutes a rectifier.

**18-15. Semiconductor Rectifiers** Semiconductor diodes, both germanium and silicon, are manufactured in quantity for use as rectifiers. A major application of such rectifiers is in the power-conversion field for converting large amounts of alternating current to direct current for use in metal production and refining, electrochemical processes for generation of gases, and for electroplating processes.

Both germanium- and silicon-rectifier equipment is available as factory assembled units with output ratings up to several thousand amperes.    Such equipment is used where formerly the ignitron rectifier and other forms of power rectifiers were used.    The voltage ranges for rectifier applications are not well defined but generally either the silicon or germanium rectifiers are applicable for required output voltages below 35 volts.    For voltages of from 35 to about 700 volts the silicon rectifier is generally applicable and above 700 volts the ignitron rectifier is normally used.

**18-16. Transistors**    As described previously, a single junction semiconductor device is capable of rectifying current.    By adding a second junction, a semiconductor device is formed which is capable of amplification.    Such a device is called a *transistor*.

A triode, or three-electrode transistor, may be of the *PNP* type consisting of two layers of *P*-type material separated by *N*-type material,

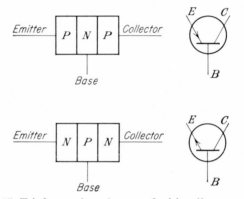

FIG. 18-15. Triode transistor forms and wiring diagram symbols.

or the *NPN* type consisting of two layers of *N*-type material separated by *P*-type material.    The arrangement of both types is shown in Fig. 18-15 together with the symbols used in wiring diagrams.    In each type, one outer layer is called the *emitter* electrode, the center layer the *base*, and the other outer layer the *collector*.    The emitter, base, and collector correspond in a general way to the cathode, grid, and plate of a triode vacuum tube.

One of the simplest circuit applications for the transistor is its use as a d-c amplifier as shown in Fig. 18-16.    The battery is connected between the emitter and collector electrodes with the load resistor in series.    Very little current can flow through the load as long as the base-emitter circuit is open.    However, when a voltage is applied to the base-emitter circuit a small base current will flow.    This small base current allows a much larger collector current to flow through the load.

The small input current in effect controls a much larger output current and amplification takes place.    This basic circuit with refinements may be used as an electronic relay in much the same way as the electron-tube relay described in Art. 18-6.

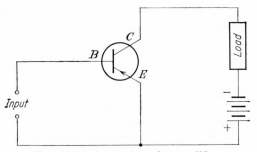

Fig. 18-16. A transistor d-c amplifier.

The transistor, because of its small size and high efficiency, is widely used in portable communications equipment, hearing aids, and other similar applications.    It is also used extensively in industrial control, in computer and logic circuitry and in many other applications where formerly electron tubes were used exclusively.

## REVIEW QUESTIONS

**1.** Name three ways in which electron tubes may be classified.

**2.** What two electrodes are necessary in all electron tubes?

**3.** How are connections made between the tube elements and the external circuits?

**4.** What is meant by the term "thermionic emission"?

**5.** What is the function of the cathode in an electron tube?

**6.** Describe two methods of heating a cathode.

**7.** What are some materials used for cathodes in thermionic tubes?

**8.** Why is the oxide-coated cathode used in most indirectly heated tubes?

**9.** What is the function of the plate or anode?

**10.** How may the current of a vacuum diode be varied?

**11.** What must be the polarity of the plate with respect to the cathode in a diode before current can flow through the tube?

**12.** Why are diodes suitable for use as rectifiers?

**13.** What is a half-wave rectifier?

**14.** What is an advantage of the full-wave rectifier over the half-wave rectifier?

**15.** How are the pulsations of the output of a rectifier tube "smoothed out"?

**16.** What are some applications of the vacuum diode tube?

**17.** What is the purpose of the grid in a vacuum triode?

**18.** Describe the action of a triode when it functions as an amplifier.

**19.** How may the triode be used as a relay?

**20.** What is the purpose of the screen grid in a tetrode?

**21.** What is meant by the term "secondary emission"?

**22.** Name the three grids used in a pentode.

**23.** Give some uses for the cathode-ray oscilloscope.

**24.** What is the space-charge effect in an electron tube?

**25.** What is the purpose of gas in an electron tube?

**26.** Describe the ionizing process in a gas-filled tube.

**27.** What are some applications of gas-filled diodes?

**28.** Why is a gas-filled tube unsuitable for use at high frequencies?  What would the action of a gas-filled tube be if attempts were made to use it to rectify an alternating voltage of, say, 100,000 cps?

**29.** What is a thyratron?

**30.** How does the action of the grid in a thyratron differ from the action of the grid in a vacuum tube?

**31.** What are some applications of the thyratron?

**32.** What is an ignitron?  How is the firing of the tube controlled?  What are some applications?

**33.** Describe the operation of the phototube.

**34.** Would you think the current carried by a phototube would be of the order of microamperes, milliamperes, or amperes?

**35.** What are some typical applications of the phototube?

**36.** What two materials are commonly used in the manufacture of semiconductor devices?

**37.** What is the effect of adding $P$-type and $N$-type impurities to semiconductor crystals?

**38.** What important function can be performed by a semiconductor diode?

**39.** Name the three electrodes of a triode transistor.  To what electrodes in a vacuum triode do these correspond in a general way?

# Appendix 1. Wiring Diagram Symbols

| Device | Standard Industrial Symbol | Other Symbols in Use |
|---|---|---|
| Battery | | |
| Capacitor | | |
| Circuit breaker, air, single-pole | | |
| Circuit breaker, oil, three-pole | | |
| Coil, nonmagnetic core | | |
| Coil, magnetic core | | |
| Coil, operating | | |
| Wire crossing, no connection | | |
| Wires connected | | |
| Ground connection | | |
| Contacts, normally closed when device is deenergized | | |
| Contacts, normally open when device is deenergized | | |
| Fuse | | |

## Appendix 1. Wiring Diagram Symbols (Continued)

| Device | Standard Industrial Symbol | Other Symbols in Use |
|---|---|---|
| Ammeter | | |
| Voltmeter | | |
| Wattmeter | | |
| D-C motor or generator armature | | |
| D-C motor or generator shunt field | | |
| D-C motor or generator series field | | |
| D-C motor or generator commutating (interpole) field | | |
| Three-phase synchronous motor or generator | | |
| Single-phase generator | | |
| Three-phase squirrel-cage motor | | |
| Fixed resistor | RES | |
| Continuously adjustable resistor | RES | |
| Adjustable contact resistor or rheostat | RES | |
| Switch, single-pole, single-throw | | |
| Switch, double-pole, double-throw, terminals shown | | |

## Appendix 1. Wiring Diagram Symbols (Continued)

| Device | Standard Industrial Symbol | Other Symbols in Use |
|---|---|---|
| Push button, normally open | | |
| Push button, normally closed | | |
| Transformer | | |
| Current transformer | | |

ELECTRON TUBES AND DEVICES

| | | |
|---|---|---|
| Directly heated cathode or filament | | |
| Indirectly heated cathode | | |
| Grid | | |
| Anode or plate | | |
| Vacuum diode | | |
| Vacuum triode | | |
| Indicates gas-filled tube | | ←TUBE ENVELOPE |
| Triode thyratron | | |
| Ignitron | | |
| Rectifier, metallic or semiconductor | | |

## Appendix 2. Dimensions, Weights, and Resistance of Bare Copper Wire, Solid

*(Courtesy of the Anaconda Wire & Cable Company)*

| Size, AWG | Diameter, mils | Area, cir mils | Weight, lb per 1,000 ft | Weight, lb per mile | Resistance, ohms per 1,000 ft 20°C (=68°F) medium hard-drawn wire* |
|---|---|---|---|---|---|
| 0000 | 460.000 | 211,600.00 | 640.5 | 3,382 | 0.05019 |
| 000 | 409.640 | 167,804.93 | 507.9 | 2,682 | 0.06329 |
| 00 | 364.800 | 133,079.04 | 402.8 | 2,127 | 0.07980 |
| 0 | 324.860 | 105,534.02 | 319.5 | 1,687 | 0.1006 |
| 1 | 289.300 | 83,694.49 | 253.3 | 1,338 | 0.1282 |
| 2 | 257.630 | 66,373.22 | 200.9 | 1,061 | 0.1617 |
| 3 | 229.420 | 52,633.54 | 159.3 | 841.2 | 0.2038 |
| 4 | 204.310 | 41,742.58 | 126.4 | 667.1 | 0.2570 |
| 5 | 181.940 | 33,102.16 | 100.2 | 529.1 | 0.3241 |
| 6 | 162.020 | 26,250.48 | 79.46 | 419.6 | 0.4087 |
| 7 | 144.280 | 20,816.72 | 63.02 | 332.7 | 0.5154 |
| 8 | 128.490 | 16,509.68 | 49.97 | 263.9 | 0.6499 |
| 9 | 114.430 | 13,094.22 | 39.63 | 209.3 | 0.8195 |
| 10 | 101.890 | 10,381.57 | 31.43 | 165.9 | 1.033 |
| 11 | 90.742 | 8,234.11 | 24.92 | 131.6 | 1.303 |
| 12 | 80.808 | 6,529.93 | 19.77 | 104.4 | 1.643 |
| 13 | 71.961 | 5,178.39 | 15.68 | 82.77 | 2.072 |
| 14 | 64.084 | 4,106.76 | 12.43 | 65.64 | 2.613 |
| 15 | 57.068 | 3,256.76 | 9.858 | 52.05 | 3.295 |
| 16 | 50.820 | 2,582.67 | 7.818 | 41.28 | 4.154 |
| 17 | 45.257 | 2,048.20 | 6.200 | 32.74 | 5.239 |
| 18 | 40.303 | 1,624.33 | 4.917 | 25.96 | 6.606 |
| 19 | 35.890 | 1,288.09 | 3.899 | 20.59 | 8.330 |
| 20 | 31.961 | 1,021.51 | 3.092 | 16.33 | 10.50 |
| 21 | 28.462 | 810.09 | 2.452 | 12.95 | 13.24 |
| 22 | 25.347 | 642.47 | 1.945 | 10.27 | 16.70 |
| 23 | 22.571 | 509.45 | 1.542 | 8.143 | 21.06 |
| 24 | 20.100 | 404.01 | 1.223 | 6.458 | 26.56 |
| 25 | 17.900 | 320.41 | 0.9699 | 5.121 | 33.49 |
| 26 | 15.940 | 254.08 | 0.7692 | 4.061 | 42.23 |
| 27 | 14.195 | 201.50 | 0.6100 | 3.221 | 53.25 |
| 28 | 12.641 | 159.79 | 0.4837 | 2.554 | 67.14 |
| 29 | 11.257 | 126.72 | 0.3836 | 2.026 | 84.66 |
| 30 | 10.025 | 100.50 | 0.3042 | 1.606 | 106.8 |
| 31 | 8.928 | 79.71 | 0.2413 | 1.274 | 134.6 |
| 32 | 7.950 | 63.20 | 0.1913 | 1.010 | 169.8 |
| 33 | 7.080 | 50.13 | 0.1517 | 0.8011 | 214.1 |
| 34 | 6.304 | 39.74 | 0.1203 | 0.6353 | 269.9 |
| 35 | 5.614 | 31.52 | 0.09542 | 0.5038 | 340.4 |
| 36 | 5.000 | 25.00 | 0.07567 | 0.3996 | 429.2 |
| 37 | 4.453 | 19.83 | 0.06001 | 0.3169 | 541.2 |
| 38 | 3.965 | 15.72 | 0.04759 | 0.2513 | 682.4 |
| 39 | 3.531 | 12.47 | 0.03774 | 0.1993 | 860.5 |
| 40 | 3.145 | 9.89 | 0.02993 | 0.1580 | 1,085 |

*The resistance values in this table are trade maximums and are higher than the average values for commercial wire. The following values for the conductivity of copper were used: 0.325 inch diameter and larger, 97.66 per cent of international annealed copper standard at 20°C.
0.324 inch diameters and smaller, 96.66 per cent of international annealed copper standard at 20°C.

# Appendix 3. Dimensions, Weights, and Resistance of Bare Copper Wire, Stranded

*(Courtesy of the Anaconda Wire & Copper Company)*

| Size, AWG or cir mils | Over-all diameter, mils | Area, cir mils | Number of strands, A.S.T.M. Class A stranding | Weight, lb per 1,000 ft | Weight, lb per mile | Resistance, ohms per 1,000 ft 20°C (=68°F) medium hard-drawn wire* |
|---|---|---|---|---|---|---|
| 5,000,000 | 2,580 | 5,000,000 | 169 | 15,890 | 83,910 | 0.002253 |
| 4,500,000 | 2,448 | 4,500,000 | 169 | 14,300 | 75,520 | 0.002504 |
| 4,000,000 | 2,307 | 4,000,000 | 169 | 12,590 | 66,490 | 0.002790 |
| 3,500,000 | 2,158 | 3,500,000 | 127 | 11,020 | 58,180 | 0.003188 |
| 3,000,000 | 1,998 | 3,000,000 | 127 | 9,353 | 49,390 | 0.003684 |
| 2,500,000 | 1,823 | 2,500,000 | 91 | 7,794 | 41,150 | 0.004421 |
| 2,000,000 | 1,630 | 2,000,000 | 91 | 6,175 | 32,600 | 0.005472 |
| 1,750,000 | 1,526 | 1,750,000 | 91 | 5,403 | 28,530 | 0.006254 |
| 1,500,000 | 1,411 | 1,500,000 | 61 | 4,631 | 24,450 | 0.007296 |
| 1,250,000 | 1,288 | 1,250,000 | 61 | 3,859 | 20,380 | 0.008755 |
| 1,000,000 | 1,152 | 1,000,000 | 61 | 3,088 | 16,300 | 0.01094 |
| 900,000 | 1,094 | 900,000 | 61 | 2,779 | 14,670 | 0.01216 |
| 800,000 | 1,031 | 800,000 | 61 | 2,470 | 13,040 | 0.01368 |
| 750,000 | 998 | 750,000 | 61 | 2,316 | 12,230 | 0.01459 |
| 700,000 | 964 | 700,000 | 61 | 2,161 | 11,410 | 0.01563 |
| 600,000 | 891 | 600,000 | 37 | 1,853 | 9,781 | 0.01824 |
| 500,000 | 813 | 500,000 | 37 | 1,544 | 8,151 | 0.02189 |
| 450,000 | 772 | 450,000 | 37 | 1,389 | 7,336 | 0.02432 |
| 400,000 | 726 | 400,000 | 19 | 1,235 | 6,521 | 0.02736 |
| 350,000 | 679 | 350,000 | 19 | 1,081 | 5,706 | 0.03127 |
| 300,000 | 629 | 300,000 | 19 | 926.3 | 4,891 | 0.03648 |
| 250,000 | 574 | 250,000 | 19 | 771.9 | 4,076 | 0.04378 |
| 0000 | 552 | 211,600 | 12 | 653.3 | 3,450 | 0.05172 |
| 000 | 492 | 167,800 | 12 | 518.1 | 2,736 | 0.06522 |
| 00 | 414 | 133,100 | 7 | 410.9 | 2,170 | 0.08223 |
| 0 | 368 | 105,500 | 7 | 325.7 | 1,720 | 0.1037 |
| 1 | 328 | 83,690 | 7 | 258.4 | 1,364 | 0.1308 |
| 2 | 292 | 66,370 | 7 | 204.9 | 1,082 | 0.1649 |
| 3 | 260 | 52,630 | 7 | 162.5 | 858.0 | 0.2079 |
| 4 | 232 | 41,740 | 7 | 128.9 | 680.5 | 0.2622 |

* The resistance values in this table are trade maximums and are higher than the average values for commercial wire. The following value of conductivity of copper was used: 96.66 per cent of international annealed copper standard at 20°C.

# Appendix 4. Full-load Currents of Motors
## (National Electrical Code)

| | Three-phase motors* | | | | | | | | |
|---|---|---|---|---|---|---|---|---|---|
| | Induction type squirrel-cage and wound-rotor, amp | | | | | Synchronous type unity power factor,‡ amp | | | |
| Horsepower rating | 110 v | 220 v† | 440 v | 550 v | 2,300 v | 220 v | 440 v | 550 v | 2,300 v |
| ½ | 4 | 2 | 1 | 0.8 | | | | | |
| ¾ | 5.6 | 2.8 | 1.4 | 1.1 | | | | | |
| 1 | 7 | 3.5 | 1.8 | 1.4 | | | | | |
| 1½ | 10 | 5 | 2.5 | 2.0 | | | | | |
| 2 | 13 | 6.5 | 3.3 | 2.6 | | | | | |
| 3 | .... | 9 | 4.5 | 4 | | | | | |
| 5 | .... | 15 | 7.5 | 6 | | | | | |
| 7½ | .... | 22 | 11 | 9 | | | | | |
| 10 | .... | 27 | 14 | 11 | | | | | |
| 15 | .... | 40 | 20 | 16 | | | | | |
| 20 | .... | 52 | 26 | 21 | | | | | |
| 25 | .... | 64 | 32 | 26 | 7 | 54 | 27 | 22 | 5.4 |
| 30 | .... | 78 | 39 | 31 | 8.5 | 65 | 33 | 26 | 6.5 |
| 40 | .... | 104 | 52 | 41 | 10.5 | 86 | 43 | 35 | 8 |
| 50 | .... | 125 | 63 | 50 | 13 | 108 | 54 | 44 | 10 |
| 60 | .... | 150 | 75 | 60 | 16 | 128 | 64 | 51 | 12 |
| 75 | .... | 185 | 93 | 74 | 19 | 161 | 81 | 65 | 15 |
| 100 | .... | 246 | 123 | 98 | 25 | 211 | 106 | 85 | 20 |
| 125 | .... | 310 | 155 | 124 | 31 | 264 | 132 | 106 | 25 |
| 150 | .... | 360 | 180 | 144 | 37 | ... | 158 | 127 | 30 |
| 200 | .... | 480 | 240 | 192 | 48 | ... | 210 | 168 | 40 |

| Direct-current motors,§ amp | | | | Single-phase motors,* amp | | | |
|---|---|---|---|---|---|---|---|
| Horsepower rating | 115 v | 230 v | 550 v | Horsepower rating | 115 v | 230 v¶ | 440 v |
| ¼ | 3 | 1.5 | .... | ⅙ | 4.4 | 2.2 | |
| ⅓ | 3.8 | 1.9 | .... | ¼ | 5.8 | 2.9 | |
| ½ | 5.4 | 2.7 | .... | ⅓ | 7.2 | 3.6 | |
| ¾ | 7.4 | 3.7 | 1.6 | ½ | 9.8 | 4.9 | |
| 1 | 9.6 | 4.8 | 2.0 | ¾ | 13.8 | 6.9 | |
| 1½ | 13.2 | 6.6 | 2.7 | 1 | 16 | 8 | |
| 2 | 17 | 8.5 | 3.6 | 1½ | 20 | 10 | |
| 3 | 25 | 12.5 | 5.2 | 2 | 24 | 12 | |
| 5 | 40 | 20 | 8.3 | 3 | 34 | 17 | |
| 7½ | 58 | 29 | 12 | 5 | 56 | 28 | |
| 10 | 76 | 38 | 16 | 7½ | 80 | 40 | 21 |
| 15 | 112 | 56 | 23 | 10 | 100 | 50 | 26 |
| 20 | 148 | 74 | 31 | | | | |
| 25 | 184 | 92 | 38 | | | | |
| 30 | 220 | 110 | 46 | | | | |
| 40 | 292 | 146 | 61 | | | | |
| 50 | 360 | 180 | 75 | | | | |
| 60 | 430 | 215 | 90 | | | | |
| 75 | 536 | 268 | 111 | | | | |
| 100 | ..... | 355 | 148 | | | | |
| 125 | ..... | 443 | 184 | | | | |
| 150 | ..... | 534 | 220 | | | | |
| 200 | ..... | 712 | 295 | | | | |

* These values of full-load current are for motors running at speeds usual for belted motors and motors with normal torque characteristics. Motors built for especially low speeds or high torques may require more running current, in which case the nameplate current rating should be used.

† For full-load currents of 208- and 200-volt motors, increase the corresponding 220-volt motor full-load current by 6 and 10 per cent, respectively.

‡ For 90 and 80 per cent power factors the above figures should be multiplied by 1.1 and 1.25, respectively.

§ These values of full-load currents are for motors running at usual speeds.

¶ To obtain full-load currents of 208- and 200-volt motors, increase corresponding 230-volt motor full-load currents by 10 and 15 per cent, respectively.

## Right Triangles

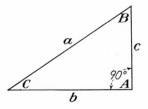

1. A right triangle is a triangle in which one angle is a right angle (90°).

2. The sum of the three angles (of any triangle) is 180°.

3. The side opposite the right angle is called the hypotenuse. Side $a$ is the hypotenuse in the above figure.

4. The square of the hypotenuse is equal to the sum of the squares of the other two sides. In the above figure,

$$a^2 = b^2 + c^2$$

or
$$a = \sqrt{b^2 + c^2}$$

Also
$$b = \sqrt{a^2 - c^2}$$

and
$$c = \sqrt{a^2 - b^2}$$

Several of the possible ratios between the sides of the right triangle shown in the above figure are listed below. These ratios are called *trigonometric functions*. A table of values of the trigonometric functions is given in Appendix 6.

5. The ratio of side $c$ to side $a$ is called the sine (sin) of angle $C$.

$$\sin C = \frac{c}{a} = \frac{\text{opposite side}}{\text{hypotenuse}}$$

6. The ratio of side $b$ to side $a$ is called the cosine (cos) of angle $C$.

$$\cos C = \frac{b}{a} = \frac{\text{adjacent side}}{\text{hypotenuse}}$$

7. The ratio of side $c$ to side $b$ is called the tangent (tan) of angle $C$.

$$\tan C = \frac{c}{b} = \frac{\text{opposite side}}{\text{adjacent side}}$$

8. The ratio of side $b$ to side $c$ is called the cotangent (cot) of angle $C$.

$$\cot C = \frac{b}{c} = \frac{\text{adjacent side}}{\text{opposite side}}$$

The following are examples using the above relationships:

**Example 1**   If angle $B$ in the above figure is 63°, find angle $C$.

$$A + B + C = 180° \qquad \text{(from relation 2)}$$
$$A = 90°$$
Therefore
$$B + C = 90°$$
$$C = 90 - 63 = 27°$$

**Example 2**   If side $c$ in the figure represents 12 ohms and side $b$ represents 16 ohms, find the angle $C$.

$$\tan C = \frac{c}{b} \qquad \text{(from relation 7)}$$

$$\tan C = \frac{12}{16} = 0.75$$

In the table of tangents (Appendix 6), the number nearest 0.75 is 0.74900 which is the tangent of 36°50′.   Thus the angle $C$ is approximately 36°50′.

**Example 3**   If side $a$ in the figure represents 200 volts and angle $C$ is 45°, find side $c$.

$$\sin C = \frac{c}{a} \qquad \text{(from relation 5)}$$
or
$$c = a \sin C$$

From the table of sines, sin 45 deg = 0.70711
    Thus
$$c = 200 \times 0.707 = 141.4 \text{ volts}$$

**Example 4**   If side $a$ in the figure is 40 units long and angle $C$ is 30°, find sides $b$ and $c$.
$$b = a \cos C \qquad \text{(from relation 6)}$$
$$b = 40 \times \cos 30°$$
$$= 40 \times 0.866 = 34.64$$
$$c = a \sin C \qquad \text{(from relation 5)}$$
$$c = 40 \sin 30°$$
$$= 40 \times 0.500 = 20$$

## Appendix 6. Trigonometric Functions

NOTE: For sines, use left-hand column of degrees and upper line of minutes. For cosines, use right-hand column of degrees and lower line of minutes.

SINE

| Angle | 0′ | 10′ | 20′ | 30′ | 40′ | 50′ | 60′ | |
|---|---|---|---|---|---|---|---|---|
| 0° | 0.00000 | 0.00291 | 0.00582 | 0.00873 | 0.01164 | 0.01454 | 0.01745 | 89 |
| 1 | 0.01745 | 0.02036 | 0.02327 | 0.02618 | 0.02908 | 0.03199 | 0.03490 | 88 |
| 2 | 0.03490 | 0.03781 | 0.04071 | 0.04362 | 0.04653 | 0.04943 | 0.05234 | 87 |
| 3 | 0.05234 | 0.05524 | 0.05814 | 0.06105 | 0.06395 | 0.06685 | 0.06976 | 86 |
| 4 | 0.06976 | 0.07266 | 0.07556 | 0.07846 | 0.08136 | 0.08426 | 0.08716 | 85° |
| 5° | 0.08716 | 0.09005 | 0.09295 | 0.09585 | 0.09874 | 0.10164 | 0.10453 | 84 |
| 6 | 0.10453 | 0.10742 | 0.11031 | 0.11320 | 0.11609 | 0.11898 | 0.12187 | 83 |
| 7 | 0.12187 | 0.12476 | 0.12764 | 0.13053 | 0.13341 | 0.13629 | 0.13917 | 82 |
| 8 | 0.13917 | 0.14205 | 0.14493 | 0.14781 | 0.15069 | 0.15356 | 0.15643 | 81 |
| 9 | 0.15643 | 0.15931 | 0.16218 | 0.16505 | 0.16792 | 0.17078 | 0.17365 | 80° |
| 10° | 0.17365 | 0.17651 | 0.17937 | 0.18224 | 0.18509 | 0.18795 | 0.19081 | 79 |
| 11 | 0.19081 | 0.19366 | 0.19652 | 0.19937 | 0.20222 | 0.20507 | 0.20791 | 78 |
| 12 | 0.20791 | 0.21076 | 0.21360 | 0.21644 | 0.21928 | 0.22212 | 0.22495 | 77 |
| 13 | 0.22495 | 0.22778 | 0.23062 | 0.23345 | 0.23627 | 0.23910 | 0.24192 | 76 |
| 14 | 0.24192 | 0.24474 | 0.24756 | 0.25038 | 0.25320 | 0.25601 | 0.25882 | 75° |
| 15° | 0.25882 | 0.26163 | 0.26443 | 0.26724 | 0.27004 | 0.27284 | 0.27564 | 74 |
| 16 | 0.27564 | 0.27843 | 0.28123 | 0.28402 | 0.28680 | 0.28959 | 0.29237 | 73 |
| 17 | 0.29237 | 0.29515 | 0.29793 | 0.30071 | 0.30348 | 0.30625 | 0.30902 | 72 |
| 18 | 0.30902 | 0.31178 | 0.31454 | 0.31730 | 0.32006 | 0.32282 | 0.32557 | 71 |
| 19 | 0.32557 | 0.32832 | 0.33106 | 0.33381 | 0.33655 | 0.33929 | 0.34202 | 70° |
| 20° | 0.34202 | 0.34475 | 0.34748 | 0.35021 | 0.35293 | 0.35565 | 0.35837 | 69 |
| 21 | 0.35837 | 0.36108 | 0.36379 | 0.36650 | 0.36921 | 0.37191 | 0.37461 | 68 |
| 22 | 0.37461 | 0.37730 | 0.37999 | 0.38268 | 0.38537 | 0.38805 | 0.39073 | 67 |
| 23 | 0.39073 | 0.39341 | 0.39608 | 0.39875 | 0.40141 | 0.40408 | 0.40674 | 66 |
| 24 | 0.40674 | 0.40939 | 0.41204 | 0.41469 | 0.41734 | 0.41998 | 0.42262 | 65° |
| 25° | 0.42262 | 0.42525 | 0.42788 | 0.43051 | 0.43313 | 0.43575 | 0.43837 | 64 |
| 26 | 0.43837 | 0.44098 | 0.44359 | 0.44620 | 0.44880 | 0.45140 | 0.45399 | 63 |
| 27 | 0.45399 | 0.45658 | 0.45917 | 0.46175 | 0.46433 | 0.46690 | 0.46947 | 62 |
| 28 | 0.46947 | 0.47204 | 0.47460 | 0.47716 | 0.47971 | 0.48226 | 0.48481 | 61 |
| 29 | 0.48481 | 0.48735 | 0.48989 | 0.49242 | 0.49495 | 0.49748 | 0.50000 | 60° |
| 30° | 0.50000 | 0.50252 | 0.50503 | 0.50754 | 0.51004 | 0.51254 | 0.51504 | 59 |
| 31 | 0.51504 | 0.51753 | 0.52002 | 0.52250 | 0.52498 | 0.52745 | 0.52992 | 58 |
| 32 | 0.52992 | 0.53238 | 0.53484 | 0.53730 | 0.53975 | 0.54220 | 0.54464 | 57 |
| 33 | 0.54464 | 0.54708 | 0.54951 | 0.55194 | 0.55436 | 0.55678 | 0.55919 | 56 |
| 34 | 0.55919 | 0.56160 | 0.56401 | 0.56641 | 0.56880 | 0.57119 | 0.57358 | 55° |
| 35° | 0.57358 | 0.57596 | 0.57833 | 0.58070 | 0.58307 | 0.58543 | 0.58779 | 54 |
| 36 | 0.58779 | 0.59014 | 0.59248 | 0.59482 | 0.59716 | 0.59949 | 0.60182 | 53 |
| 37 | 0.60182 | 0.60414 | 0.60645 | 0.60876 | 0.61107 | 0.61337 | 0.61566 | 52 |
| 38 | 0.61566 | 0.61795 | 0.62024 | 0.62251 | 0.62479 | 0.62706 | 0.62932 | 51 |
| 39 | 0.62932 | 0.63158 | 0.63383 | 0.63608 | 0.63832 | 0.64056 | 0.64279 | 50° |
| 40° | 0.64279 | 0.64501 | 0.64723 | 0.64945 | 0.65166 | 0.65386 | 0.65606 | 49 |
| 41 | 0.65606 | 0.65825 | 0.66044 | 0.66262 | 0.66480 | 0.66697 | 0.66913 | 48 |
| 42 | 0.66913 | 0.67129 | 0.67344 | 0.67559 | 0.67773 | 0.67987 | 0.68200 | 47 |
| 43 | 0.68200 | 0.68412 | 0.68624 | 0.68835 | 0.69046 | 0.69256 | 0.69466 | 46 |
| 44 | 0.69466 | 0.69675 | 0.69883 | 0.70091 | 0.70298 | 0.70505 | 0.70711 | 45 |
| | 60′ | 50′ | 40′ | 30′ | 20′ | 10′ | 0′ | Angle |

COSINE

369

## Appendix 6. Trigonometric Functions (Continued)

**SINE**

| Angle | 0′ | 10′ | 20′ | 30′ | 40′ | 50′ | 60′ | |
|---|---|---|---|---|---|---|---|---|
| 45° | 0.70711 | 0.70916 | 0.71121 | 0.71325 | 0.71529 | 0.71732 | 0.71934 | 44 |
| 46 | 0.71934 | 0.72136 | 0.72337 | 0.72537 | 0.72737 | 0.72937 | 0.73135 | 43 |
| 47 | 0.73135 | 0.73333 | 0.73531 | 0.73728 | 0.73924 | 0.74120 | 0.74314 | 42 |
| 48 | 0.74314 | 0.74509 | 0.74703 | 0.74896 | 0.75088 | 0.75280 | 0.75471 | 41 |
| 49 | 0 75471 | 0.75661 | 0.75851 | 0.76041 | 0.76229 | 0.76417 | 0.76604 | 40° |
| 50° | 0.76604 | 0.76791 | 0.76977 | 0.77162 | 0.77347 | 0.77531 | 0.77715 | 39 |
| 51 | 0.77715 | 0.77897 | 0.78079 | 0.78261 | 0.78442 | 0.78622 | 0.78801 | 38 |
| 52 | 0 78801 | 0.78980 | 0.79158 | 0.79335 | 0.79512 | 0.79688 | 0.79864 | 37 |
| 53 | 0 79864 | 0.80038 | 0.80212 | 0.80386 | 0.80558 | 0.80730 | 0.80902 | 36 |
| 54 | 0.80902 | 0.81072 | 0.81242 | 0.81412 | 0.81580 | 0.81748 | 0.81915 | 35° |
| 55° | 0.81915 | 0.82082 | 0.82248 | 0.82413 | 0.82577 | 0.82741 | 0.82904 | 34 |
| 56 | 0.82904 | 0.83066 | 0.83228 | 0.83389 | 0.83549 | 0.83708 | 0.83867 | 33 |
| 57 | 0.83867 | 0.84025 | 0.84182 | 0.84339 | 0.84495 | 0.84650 | 0.84805 | 32 |
| 58 | 0.84805 | 0.84959 | 0.85112 | 0.85264 | 0.85416 | 0.85567 | 0.85717 | 31 |
| 59 | 0.85717 | 0.85866 | 0.86015 | 0.86163 | 0.86310 | 0.86457 | 0.86603 | 30° |
| 60° | 0.86603 | 0.86748 | 0.86892 | 0.87036 | 0.87178 | 0.87321 | 0.87462 | 29 |
| 61 | 0.87462 | 0.87603 | 0.87743 | 0.87882 | 0.88020 | 0.88158 | 0.88295 | 28 |
| 62 | 0.88295 | 0.88431 | 0.88566 | 0.88701 | 0.88835 | 0.88968 | 0.89101 | 27 |
| 63 | 0.89101 | 0.89232 | 0.89363 | 0.89493 | 0.89623 | 0.89752 | 0.89879 | 26 |
| 64 | 0.89879 | 0.90007 | 0.90133 | 0.90259 | 0.90383 | 0.90507 | 0.90631 | 25° |
| 65° | 0.90631 | 0.90753 | 0.90875 | 0.90996 | 0.91116 | 0.91236 | 0.91355 | 24 |
| 66 | 0.91355 | 0.91472 | 0.91590 | 0.91706 | 0.91822 | 0.91936 | 0.92050 | 23 |
| 67 | 0.92050 | 0.92164 | 0.92276 | 0.92388 | 0.92499 | 0.92609 | 0.92718 | 22 |
| 68 | 0.92718 | 0.92827 | 0.92935 | 0.93042 | 0.93148 | 0.93253 | 0.93358 | 21 |
| 69 | 0.93358 | 0.93462 | 0.93565 | 0.93667 | 0.93769 | 0.93869 | 0.93969 | 20° |
| 70° | 0.93969 | 0.94068 | 0.94167 | 0.94264 | 0.94361 | 0.94457 | 0.94552 | 19 |
| 71 | 0.94552 | 0.94646 | 0.94740 | 0.94832 | 0.94924 | 0.95015 | 0.95106 | 18 |
| 72 | 0.95106 | 0.95195 | 0.95284 | 0.95372 | 0.95459 | 0.95545 | 0.95630 | 17 |
| 73 | 0.95630 | 0.95715 | 0.95799 | 0.95882 | 0.95964 | 0.96046 | 0.96126 | 16 |
| 74 | 0.96126 | 0.96206 | 0.96285 | 0.96363 | 0.96440 | 0.96517 | 0.96593 | 15° |
| 75° | 0.96593 | 0.96667 | 0.96742 | 0.96815 | 0.96887 | 0.96959 | 0.97030 | 14 |
| 76 | 0.97030 | 0.97100 | 0.97169 | 0.97237 | 0.97304 | 0.97371 | 0.97437 | 13 |
| 77 | 0.97437 | 0.97502 | 0.97566 | 0.97630 | 0.97692 | 0.97754 | 0.97815 | 12 |
| 78 | 0.97815 | 0.97875 | 0.97934 | 0.97992 | 0.98050 | 0.98107 | 0.98163 | 11 |
| 79 | 0.98163 | 0.98218 | 0.98272 | 0.98325 | 0.98378 | 0.98430 | 0.98481 | 10° |
| 80° | 0.98481 | 0.98531 | 0.98580 | 0.98629 | 0.98676 | 0.98723 | 0.98769 | 9 |
| 81 | 0.98769 | 0.98814 | 0.98858 | 0.98902 | 0.98944 | 0.98986 | 0.99027 | 8 |
| 82 | 0.99027 | 0.99067 | 0.99106 | 0.99144 | 0.99182 | 0.99219 | 0.99255 | 7 |
| 83 | 0.99255 | 0.99290 | 0.99324 | 0.99357 | 0.99390 | 0.99421 | 0.99452 | 6 |
| 84 | 0.99452 | 0.99482 | 0.99511 | 0.99540 | 0.99567 | 0.99594 | 0.99619 | 5° |
| 85° | 0.99619 | 0.99644 | 0.99668 | 0.99692 | 0.99714 | 0.99736 | 0.99756 | 4 |
| 86 | 0.99756 | 0.99776 | 0.99795 | 0.99813 | 0.99831 | 0.99847 | 0.99863 | 3 |
| 87 | 0.99863 | 0.99878 | 0.99892 | 0.99905 | 0.99917 | 0.99929 | 0.99939 | 2 |
| 88 | 0.99939 | 0.99949 | 0.99958 | 0.99966 | 0.99973 | 0.99979 | 0.99985 | 1 |
| 89 | 0.99985 | 0.99989 | 0.99993 | 0.99996 | 0.99998 | 1.00000 | 1.00000 | 0° |
| | 60′ | 50′ | 40 | 30′ | 20′ | 10′ | 0′ | Angle |

**COSINE**

## Appendix 6. Trigonometric Functions (Continued)

NOTE: For tangents, use left-hand column of degrees and upper line of minutes. For cotangents, use right-hand column of degrees and lower line of minutes.

### TANGENT

| Angle | 0' | 10' | 20' | 30' | 40' | 50' | 60' | |
|---|---|---|---|---|---|---|---|---|
| 0° | 0.00000 | 0.00291 | 0.00582 | 0.00873 | 0.01164 | 0.01455 | 0.01746 | 89 |
| 1 | 0.01746 | 0.02036 | 0.02328 | 0.02619 | 0.02910 | 0.03201 | 0.03492 | 88 |
| 2 | 0.03492 | 0.03783 | 0.04075 | 0.04366 | 0.04658 | 0.04949 | 0.05241 | 87 |
| 3 | 0.05241 | 0.05533 | 0.05824 | 0.06116 | 0.06408 | 0.06700 | 0.06993 | 86 |
| 4 | 0.06993 | 0.07285 | 0.07578 | 0.07870 | 0.08163 | 0.08456 | 0.08749 | 85° |
| 5° | 0.08749 | 0.09042 | 0.09335 | 0.09629 | 0.09923 | 0.10216 | 0.10510 | 84 |
| 6 | 0.10510 | 0.10805 | 0.11099 | 0.11394 | 0.11688 | 0.11983 | 0.12278 | 83 |
| 7 | 0.12278 | 0.12574 | 0.12869 | 0.13165 | 0.13461 | 0.13758 | 0.14054 | 82 |
| 8 | 0.14054 | 0.14351 | 0.14648 | 0.14945 | 0.15243 | 0.15540 | 0.15838 | 81 |
| 9 | 0.15838 | 0.16137 | 0.16435 | 0.16734 | 0.17033 | 0.17333 | 0.17633 | 80° |
| 10° | 0.17633 | 0.17933 | 0.18233 | 0.18534 | 0.18835 | 0.19136 | 0.19438 | 79 |
| 11 | 0.19438 | 0.19740 | 0.20042 | 0.20345 | 0.20648 | 0.20952 | 0.21256 | 78 |
| 12 | 0.21256 | 0.21560 | 0.21864 | 0.22169 | 0.22475 | 0.22781 | 0.23087 | 77 |
| 13 | 0.23087 | 0.23393 | 0.23700 | 0.24008 | 0.24316 | 0.24624 | 0.24933 | 76 |
| 14 | 0.24933 | 0.25242 | 0.25552 | 0.25862 | 0.26172 | 0.26483 | 0.26795 | 75° |
| 15° | 0.26795 | 0.27107 | 0.27419 | 0.27732 | 0.28046 | 0.28360 | 0.28675 | 74 |
| 16 | 0.28675 | 0.28990 | 0.29305 | 0.29621 | 0.29938 | 0.30255 | 0.30573 | 73 |
| 17 | 0.30573 | 0.30891 | 0.31210 | 0.31530 | 0.31850 | 0.32171 | 0.32492 | 72 |
| 18 | 0.32492 | 0.32814 | 0.33136 | 0.33460 | 0.33783 | 0.34108 | 0.34433 | 71 |
| 19 | 0.34433 | 0.34758 | 0.35085 | 0.35412 | 0.35740 | 0.36068 | 0.36397 | 70° |
| 20° | 0.36397 | 0.36727 | 0.37057 | 0.37388 | 0.37720 | 0.38053 | 0.38386 | 69 |
| 21 | 0.38386 | 0.38721 | 0.39055 | 0.39391 | 0.39727 | 0.40065 | 0.40403 | 68 |
| 22 | 0.40403 | 0.40741 | 0.41081 | 0.41421 | 0.41763 | 0.42105 | 0.42447 | 67 |
| 23 | 0.42447 | 0.42791 | 0.43136 | 0.43481 | 0.43828 | 0.44175 | 0.44523 | 66 |
| 24 | 0.44523 | 0.44872 | 0.45222 | 0.45573 | 0.45924 | 0.46277 | 0.46631 | 65° |
| 25° | 0.46631 | 0.46985 | 0.47341 | 0.47698 | 0.48055 | 0.48414 | 0.48773 | 64 |
| 26 | 0.48773 | 0.49134 | 0.49495 | 0.49858 | 0.50222 | 0.50587 | 0.50953 | 63 |
| 27 | 0.50953 | 0.51319 | 0.51688 | 0.52057 | 0.52427 | 0.52798 | 0.53171 | 62 |
| 28 | 0.53171 | 0.53545 | 0.53920 | 0.54296 | 0.54673 | 0.55051 | 0.55431 | 61 |
| 29 | 0.55431 | 0.55812 | 0.56194 | 0.56577 | 0.56962 | 0.57348 | 0.57735 | 60° |
| 30° | 0.57735 | 0.58124 | 0.58513 | 0.58905 | 0.59297 | 0.59691 | 0.60086 | 59 |
| 31 | 0.60086 | 0.60483 | 0.60881 | 0.61280 | 0.61681 | 0.62083 | 0.62487 | 58 |
| 32 | 0.62487 | 0.62892 | 0.63299 | 0.63707 | 0.64117 | 0.64528 | 0.64941 | 57 |
| 33 | 0.64941 | 0.65355 | 0.65771 | 0.66189 | 0.66608 | 0.67028 | 0.67451 | 56 |
| 34 | 0.67451 | 0.67875 | 0.68301 | 0.68728 | 0.69157 | 0.69588 | 0.70021 | 55° |
| 35° | 0.70021 | 0.70455 | 0.70891 | 0.71329 | 0.71769 | 0.72211 | 0.72654 | 54 |
| 36 | 0.72654 | 0.73100 | 0.73547 | 0.73996 | 0.74447 | 0.74900 | 0.75355 | 53 |
| 37 | 0.75355 | 0.75812 | 0.76272 | 0.76733 | 0.77196 | 0.77661 | 0.78129 | 52 |
| 38 | 0.78129 | 0.78598 | 0.79070 | 0.79544 | 0.80020 | 0.80498 | 0.80978 | 51 |
| 39 | 0.80978 | 0.81461 | 0.81946 | 0.82434 | 0.82923 | 0.83415 | 0.83910 | 50° |
| 40° | 0.83910 | 0.84407 | 0.84906 | 0.85408 | 0.85912 | 0.86419 | 0.86929 | 49 |
| 41 | 0.86929 | 0.87441 | 0.87955 | 0.88473 | 0.88992 | 0.89515 | 0.90040 | 48 |
| 42 | 0.90040 | 0.90569 | 0.91099 | 0.91633 | 0.92170 | 0.92709 | 0.93252 | 47 |
| 43 | 0.93252 | 0.93797 | 0.94345 | 0.94896 | 0.95451 | 0.96008 | 0.96569 | 46 |
| 44 | 0.96569 | 0.97133 | 0.97700 | 0.98270 | 0.98843 | 0.99420 | 1.00000 | 45° |
| | 60' | 50' | 40' | 30' | 20' | 10' | 0' | Angle |

### COTANGENT

## Appendix 6. Trigonometric Functions (Continued)

### TANGENT

| Angle | 0′ | 10′ | 20′ | 30′ | 40′ | 50′ | 60′ | |
|---|---|---|---|---|---|---|---|---|
| **45°** | 1.00000 | 1.00583 | 1.01170 | 1.01761 | 1.02355 | 1.02952 | 1.03553 | **44** |
| **46** | 1.03553 | 1.04158 | 1.04766 | 1.05378 | 1.05994 | 1.06613 | 1.07237 | **43** |
| **47** | 1.07237 | 1.07864 | 1.08496 | 1.09131 | 1.09770 | 1.10414 | 1.11061 | **42** |
| **48** | 1.11061 | 1.11713 | 1.12369 | 1.13029 | 1.13694 | 1.14363 | 1.15037 | **41** |
| **49** | 1.15037 | 1.15715 | 1.16398 | 1.17085 | 1.17777 | 1.18474 | 1.19175 | **40°** |
| **50°** | 1.19175 | 1.19882 | 1.20593 | 1.21310 | 1.22031 | 1.22758 | 1.23490 | **39** |
| **51** | 1.23490 | 1.24227 | 1.24969 | 1.25717 | 1.26471 | 1.27230 | 1.27994 | **38** |
| **52** | 1.27994 | 1.28764 | 1.29541 | 1.30323 | 1.31110 | 1.31904 | 1.32704 | **37** |
| **53** | 1.32704 | 1.33511 | 1.34323 | 1.35142 | 1.35968 | 1.36800 | 1.37638 | **36** |
| **54** | 1.37638 | 1.38484 | 1.39336 | 1.40195 | 1.41061 | 1.41934 | 1.42815 | **35°** |
| **55°** | 1.42815 | 1.43703 | 1.44598 | 1.45501 | 1.46411 | 1.47330 | 1.48256 | **34** |
| **56** | 1.48256 | 1.49190 | 1.50133 | 1.51084 | 1.52043 | 1.53010 | 1.53986 | **33** |
| **57** | 1.53986 | 1.54972 | 1.55966 | 1.56969 | 1.57981 | 1.59002 | 1.60033 | **32** |
| **58** | 1.60033 | 1.61074 | 1.62125 | 1.63185 | 1.64256 | 1.65337 | 1.66428 | **31** |
| **59** | 1.66428 | 1.67530 | 1.68643 | 1.69766 | 1.70901 | 1.72047 | 1.73205 | **30°** |
| **60°** | 1.73205 | 1.74375 | 1.75556 | 1.76749 | 1.77955 | 1.79174 | 1.80405 | **29** |
| **61** | 1.80405 | 1.81649 | 1.82906 | 1.84177 | 1.85462 | 1.86760 | 1.88073 | **28** |
| **62** | 1.88073 | 1.89400 | 1.90741 | 1.92098 | 1.93470 | 1.94858 | 1.96261 | **27** |
| **63** | 1.96261 | 1.97681 | 1.99116 | 2.00569 | 2.02039 | 2.03526 | 2.05030 | **26** |
| **64** | 2.05030 | 2.06553 | 2.08094 | 2.09654 | 2.11233 | 2.12832 | 2.14451 | **25°** |
| **65°** | 2.14451 | 2.16090 | 2.17749 | 2.19430 | 2.21132 | 2.22857 | 2.24604 | **24** |
| **66** | 2.24604 | 2.26374 | 2.28167 | 2.29984 | 2.31826 | 2.33693 | 2.35585 | **23** |
| **67** | 2.35585 | 2.37504 | 2.39449 | 2.41421 | 2.43422 | 2.45451 | 2.47509 | **22** |
| **68** | 2.47509 | 2.49597 | 2.51715 | 2.53865 | 2.56046 | 2.58261 | 2.60509 | **21** |
| **69** | 2.60509 | 2.62791 | 2.65109 | 2.67462 | 2.69853 | 2.72281 | 2.74748 | **20°** |
| **70°** | 2.74748 | 2.77254 | 2.79802 | 2.82391 | 2.85023 | 2.87700 | 2.90421 | **19** |
| **71** | 2.90421 | 2.93189 | 2.96004 | 2.98868 | 3.01783 | 3.04749 | 3.07768 | **18** |
| **72** | 3.07768 | 3.10842 | 3.13972 | 3.17159 | 3.20406 | 3.23714 | 3.27085 | **17** |
| **73** | 3.27085 | 3.30521 | 3.34023 | 3.37594 | 3.41236 | 3.44951 | 3.48741 | **16** |
| **74** | 3.48741 | 3.52609 | 3.56557 | 3.60588 | 3.64705 | 3.68909 | 3.73205 | **15°** |
| **75°** | 3.73205 | 3.77595 | 3.82083 | 3.86671 | 3.91364 | 3.96165 | 4.01078 | **14** |
| **76** | 4.01078 | 4.06107 | 4.11256 | 4.16530 | 4.21933 | 4.27471 | 4.33148 | **13** |
| **77** | 4.33148 | 4.38969 | 4.44942 | 4.51071 | 4.57363 | 4.63825 | 4.70463 | **12** |
| **78** | 4.70463 | 4.77286 | 4.84300 | 4.91516 | 4.98940 | 5.06584 | 5.14455 | **11** |
| **79** | 5.14455 | 5.22566 | 5.30928 | 5.39552 | 5.48451 | 5.57638 | 5.67128 | **10°** |
| **80°** | 5.67128 | 5.76937 | 5.87080 | 5.97576 | 6.08444 | 6.19703 | 6.31375 | **9** |
| **81** | 6.31375 | 6.43484 | 6.56055 | 6.69116 | 6.82694 | 6.96823 | 7.11537 | **8** |
| **82** | 7.11537 | 7.26873 | 7.42871 | 7.59575 | 7.77035 | 7.95302 | 8.14435 | **7** |
| **83** | 8.14435 | 8.34496 | 8.55555 | 8.77689 | 9.00983 | 9.25530 | 9.51436 | **6** |
| **84** | 9.51436 | 9.78817 | 10.0780 | 10.3854 | 10.7119 | 11.0594 | 11.4301 | **5°** |
| **85°** | 11.4301 | 11.8262 | 12.2505 | 12.7062 | 13.1969 | 13.7267 | 14.3007 | **4** |
| **86** | 14.3007 | 14.9244 | 15.6048 | 16.3499 | 17.1693 | 18.0750 | 19.0811 | **3** |
| **87** | 19.0811 | 20.2056 | 21.4704 | 22.9038 | 24.5418 | 26.4316 | 28.6363 | **2** |
| **88** | 28.6363 | 31.2416 | 34.3678 | 38.1885 | 42.9641 | 49.1039 | 57.2900 | **1** |
| **89** | 57.2900 | 68.7501 | 85.9398 | 114.589 | 171.885 | 343.774 | ∞ | **0°** |
| | **60′** | **50′** | **40′** | **30′** | **20′** | **10′** | **0′** | Angle |

### COTANGENT

Vectors when represented as complex quantities consist of two components, a *real* and a *quadrature* component. Graphically, the real components are represented by points along a horizontal axis, and the quadrature components are represented by points along a vertical axis, as shown in Fig. A-1. The point of intersection of the two axes is called the *origin point O*. Positive values of the real components are represented by points to the right of the origin $O$ and negative values to the left of the origin. Positive values of the quadrature components are represented by points above the origin $O$ and negative values by points below the origin.

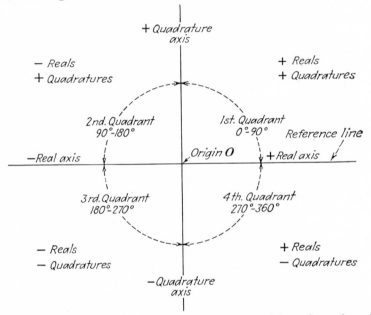

Fɪɢ. A-1. Diagram showing the four quadrants with the positive and negative values of vector components in each.

The four sections of the plane as divided by the two axes are called *quadrants* and are numbered as shown. The horizontal line to the right of the origin is called the *reference line*. Starting at the reference line and proceeding in a counterclockwise direction, the first quadrant contains all angles from 0 to 90°; the second quadrant, 90 to 180°; the third quadrant, 180 to 270°; and the fourth, 270 to 360°.

The real and quadrature components of a vector in any quadrant are the projections of that vector on the horizontal and vertical axes of the quadrant in which the vector lies. For example, in Fig. A-2, the vector $C$ has a real component $a$ (the projection on the horizontal axis) and a quadrature component $jb$ (the projection on the vertical axis). The operator $j$ is used with the quadrature component to indicate that this component is at right angles to the real component.

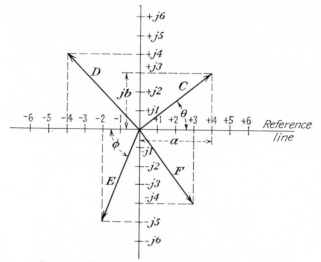

Fɪɢ. A-2. Diagram to illustrate vector notation.

In accordance with the convention stated, both the real and quadrature components of vectors in the first quadrant have positive values. Mathematically, the vector $C$ can be written

$$C = a + jb$$

Using the numerical values shown in Fig. A-2, the vector $C$ is

$$C = 4 + j3$$

As can be seen in Figs. A-1 and A-2, vectors in the second quadrant have negative real and positive quadrature components, those in the third quadrant have negative real and negative quadrature components, and those in the fourth quadrant have positive real and negative quadrature components. The vectors $D$, $E$, and $F$ in Fig. A-2 are expressed numerically as

$$D = -4 + j4$$
$$E = -2 - j5$$
and
$$F = +3 - j4$$

The angle that a vector makes with the horizontal is the angle whose tangent is the quadrature component divided by the real component. For example, the angle $\theta$ between the vector $C$ and the horizontal in

Fig. A-2 is

$$\tan \theta = \frac{b}{a} = \frac{3}{4} = 0.75$$
$$\theta = 36°52'$$

Similarly, the angle $\phi$ for the vector $E$ is

$$\tan \phi = \frac{5}{2} = 2.50$$
$$\phi = 68°12'$$

Thus the magnitude and the angular position of a vector is determined fully by the expression $a + jb$, the magnitude being $\sqrt{a^2 + b^2}$ and the angle from the horizontal being the angle whose tangent is $b/a$. The vector form $a + jb$ is sometimes called the *rectangular form of vector notation*.

Another way of expressing a vector is the so-called *polar* form $C/\underline{\theta°}$, where $C$ is the magnitude of the vector and $\theta$ is the angular position of the vector with respect to the reference line. Using this notation, the vector $C$ in Fig. A-2 may be represented numerically as $5/\underline{36°52'}$ and the vector $E$ as $5.39/\underline{248°12'}$.

Both the rectangular and the polar forms of vectors are useful, and many times it is necessary to convert from one form to the other. In Fig. A-2

$$a = C \cos \theta \quad \text{and} \quad b = C \sin \theta$$

So the form $a + jb$ may be written as

$$C(\cos \theta + j \sin \theta)$$

Again referring to Fig. A-2, if the vector $C$ is given as $5/\underline{36°52'}$, it can be changed to the $a + jb$ form by writing

$$\begin{aligned} C &= 5(\cos 36°52' + j \sin 36°52') \\ &= 5(0.8 + j0.6) \\ &= 4 + j3 \end{aligned}$$

Furthermore, if the vector $E$ is represented as $5.39/\underline{248°12'}$, it is known that this vector is in the third quadrant, since the angle is between 180 and 270 deg. Thus the vector makes an angle of $248°12' - 180°$, or $68°12'$ with the horizontal. Since it is in the third quadrant, both the real and the quadrature components will have negative values. Thus

$$\begin{aligned} E &= 5.39(- \cos 68°12' - j \sin 68°12') \\ &= 5.39(-0.37 - j0.93) \\ &= -2 - j5 \end{aligned}$$

As is shown in the text, currents and voltages are conveniently represented as vectors. Both currents and voltages then may be expressed as complex quantities. Although impedances are not strictly vector quantities, it is convenient to express impedances as complex quantities. Resistances are represented as real components and reactances as quadrature components. In general, impedance is expressed in the rectangular form as

$$Z = R + j(X_L - X_C)$$

and in the polar form

$$Z\underline{/\theta^\circ}$$

Complex quantities representing vectors in general may be subjected to the usual algebraic operations such as addition, subtraction, multiplication, and division. The $a + jb$ or rectangular form is the more convenient form when adding or subtracting vectors, while the $C\underline{/\theta^\circ}$ or polar form is the more convenient form when multiplying or dividing vectors.

**Addition and Subtraction of Vectors**   To add or subtract vectors expressed as complex quantities, the real and quadrature components are added or subtracted separately, and their sums or differences are combined to form the resultant vector.

**Example 1**   Find the vector sum of the two voltages $100\underline{/0^\circ}$ volts and $100\underline{/30^\circ}$ volts. (Refer to Example 4 and Fig. 8-7 in Art. 8-9 in the text.)

The two vectors expressed in complex form are

$$100\underline{/0^\circ} = 100(\cos 0^\circ + j \sin 0^\circ)$$
$$= 100(1 + j0)$$
$$= 100 + j0$$

and

$$100\underline{/30^\circ} = 100(\cos 30^\circ + j \sin 30^\circ)$$
$$= 100(0.866 + j0.5)$$
$$= 86.6 + j50$$

Adding the two vectors

$$\begin{array}{r} 100\phantom{.0} + j0 \\ 86.6 + j50 \\ \hline 186.6 + j50 \end{array}$$

The magnitude of the resultant voltage is

$$\sqrt{(186.6)^2 + (50)^2} = 193.2 \text{ volts}$$

The resultant angle is

$$\tan \theta = \frac{50}{186.6} = 0.268$$

$$\theta = 15 \text{ deg}$$

The sum of the voltages is, therefore, $193.2\underline{/15^\circ}$ volts

**Example 2**   The total current supplied to the two branches of a single-phase parallel circuit is $40\underline{/315°}$ amp.   The current in branch No. 1 is $20\underline{/0°}$ amp.

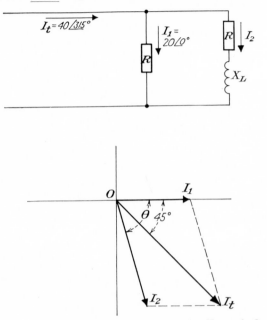

FIG. A-3. Circuit and vector diagrams for Example 2.

What is the current in branch No. 2?   The circuit and vector diagrams are shown in Fig. A-3.

$$I_t = 40\underline{/315°} = 40(\cos 45° - j \sin 45°)$$
$$= 40(0.707 - j0.707)$$
$$= 28.28 - j28.28$$
$$I_1 = 20\underline{/0°} = 20(\cos 0° + j \sin 0°)$$
$$= 20(1 + j0)$$
$$= 20 + j0$$

Subtracting $I_1$ from $I_t$

$$
\begin{array}{r}
28.28 - j28.28 \\
-(+20 \quad + j0) \\
\hline
I_2 = \quad + 8.28 - j28.28
\end{array}
$$

The magnitude of the current $I_2$ in the second branch is

$$\sqrt{(8.28)^2 + (28.28)^2} = 29.5 \text{ amp}$$

and the angle is

$$\tan \theta = \frac{-28.28}{8.28} = -3.415$$
$$\theta = -73°41'$$

It should be noted that the angle $\theta$ has a negative value.   This indicates that the angular position of $I_2$ is $73°41'$ in the *clockwise* direction from the reference line since, by convention, positive angles are measured in a counter-clockwise direction from the reference line. A vector with an angle of 73°41′ in the clockwise direction from the reference line is of course in the fourth quadrant. This is evident also from the fact that the real component of $I_2$ is positive and the quadrature component is negative. The angle $-73°41′$ may be expressed as a positive angle by subtracting from 360°:

$$360° - 73°41′ = 286°19′$$

The current $I_2$ then may be expressed in the polar form either as $29.5/{-73°41′}$ or $29.5/286°19′$ amp.

**Multiplication of Vectors** The product of two vectors $A/\theta°$ and $B/\phi°$ is $AB/\theta° + \phi°$.

**Example 3** What is the voltage across an impedance of $40/20°$ ohms when a current of $6/40°$ amp flows through it?

$$E = IZ = 6/40° \times 40/20°$$
$$= 6 \times 40/40° + 20°$$
$$= 240/60° \text{ volts}$$

**Division of Vectors** The quotient of two vectors $A/\theta°$ and $B/\phi°$ is $\dfrac{A}{B} /\theta° - \phi°$.

**Example 4** What is the current in a circuit that has a resistance of 12 ohms and an inductive reactance of 16 ohms in series when a voltage of $120/0°$ volts is applied?

$$I = \frac{E}{Z}$$
$$E = 120/0°$$
$$Z = 12 + j16 = 20/53°8′$$
$$I = \frac{120/0°}{20/53°8′}$$
$$= \frac{120}{20} /0° - 53°8′$$
$$= 6/{-53°8′} \text{ amp}$$

This angle may be expressed as a positive angle by subtracting from 360°:

$$360° - 53°8′ = 306°52′$$

Thus $$I = 6/{-53°8′}$$

or $$I = 6/306°52′ \text{ amp}$$

# REFERENCES

## HANDBOOKS AND REFERENCE BOOKS

*Standard Handbook for Electrical Engineers,* 9th ed., ARCHER E. KNOWLTON, Editor-in-Chief, McGraw-Hill Book Company, Inc., New York, 1957.

*Electrical Engineers' Handbook,* 4th ed., (two volumes), HAROLD PENDER, Editor-in-Chief, John Wiley & Sons, Inc., New York, 1949 (Electric Power Volume), 1950 (Communication-Electronics Volume).

*American Electricians' Handbook,* 7th ed., TERRELL CROFT, McGraw-Hill Book Company, Inc., New York, 1953.

*National Electrical Code,* National Fire Protection Association, Boston, 1959.

*National Electrical Code Handbook,* 9th ed., ARTHUR L. ABBOTT, revised by CHARLES L. SMITH, McGraw-Hill Book Company, Inc., New York, 1957.

*Electrical Transmission and Distribution Reference Book,* Central Station Engineers, Westinghouse Electric Corporation, East Pittsburgh, Penna., 1950.

*Industrial Electronics Reference Book,* Electronics Engineers of the Westinghouse Electric Corporation, John Wiley & Sons, Inc., New York, 1948.

*Radio Engineering Handbook,* 5th ed., KEITH HENNEY, Editor-in-Chief, McGraw-Hill Book Company, Inc., New York, 1959.

*Radio Engineers' Handbook,* FREDERICK E. TERMAN, McGraw-Hill Book Company, Inc., New York, 1943.

*The Radio Manual,* 4th ed., GEORGE E. STERLING and ROBERT B. MONROE, D. Van Nostrand Company, Inc., Princeton, N.J., 1950.

*The Radio Amateur's Handbook,* 40th ed., The American Radio Relay League, West Hartford, Conn., 1960.

*The Lineman's Handbook,* 3d ed., EDWIN B. KURTZ, McGraw-Hill Book Company, Inc., New York, 1955.

*Industrial Electronics Handbook,* WILLIAM D. COCKRELL, Editor-in-Chief, McGraw-Hill Book Company, Inc., New York, 1958.

*Industrial Power Systems Handbook,* DONALD L. BEEMAN, McGraw-Hill Book Company, Inc., New York, 1955.

## PRINCIPLES AND CIRCUITS

*Principles of Electrical Engineering,* 4th ed., W. H. TIMBIE and VANNEVAR BUSH, John Wiley & Sons, Inc., New York, 1951.

*Introduction to Electrical Engineering,* 3d ed., GEORGE V. MUELLER, McGraw-Hill Book Company, Inc., New York, 1957.

*Introductory Electrical Engineering*, GEORGE F. CORCORAN and HENRY R. REED, John Wiley & Sons, Inc., New York, 1957.

*A Course in Electrical Engineering*, 4th ed., (two volumes), CHESTER L. DAWES, McGraw-Hill Book Company, Inc., New York, 1952 (vol. 1) and 1947 (vol. 2).

*Principles and Practice of Electrical Engineering*, 7th ed., ALEXANDER GRAY and G. A. WALLACE, McGraw-Hill Book Company, Inc., New York, 1955.

*Basic Theory in Electrical Engineering*, ROYCE G. KLOEFFLER and KARL L. SITZ, The Macmillan Company, New York, 1955.

*Analysis of Alternating-current Circuits*, WILBUR R. LEPAGE, McGraw-Hill Book Company, Inc., New York, 1952.

*Alternating-current Circuits*, 3d ed., RUSSELL M. KERCHNER and GEORGE F. CORCORAN, John Wiley & Sons, Inc., New York, 1951.

## MACHINERY AND EQUIPMENT

*Direct-current Machinery*, GROVER S. BLALOCK, McGraw-Hill Book Company, Inc., New York, 1947.

*Direct-current Machinery*, 2d ed., ROYCE G. KLOEFFLER, RUSSELL M. KERCHNER, and JESSE L. BRENNEMAN, The Macmillan Company, New York, 1948.

*D-C and A-C Machines*, M. LIWCHITZ-GARIK and ROBERT T. WEIL, JR., D. Van Nostrand Company, Inc., Princeton, N.J., 1952.

*Connecting and Testing Direct-current Machines*, 3d ed., F. A. ANNETT and A. C. ROE, McGraw-Hill Book Company, Inc., New York, 1955.

*Electrical Machinery*, 3d ed., F. A. ANNETT, McGraw-Hill Book Company, Inc., New York, 1950.

*Principles of Alternating-current Machinery*, 4th ed., RALPH R. LAWRENCE and HENRY E. RICHARDS, McGraw-Hill Book Company, Inc., New York, 1953.

*Theory of Alternating-current Machinery*, 2d ed., ALEXANDER S. LANGSDORF, McGraw-Hill Book Company, Inc., New York, 1955.

*Alternating-current Machines*, 3d ed., A. F. PUCHSTEIN, T. C. LLOYD, and A. G. CONRAD, John Wiley & Sons, Inc., New York, 1954.

*Electric Generation: Steam Stations*, BERNHARDT G. A. SKROTZKI (ed.), McGraw-Hill Book Company, Inc., New York, 1956.

*Electric Generation: Hydro, Diesel, and Gas-turbine Stations*, BERNHARDT G. A. SKROTZKI (ed.), McGraw-Hill Book Company, Inc., New York, 1956.

*Electric Transmission and Distribution*, BERNHARDT G. A. SKROTZKI (ed.), McGraw-Hill Book Company, Inc., New York, 1954.

*Electrical System Design*, J. F. MCPARTLAND, McGraw-Hill Book Company, Inc., New York, 1956.

*Transformer Principles and Practice*, 2d ed., J. B. GIBBS, McGraw-Hill Book Company, Inc., New York, 1950.

*Transformer Engineering*, 2d ed., L. F. BLUME, G. CAMILLI, A. BOYAJIAN, and V. M. MONTSINGER, John Wiley & Sons, Inc., New York, 1951.

*Magnetic Circuits and Transformers*, M.I.T. ELECTRICAL ENGINEERING STAFF, John Wiley & Sons, Inc., New York, 1943.

*Electric Motors in Industry*, THERON C. JOHNSON (ed.), John Wiley & Sons, Inc., New York, 1942.

*Fractional Horsepower Electric Motors*, 2d ed., CYRIL G. VEINOTT, McGraw-Hill Book Company, Inc., New York, 1948.

*Troubles of Electrical Equipment: Their Symptoms, Causes, and Remedy*, 3d ed., H. E. STAFFORD, McGraw-Hill Book Company, Inc., New York, 1947.

*Power Capacitors*, R. E. MARBURY, McGraw-Hill Book Company, Inc., New York, 1949.

*The Art and Science of Protective Relaying*, C. RUSSELL MASON, John Wiley & Sons, Inc., New York, 1956.

*Storage Batteries*, 4th ed., GEORGE WOOD VINAL, John Wiley & Sons, Inc., New York, 1955.

## CONTROL

*Controllers for Electric Motors*, 2d ed., H. D. JAMES and L. E. MARKLE, McGraw-Hill Book Company, Inc., New York, 1952.

*Magnetic Control of Industrial Motors*, 2d ed., GERHART W. HEUMANN, John Wiley & Sons, Inc., New York, 1954.

*Control of Electric Motors*, 3d ed., PAISLEY B. HARWOOD, John Wiley & Sons, Inc., New York, 1952.

*Electronic Motor and Welder Controls*, GEORGE M. CHUTE, McGraw-Hill Book Company, Inc., New York, 1951.

*Industrial Electronic Control*, 2d ed., WILLIAM D. COCKRELL, McGraw-Hill Book Company, Inc., New York, 1950.

## ELECTRICAL MEASUREMENTS

*Electrical Measurements*, 2d ed., FRANK A. LAWS, McGraw-Hill Book Company, Inc., New York, 1938.

*Electrical Measurements in Theory and Application*, 4th ed., ARTHUR W. SMITH, McGraw-Hill Book Company, Inc., New York, 1948.

*Electrical Measurements and Their Applications*, WALTER C. MICHELS, D. Van Nostrand Company, Inc., Princeton, N.J., 1957.

*Electronic Measurements*, 2d ed., F. E. TERMAN and J. M. PETTIT, McGraw-Hill Book Company, Inc., New York, 1952.

*Electrical Measurements*, FOREST K. HARRIS, John Wiley & Sons, Inc., New York, 1952.

*Applied Electrical Measurements*, ISAAC FERN KINNARD, John Wiley & Sons Inc., New York, 1956.

*Manual of Electrical Instruments*, General Electric Company, Schenectady, 1949.

*Manual of Instrument Transformers*, General Electric Company, Schenectady, 1950.

*Manual of Watthour Meters*, General Electric Company, Schenectady, 1950.

*Electrical Meterman's Handbook*, 6th ed., Edison Electric Institute, New York, 1950.

## ELECTRONICS AND COMMUNICATION

*Electron-tube Circuits*, 2d ed., SAMUEL SEELY, McGraw-Hill Book Company, Inc., New York, 1958.

*A Primer of Electronics and Radiant Energy*, 2d ed., DON P. CAVERLY, McGraw-Hill Book Company, Inc., New York, 1952.

*Electronics in Industry*, 2d ed., GEORGE M. CHUTE, McGraw-Hill Book Company, Inc., New York, 1956.

*Practical Industrial Electronics*, F. A. ANNETT, McGraw-Hill Book Company, Inc., New York, 1952.

*Engineering Electronics*, JOHN D. RYDER, McGraw-Hill Book Company, Inc., New York, 1957.

*Electronics and Electron Devices*, 3d ed., ARTHUR L. ALBERT, The Macmillan Company, New York, 1956.

*Electronic and Radio Engineering*, 4th ed., FREDERICK E. TERMAN, McGraw-Hill Book Company, Inc., New York, 1955.

*The Electrical Fundamentals of Communication*, 2d ed., ARTHUR L. ALBERT, McGraw-Hill Book Company, Inc., New York, 1952.

*Communication Engineering*, 3d ed., W. L. EVERITT and G. E. ANNER, McGraw-Hill Book Company, Inc., New York, 1956.

*Electrical Communication*, 3d ed., ARTHUR L. ALBERT, John Wiley & Sons, Inc., New York, 1950.

*Elements of Radio Servicing*, 2d ed., WILLIAM MARCUS and ALEX LEVY, McGraw-Hill Book Company, Inc., New York, 1955.

# VISUAL BIBLIOGRAPHY

The visual materials listed below and on the following pages can be used to supplement the material in this book. It is recommended, however, that a film selected from this list be reviewed before it is used in order to determine its suitability for a particular group.

Both motion pictures and filmstrips are included in this list of visual materials, and the character of each one is indicated by the self-explanatory abbreviations "MP" and "FS." Immediately following this identification is the name of the producer, and if the distributor is different from the producer, the name of the distributor follows the name of the producer. Abbreviations are used for the names of producers and distributors, and these abbreviations are identified in the list of producers and distributors (with their addresses) at the end of the bibliography. In most instances, the films listed in this bibliography can be borrowed or rented from local or state 16-mm film libraries. All the motion pictures are 16-mm sound films, and the filmstrips are 35-mm silent films.

No attempt has been made to include in this bibliography all the films on electricity and electric machines. For such a listing, film users should consult "Educational Film Guide," a standard reference book which is available in most school and public libraries. The following films have been selected to supplement the particular material covered in this book, and for the convenience of readers they are classified according to various chapters of the book, although many of the films can be used equally well with the material in other chapters.

## Chapter 1

*Amperes, Volts, and Ohms* (MP, USN/UWF, 8 min). Explains the meaning, relationship, and measurement of amperes, volts, and ohms. (Correlated filmstrip, 23 fr)

*Basic Electricity* (MP, ISAF/UWF, 20 min color). An animated cartoon explaining the fundamentals of electricity, including voltage, current, resistance, magnetic fields, induction, primary and secondary coils, series and parallel circuits.

*Basic Electricity* (FS series, Handy). Twelve filmstrips with the following titles:

| | |
|---|---|
| *Magnetism* (62 fr) | *The Generator* (77 fr) |
| *Static Electricity* (73 fr) | *Alternating Current* (90 fr) |
| *Current Electricity* (74 fr) | *Electric Motors* (66 fr) |
| *The Electric Cell* (50 fr) | *Applications, Part* 1 (60 fr) |

*The Storage Battery* (83 fr)     *Applications, Part 2* (56 fr)
*Electromagnetism* (55 fr)     *Electric Meters* (83 fr)

*Basic Electronics* (MP, USAF/UWF, 17 min color).   An animated cartoon explaining the meaning of atoms and electrons, vacuum tube, cathode, rectifier tube, amplifier tube, grid, and bridge circuits.

*Current and Electromotive Force* (MP, USN/UWF, 11 min).   Explains electron theory, the arrangement of molecules, building up of current, conductors, emf, resistance, and chemical and mechanical sources of emf.   (Correlated filmstrip, 38 fr)

*The Electron: An Introduction* (MP, USOE/UWF, 16 min).   Nature of electrons; electron flow in solid conductors; emf; types and control of electron flow; electron flow and magnetic fields; and induced electron flow.   (Correlated filmstrip, 40 fr)

*Electrostatics* (MP, EBF, 11 min).   Explains positive and negative electrification, role of insulators and conductors, movement of charges in the electroscope, the Compton electrometer, and lightning as nature's display of static electricity.

*Elements of Electrical Circuits* (MP, EBF, 11 min).   Explains the nature of electric currents and circuits, electron motions, conductors, insulators, and factors affecting resistance.   Contains animated drawings and photographic demonstrations.   (Correlated filmstrip, 89 fr)

*Measurement of Electricity* (MP, Cor, 11 min).   Explains the definitions and physical concepts involved in the four basic units of electrical measure— volt, ampere, ohm, and watt.

*Principles of Electricity* (MP, GE, 20 min color).   Explains the actions of electrons within an atom, the principles involved in the flow of current, magnetism and magnetic fields, and the meanings of volt, ampere, and ohm.

*What Is Electricity?* (MP, EBF, 13 min).   Provides a background for studying the nature of electricity.

## Chapter 2

*Ohm's Law* (MP, USA/UWF, 19 min).   Explains the elements of electricity; electric energy, its source, transmission, and use; composition of matter; use of force and energy; how Ohm's law functions; resistance; and the purpose and use of meters.

*Series and Parallel Circuits* (MP, EBF, 11 min).   Explains the relationship between and among resistance, current, and voltage in series circuits and in parallel circuits; the advantages of each type of circuit; and a simple series-parallel combination circuit.   (Correlated filmstrip, 86 fr)

## Chapter 3

*The Primary Cell* (MP, EBF, 11 min).   Demonstrates by animation the ionization of an electrolyte, electron flow, action at electrodes, polarization, and function of the depolarizer.   Shows the characteristics and uses of a single cell and of cells connected as a battery in series and in parallel.

*Storage Battery Operation* (FS, McGraw, 48 fr).   Shows the construction of a storage battery and explains the various operations of the battery.

*Storage Battery Principles* (FS, McGraw, 36 fr).   Explains the principles of the storage battery, effects of charging and discharging, specific gravity, and use of the hydrometer.

*The Story of a Storage Battery* (MP, USBM, 32 min).   Explains by animation the principle of a storage battery; shows the operations in the manufacture of storage batteries; gives instructions on the care of batteries; illustrates industrial and domestic uses of batteries.

*Voltaic Cell, Dry Cell, and Storage Battery* (MP, USA/UWF, 18 min). Explains the principles of a voltaic cell, a dry cell, and a storage battery.

## Chapter 4

*Magnetism* (MP, EBF, 16 min).   Discusses the laws of polarity, the magnetic field, and terrestrial magnetism; shows a variety of applications of magnetism to modern civilization.

## Chapter 5

*Electrodynamics* (MP, EBF, 11 min).   Explains the principles of current electricity and electromagnetism, including magnetic field of a coil, electromagnets, magnetic hypothesis, recalescence, induction by electric currents, and transformers.

*Electrons* (MP, EBF, 11 min).   Illustrates the hypothesis that electricity consists of unit elementary charges.   Includes demonstrations of conduction of electricity, Faraday's laws, valence, movement of charges in vacuum tubes, operation of photoelectric cells, and reproduction of sound on film.

*Inductance* (MP, USN/UWF, 35 min).   Shows how a magnetic force reacts around a coil, illustrates the nature of self-inductance, and shows how to increase the inductance of a coil.   (Correlated filmstrip, 38 fr)

## Chapter 6

*Principle of the Generator* (MP, McGraw, 10 min).   Uses animation to explain the principles of electromagnetic induction and to relate these principles to the operation of the transformer.

## Chapter 7

*Direct Current Controllers* (MP, USOE/UWF, 15 min).   Shows shunt motors and d-c controllers in operation; and by animation, a d-c faceplate controller connected to a shunt motor.   (Correlated filmstrip, 27 fr)

*D.C. Motor. Part 1: Mechanical Overhaul* (MP, USOE/UWF, 20 min). How to test for electrical and mechanical faults; dismantle d-c motor; turn the commutator; repair and replace field coils; assemble the motor; and adjust and make final tests.   (Correlated filmstrip, 37 fr)

*D.C. Motor. Part 2: Rewinding* (MP, USOE/UWF, 37 min).   How to dismantle and clean an armature core; determine commutator pitch; reinsulate the core; insert coils; band an armature; shape coil ends; lay in and solder leads; balance and impregnate the armature; and turn a commutator. (Correlated filmstrip, 43 fr)

*Motor Selection and Application* (FS series, GE). Ten filmstrips, 30-50 fr each, with accompanying records averaging 20-25 min each, comprising a course on motors. Titles are:

> *The Fundamentals of Motors*
> *The Types of Motors*
> *Fundamentals of Motor Selection*
> *The Selection and Application of AC Polyphase Induction Motors*
> *The Selection and Application of Single Phase Integral Horsepower Motors*
> *The Selection and Application of DC Motors*
> *The Selection and Application of Synchronous Motors*
> *The Selection and Application of Adjustable Speed Drives*
> *The Selection and Application of Gear Motors*
> *The Selection and Application of Fractional Horsepower Motors*

## Chapter 8

*Alternating Current* (FS, USAF/UWF, 50 fr). An elementary introduction to the principles of alternating current. Demonstrates and explains Lenz' law, simple wave alternator, frequency, effective value, voltage-current-time relationship, and power.

*Capacitance* (MP, USN/UWF, 31 min). Demonstrates electron flow through a circuit, the charging and discharging of condensers, variations of a charge on a condenser in relation to time, and the behavior of capacitance with alternating current. (Correlated filmstrip, 22 fr)

*An Introduction to Vectors: Coplanar Concurrent Forces* (MP, USOE/UWF, 22 min). Explains the meaning of scalar and vector quantities; how to add scalars and vectors; methods of vector composition and vector resolution; relationship between vector composition and vector resolution; and how vectors may be used to solve engineering problems. (Correlated filmstrip, 36 fr)

*RCL: Resistance, Capacitance, Inductance* (MP, USN/UWF, 34 min). Explains current and voltage in relation to time; voltage and current curves; the relationship of current and voltage; the measurement of voltage at source; the addition of phase components; and the effect of impedance on resonance.

## Chapter 9

*Single-Phase and Polyphase Circuits* (MP, USOE/UWF, 17 min). Explains a single-phase synchronous generator; the use of sine curves to illustrate flow changes; a two-phase and a three-phase system; and ways to simplify wiring. (Correlated filmstrip, 51 fr)

## Chapter 13

*Across-the-Line Starters* (MP, USOE/UWF, 15 min). Theory and operation of a manually operated thermal overload switch, a magnetically operated across-the-line starter, a drum reversing switch for a three-phase motor, and a magnetic reversing switch. (Correlated filmstrip, 37 fr)

*Reduced Voltage Starters* (MP, USOE/UWF, 23 min). Principle of the transformer; operation of a manual starting compensator, thermal overload relay, and automatic starting compensator. (Correlated filmstrip, 46 fr)

*Rotating Magnetic Fields* (MP, USOE/UWF, 13 min). Explains a rotating magnetic-field pattern; three-phase winding in a demonstration stator; factors that cause rotation of the magnetic field; and the construction of polyphase motors. (Correlated filmstrip, 44 fr)

*Squirrel-Cage Rotor Principles* (MP, USOE/UWF, 10 min). Laws of magnetism and induced emf.; electron flow in squirrel-cage rotor setting up magnetic poles which create torque; construction of squirrel-cage rotors. (Correlated filmstrip, 28 fr)

*Three-Phase Motor. Part 1: Preparing to Rewind* (MP, USOE/UWF, 17 min). How to interpret and record nameplate data of a three-phase motor; identify the line and finish leads; remove coils and determine coil span; use a coil winding machine; and end-tape machine-wound coils. (Correlated filmstrip, 35 fr)

*Three-Phase Motor. Part 2: Rewinding* (MP, USOE/UWF, 17 min). How to insert mush coils and separators or "willies"; fold, trim, and wedge slot insulation around windings; insert phase insulation, and make a delta connection. (Correlated filmstrip, 31 fr)

*Wound Rotor Controllers* (MP, USOE/UWF, 17 min). Wound rotor motor principles; operation of a faceplate controller, drum-type nonreversing controller, drum-type reversing controller, and automatic magnetic starter for a wound rotor motor. (Correlated filmstrip, 40 fr)

## Chapter 15

*Repulsion-Induction Motor: General Overhaul* (MP, USOE/UWF, 25 min). How to check a repulsion-induction motor for electrical and mechanical faults; dismantle it; remove a damaged coil; wind and insulate a new coil; and assemble and lubricate the motor. (Correlated filmstrip, 33 fr)

*Repulsion Motor Principles* (MP, USOE/UWF, 18 min). Explains construction of repulsion motor; rotor circuits and effect of brush position; short-circuiting and brush-lifting mechanism; and applications of repulsion motors. (Correlated filmstrip, 40 fr)

*Split-Phase Motor Principles* (MP, USOE/UWF, 17 min). Construction of stator and rotor; comparison of winding in two-phase stator with split-phase stator; effects of winding resistances and inductive reactances; and use of capacitor to produce phase displacement. (Correlated filmstrip, 48 fr)

*Split-Phase Motor: Rewinding* (MP, USOE/UWF, 28 min). How to test a split-phase motor for electrical and mechanical faults; dismantle and strip the stator; rewind the stator; form and install skein windings; insulate; lace, dip, and bake the stator; and assemble, lubricate, and test the motor. (Correlated filmstrip, 40 fr)

Chapter 17

*Circuit Testing with Meters and Multimeters. Part 1: Theory* (MP, USA/
UWF, 30 min). Explains the theory and construction of meters and
shows various types of meters used for circuit testing and associated external
equipment.

*Circuit Testing with Meters and Multimeters. Part 2: Practical Application*
(MP, USA/UWF, 37 min). Demonstrates how to use meters in testing transformers, capacitors, resistors, telephone loop circuits, etc.

*Volt Ohmmeter Operation* (MP, USN/UWF, 15 min). Shows how to operate
a volt ohmmeter, Weston, and other types, including the selection of the proper
scale range, adjustment for zero on the scale, and the setup for either d-c or
a-c current.

Chapter 18

*The Cathode Ray Tube: How It Works* (MP, USN/UWF, 15 min). Demonstrates the construction and function of various parts of the cathode-ray tube.
Explains electrostatic and electromagnetic deflection and how varied currents
affect the position of the spot of light on the scope.

*The Diode: Principles and Applications* (MP, USOE/UWF, 17 min). Principles of electron flow across a gap; basic features of the diode tube; control of
electron flow in the tube; photoelectric cells; X-ray tubes; and the diode as a
rectifier. (Correlated filmstrip, 58 fr)

*Principles of Gas-Filled Tubes* (MP, USOE/UWF, 15 min). Theory of ionization applied to gas-filled tubes; control of current in circuits employing gas-
filled tubes; use of the gas diode as a rectifier; action of the grid in a gas triode;
and application of the gas triode as a grid-controlled rectifier. (Correlated
filmstrip, 36 fr)

*The Triode: Amplification* (MP, USOE/UWF, 14 min). Principles of the
diode and triode; electric fields; a triode amplifier circuit; amplification of d-c
voltage changes; alternating voltages; distortion; amplification of audio-fre-
quency signals. (Correlated filmstrip, 36 fr)

*Vacuum Tubes* (MP, EBF, 11 min). Explains, by animated drawings, the
operation of a radio vacuum tube in terms of its filament, plate, and grid circuits. Illustrates its functions as an amplifier to operate the loudspeaker, as a
rectifier in detection, and as an oscillator to generate the carrier wave.

*Vacuum Tubes: Electron Theory and the Diode Tube* (MP, USAF/UWF,
16 min). Explains electron behavior in matter, electron sources in vacuum
tubes, symbols of tubes, functioning of tube in a circuit, and effect of plate
voltage changes, space charge, and diode and duo-diode as rectifiers.

Main Sources of Films Listed

Cor—Coronet Films, Coronet Bldg., Chicago 1, Ill.
EBF—Encyclopaedia Britannica Films, Inc., 1150 Wilmette Ave., Wilmette,
Ill.
GE—General Electric Co., 1 River Rd., Schenectady 5, N.Y.

Handy—Jam Handy Organization, 2821 E. Grand Blvd., Detroit, Mich.

McGraw—McGraw-Hill Book Co., Text-Film Dept., 330 W. 42 St., New York 36, N.Y.

*USA—U.S. Dept. of the Army, Washington 25, D.C.

*USAF—U.S. Dept. of the Air Force, Washington 25, D.C.

USBM—U.S. Bureau of Mines, 4800 Forbes St., Pittsburgh, Pa.

*USN—U.S. Dept. of the Navy, Washington 25, D.C.

*USOE—U.S. Office of Education, Washington 25, D.C.

UWF—United World Films, Inc., 1445 Park Ave., New York 29, N.Y.

* Films distributed by United World Films, Inc.

# INDEX